GLASGOW UNIVERSITY PUBLICATIONS
LXXXII

AN
EIGHTEENTH CENTURY LECTURESHIP
IN CHEMISTRY

" *Every scientific idea, however esoteric, is thoroughly human from its birth to its perfection* "

GEORGE SARTON

" *Now Watt's impulse came from Black, the man who, besides his work on heat, began the chemical revolution. We have thus reached the very centre of things* "

A. T. PLEDGE

" *It is always by the successive labors of Several that an art is brought to perfection. . . . The Case is, a second improves upon it, a third puts it in execution ; and all claim the honor of the invention* "

WILLIAM CULLEN

WILLIAM CULLEN

An Eighteenth Century Lectureship in Chemistry

Essays and Bicentenary Addresses relating to
the Chemistry Department (1747)
of
Glasgow University (1451)

With a Foreword by

J. W. COOK, F.R.S.

REGIUS PROFESSOR OF CHEMISTRY

Edited by

ANDREW KENT, M.A., Ph.D.

GLASGOW

JACKSON, SON & COMPANY

PUBLISHERS TO THE UNIVERSITY

1950

FOREWORD

By J. W. Cook

IN THE year 1947 there was celebrated the bicentenary of an event which was of considerable significance even in the long and illustrious history of the University of Glasgow. For it was in 1747 that William Cullen took up his appointment as Lecturer in Chemistry. To mark the bicentenary, a series of four lectures was arranged and the present volume was planned. The lectures were delivered in May, 1947, and are now reproduced as four chapters of the present volume. In addition, the book contains a series of articles which together give a most interesting account of the chemical personalities in Glasgow of the latter half of the eighteenth century and the early nineteenth century, of the environment in which they lived and worked, and of the ways in which their activities influenced current developments in science, in industry and in medicine. It is not then the purpose of this book to serve as a complete history of chemistry in Glasgow University, and scant attention has been paid to the Victorian era. Modern chemistry in Glasgow has, however, been dealt with by A. R. Todd, who gives an interesting and balanced assessment of later activities.

The essays which follow are by no means limited in their interest to the accounts which they give of eighteenth-century Glasgow and of the men, including the illustrious Joseph Black, who were helping to lay the foundations of chemistry. In 1951 the University of Glasgow will celebrate the quingentenary of its foundation, and the present series of essays will be of interest also against the larger background of that celebration.

Moreover, the lecturers in chemistry, and indeed the first two professors, were generally doctors of medicine, and their chemical teaching formed part of the medical curriculum. Before the time of William Cullen there had been very little systematic instruction in medicine in the University of Glasgow, and the inauguration of the Lectureship in Chemistry may justly be claimed to mark the beginning of the Glasgow Medical School, wherein Cullen, Joseph Black and Thomas Charles Hope were also professors of Medicine ; and there was a close association between chemistry and other subjects of medical instruction, such as botany and materia medica.

In due time the Lectureship established in 1747 was elevated to a Regius Chair of chemistry, and as the present incumbent of that chair I am very conscious of the long and honourable tradition which I have inherited. In 1919 the Gardiner Chair of chemistry was instituted, and Professor J. M. Robertson, who now occupies it, joined with me in sponsoring the celebrations of the bicentenary of the department.

Grateful thanks are due to the Publications Standing Committee of the University of Glasgow, which has undertaken the publication of these commemorative lectures and essays.

We are deeply indebted to all those distinguished contributors who have so freely given of their time and powers to make this volume a worthy memento of an interesting anniversary and an authoritative and permanent record of an important period in the history of Scottish chemistry. Lastly, I should like to express my gratitude to my colleague, Dr. Andrew Kent, who has carried out the arduous task of editing this book and supervising its preparation for the press.

November, 1949.

EDITORIAL

THAT THE purpose of this volume has been extensively and generously supported will be evident from the list of contributors. Their essays and addresses have been arranged to illustrate the men, the ideas and the associations impingent on the early history and later progress of chemical teaching and research at Glasgow University. This book may appeal most widely in its reflection on a period when the science, emerging at length from materia medica and alchemy, excited something of that public interest enjoyed by the atomic physics of to-day.

There may be, too, some actual need for a review of achievement, in the interest of not only the less illustrious figures considered here. A recent much-publicised book on Glasgow contains no mention of Joseph Black : E. J. Holmyard has commented, in appraisal of a modern history of chemistry, that this name " does not appear in the index or, apparently, in the text ". These are surely underemphases.

Of the ancillary material, Dr. George Thomson has very kindly prepared the author-index, the list of appointments since 1747 and that for 1947. This last succinctly summarises the present, growing responsibilities of a department which in its first century was conducted single-handed and at times, indeed, only as an adjunct to other duties. The subject-index has been contrived primarily to provide cross-references to mention of the same topic by different authorities.

The extra-mural contributions to this volume, in their first form, have been in my hands since 1947. It will be recognised that the editing and production of a joint enterprise of this kind, in postwar circumstances, has encountered some unwelcome delays. It is a pleasure to express thanks now for the patient goodwill of the distinguished authors with whom I have enjoyed the stimulus of collaboration, and for the guidance in technical matters of Mr. Alan S. Jackson.

CHEMISTRY DEPARTMENT,
GLASGOW UNIVERSITY,

November, 1949

ACKNOWLEDGEMENTS

GRATEFUL THANKS are offered for much effective interest and help to Dr. W. R. Cunningham, the University Librarian, and to his staff, in particular Mrs. W. E. Muir, the member of that staff associated with the Chemistry Department : to the Librarian, the Free Library, Paisley, for the loan of White's MSS. of Cullen's lectures and permission to reproduce extracts therefrom : to the editor of *Endeavour* for permission to reprint the article on Hope by Professor James Kendall, and for the loan of the block of the portrait : to the Wellcome Historical Medical Museum for the block of the portrait of Robert Cleghorn : to the Royal Society of Edinburgh for a photograph of the Robison portrait in its possession and permission to reproduce it : to the Royal Philosophical Society of Glasgow for permission to reproduce the portrait of Thomas Thomson in its possession : to Professor John Read for photographs of Joseph Black from the Raeburn portrait and the Kay cartoon : to Professor C. J. Fordyce, Dr. G. W. Tyrell and Dr. J. A. Cranston for apposite articles and references : to the trustees of Dr. John Cowan for a block of the class-ticket issued by William Irvine : to Sheriff K. D. Cullen for the loan of MSS. of William Cullen's lectures : and to Professor A. Browning for some helpful advice.

LIST OF CONTENTS

*Substance of a Bicentenary Lecture

ix

* Substance of a Bicentenary Lecture

LIST OF ILLUSTRATIONS

xi

SENIOR APPOINTMENTS IN CHEMISTRY AT GLASGOW UNIVERSITY

Lecturers in Chemistry

1747–55. William Cullen, M.D. (p. 49).

1756–66. Joseph Black, M.D. (p. 78).

1766–69. John Robison, M.A., LL.D. (p. 126).

1769–87. William Irvine, M.D. (p. 140).

1787–91. Thomas Charles Hope, M.D. (p. 157).

1791–1817. Robert Cleghorn, M.D. (p. 164).

1817–18. Thomas Thomson, M.D., F.R.S. (p. 176).

Regius Professors

1818–52. Thomas Thomson, M.D., F.R.S.

1852–74. Thomas Anderson. 1819 (2nd July)—1874 (2nd Nov.).
Leith High School, Edinburgh Academy, University of Edinburgh (M.D., 1841). Hon. D.C.L. (*Nova Scotia*), LL.D. (*Glas.*). Chemist to the Highland and Agricultural Society, 1848–74. Royal Medallist of the Royal Society, 1872. Author of *Elements of Agricultural Chemistry*, and of other memoirs on the chemistry of agriculture and of alkaloids.

1874–1915. John Ferguson. 1837 (23rd Jan.)—1916 (2nd Nov.).
High School and University (B.A., 1861, M.A., 1862) of Glasgow. Hon. LL.D. (*Glas.*). Private Assistant to Thomas Anderson ; Assistant in chemistry (*Glasgow*) 1869. Author of *Bibliotheca Chemica*, and of numerous memoirs on the history of chemistry.

1919–37. George Gerald Henderson. 1862 (30th Jan.)—1942 (28th Sept.).
Universities of Glasgow (B.Sc., 1881, M.A., 1884, D.Sc., 1890), and Leipzig. F.R.S.,

1916. Hon. LL.D., (*Glasgow* and *St. Andrews*), D.Sc., (*Belfast*). Assistant in Chemistry, (*Glasgow*) 1884. Lecturer (*Queen Margaret College*) 1889. Freeland Professor (*Glasgow and West of Scotland Technical College*) 1892. Author of *Catalysis in Industrial Chemistry* and other textbooks, and of numerous memoirs chiefly on the chemistry of terpenes. Sometime President of the Chemical Society, of the Society of Chemical Industry, and of the Institute of Chemistry.

1938–39.   George Barger. 1878–1939 (6th Jan.).

School in Utrecht ; University College, London, and King's College, Cambridge. M.A., D.Sc. F.R.S., 1919. Hon. Graduate of Heidelberg, Lausanne, Liverpool, Michigan, Padua and Utrecht. Demonstrator in botany (*Brussels*) 1901. Wellcome Physiological Research Laboratories, 1903. Head of department of chemistry (*Goldsmith's College, London*) 1909. Professor of Chemistry (*Royal Holloway College, London*) 1913. Chemist, Medical Research Committee, 1914. Professor of Chemistry in relation to Medicine (*Edinburgh*) 1919. Author of *Ergot and Ergotism* and other text-books, and of numerous papers on the chemistry of alkaloids.

1939–   James Wilfred Cook.

Sloane School, Chelsea, and University College, London (D.Sc., Ph.D.). F.R.S., 1938. Demonstrator and later Lecturer in Organic Chemistry (*Sir John Cass Technical Institute*) 1920. Research Chemist, Department of Scientific and Industrial Research, 1928 ; and the Royal Cancer Hospital (Free), 1929. Reader in Pathological Chemistry (*London*) 1932. Professor of Chemistry (*London*) 1935. Author of numerous papers on organic chemistry, especially in relation to cancer. President of the Royal Institute of Chemistry, 1949.

PLATE I

University of Glasgow

LECTURESHIP IN CHEMISTRY
BICENTENARY

In celebration of the two hundredth anniversary of the inauguration of the teaching of Chemistry in the University the following Lectures will be delivered in the Chemistry Lecture Theatre, on Fridays during May at 7.30 p.m.

9th MAY—DOUGLAS GUTHRIE, M.D., F.R.C.S.E., F.R.S.E., on
"William Cullen and His Times."
(Chairman: His Grace the Duke of Hamilton, P.C., G.C.V.O.)

16th MAY—Professor JOHN READ, M.A., Ph.D., Sc.D., F.R.S., on
"Joseph Black, the Teacher and the Man."
(Chairman: Professor J. Monteath Robertson, M.A., D.Sc., F.R.S.)

23rd MAY—ALEXANDER FLECK, D.Sc., F.R.I.C., on
"Scottish Industrial Development of the Cullen-Black Period."
(Chairman: Andrew McCance, D.Sc., F.R.S.)

30th MAY—Professor A. R. TODD, D.Sc., D.Phil., F.R.S., on
"Glasgow Chemistry in the Twentieth Century."
(Chairman: Professor J. W. Cook, D.Sc., F.R.S.)

These Lectures are open without Ticket to Members of the University and to others who are interested.

Announcement of Bicentenary Lectures, 1947

PLATE II

E S S A Y S

ON THE

CONSTRUCTION AND GRADUATION

F

THERMOMETERS,

AND ON THE

HEATING AND COOLING

OF

B O D I E S.

BY GEORGE MARTINE, M. D.

A NEW EDITION,
WITH NOTES AND CONSIDERABLE ADDITIONS,

ESPECIALLY THE

TABLES of the Different SCALES OF HEAT,
exhibited by DR. BLACK, in his Annual
Course of Chemistry.

EDINBURGH:
PRINTED FOR AND SOLD BY WILLIAM CREECH.

MDCCXCII.

Extracts from Martine's *Essays* (1740) as a text-book of the seventeen-nineties. In the advertisement it is stated that " this book is recommended by Dr. Black to the Students attending his classes " (cf. p. 6).
(Glasgow University Library)

Gardiner Professors

1919–42.   Thomas Stewart Patterson. 1872 (July)—1949 (14th Feb.).

Greenock Academy, Merchiston Castle School, Andersonian College, Glasgow, and Heidelberg University (Ph.D., 1895). D.Sc., (*London*, 1909). D.Sc., (1911) and Hon. LL.D., (*Glas.*). Assistant (*Yorkshire College*) 1896. Lecturer in Organic Chemistry (*Glasgow*) 1904. Author of numerous memoirs on the history of chemistry and on the chemistry of optically active organic compounds.

1942–   John Monteath Robertson.

Perth Academy, and Glasgow University (M.A., Ph.D., D.Sc.). F.R.S., 1945. Staff of Davy Faraday Laboratory, Royal Institution, 1930. Senior Lecturer in physical chemistry, (*Sheffield*) 1939. Author of numerous papers and articles on chemical, physical and X-ray diffraction subjects.

THE LECTURESHIP AT GLASGOW

Andrew Kent

IN THE year 1747, Scotsmen could look back on some sixty
years of almost unprecedented domestic peace, assured by the
Revolution of 1688, and on some forty years of growing
prosperity, resulting from the Union of Parliaments in 1707. It
is true that tranquillity had been interrupted by the brief Jacobite
violence of 1715 and 1745, and that the new bustle of trade and
transport had been unevenly distributed in favour of Glasgow
and of other parts which looked across the Atlantic ocean.
None the less the overall atmosphere was one of peace and
prosperity, conducive to hopeful and progressive views in every
department of human endeavour ; few could anticipate ensuing
decades well-nigh as compact of war and revolution as our own.

One instant need had been to restore, after the successful
Revolution, the torn fabric of the country's persecuted Kirk, to
restate its doctrines and restaff its empty parishes. " Glasgow
was a market and University town " writes G. M. Trevelyan,
" with a population of 12,500, an outpost of Southern civilisation
against the Highland tribes, the capital of the Covenanting
West." [1] It was this and something more : it was the cultural
capital of Ulster—then, in Dewar Gibb's phrase, " Scotland's
most successful colony " [2]—and a resort of nonconformists from
England and elsewhere. The Arts Faculty of the College played
an important part in meeting local requirements, and in restoring
presbyterian Ulster. It educated many Scots-Irish clergymen
and their relatives, attracted dissenters from England and the
colonies. Professor (" Common Sense ") Reid might indulge in
humorous vilification of " the stupid Irish teagues " who
thronged his classes of Moral Philosophy : their numbers, at
times one third of the student body, were important to the
structure of their Alma Mater. [3]

The continuance of this tradition meant that, in notable
attempts to elucidate the ancient mystery of Fire, Science at

A
1

Glasgow had benefit from the contributions of Ulstermen like Joseph Black, Adair Crawford, William Thomson (Lord Kelvin) and other nonconformists. Conversely her academic influence was then most effectively spread by transfer of staff or students to other dissenting seats of learning at home or abroad. So, for example, the Scots chemist Dr. John McLean proceeded from Glasgow to the College of New Jersey, Princeton, Massachusetts, to expound the views of Black and Irvine in what D. A. Stauffer calls " the religious and educational capital of Scotch-Irish America ".[4]

Although the first half of the eighteenth century saw a welcome increase in the number of students at Glasgow, this academic prosperity was confined almost entirely to the Faculty of Arts, whose chair of Natural Philosophy comprised the physical science of its day. The Faculty of Medicine was stagnant ; few students attended its two professors, who were examiners rather than tutors for the doctorate of Medicine. Physicians, as opposed to their lesser brethren, " chirurgeons " and apothecaries, were in chronically short supply in the prosperous expanding town.[5]

Under pressure from such as Dr. Cullen, the College authorities finally agreed to remedy this state of affairs by establishing Lectureships, within the Faculty of Medicine, in Materia Medica, Botany and Chemistry. The preliminary negotiations were lengthy and may not have been accelerated by the town's brief surrender to the sullen Highlanders of Charles Stuart's unhappy host. The first start was nearly a false one : the illness of Mr. Carrick,[6] Cullen's assistant who undertook the chemistry class, prevented his delivery of all but a few preliminary lectures in the session 1747-8 ; and Cullen himself stepped into the breach to maintain a continuity which has continued to this day.

The creation of such lectureships, whose incumbents, reappointed annually, had the full responsibilities of professors without the equivalent status and emoluments, resulted mainly from the selfish outlook of the original professoriate. This form of appointment was an innovation in academic circles of that day, and had no precedent in the experience of that much-travelled Viennese, Joseph Frank : [7] some confusion as to title reflects its ambiguous nature. In extra-mural publications, Irvine and Cleghorn are generally awarded the honorific

" Professor ", and at least one incumbent refers to his " chemical chair " at Glasgow.[8]

Handicapped in status, the lectureships were further affected by the uncertain fortunes of the new medical school before its final success was assured by the provision of an adequate hospital (the Royal Infirmary) in 1794, and by the grisly requirements of counter-Napoleonic campaigns.[9] Meantime the higher reputation and recompense accruing from corresponding exertions at Edinburgh University cost Glasgow chemistry and medicine the services of Cullen, Black and Hope : Robison soon departed for a more profitable Russian appointment ; and Irvine was negotiating a Spanish one at the time of his death.

Any official stipends were low, and the major recompense of many appointments came from the fees of such as could be persuaded to enrol or re-enrol. Expository grace and power were correspondingly valuable. Charles Hope and Joseph Black were exceptionally attractive in this respect. Cullen, once in Edinburgh, " touched fees " from increasing classes, some of whose members were charmed into five successive re-enrolments.[10] Dr. Frank did not rank Thomas Thomson with the inspiring Fourcroy, yet could compare him in lucidity with Vauquelin.[11]

Latin was still, as in Cullen's botany class, the usual language of praelection, but chemistry was from its beginning conducted in English or at least in braid Scots. If this were little welcome to any Gaelic Bajans from the western Highlands, it must otherwise have broadened the appeal of the subject in an age when the academic teacher had need at times to orate for his supper.

The new department, then, was not lacking in eloquent luminosity ; but this alone could not immediately influence Glasgow's relative dearth of intending physicians. Any professor might fall back on his endowments : some did not choose to teach ; and one, William Cross, professor of law, could scarcely be induced to visit the University.[12] The lecturers, unless they were academic pluralists, had little material solace for empty class-rooms ; and the co-ordinated group of lectureships soon broke down. The relative and continuous vitality of Chemistry was due to special circumstances.

With occasional exceptions such as the original short courses at King's College, Aberdeen,[13] chemistry in eighteenth century Scottish universities was a Paracelsean adjunct to medical science. Formal association with Medicine at Glasgow endured indeed until the twentieth century.[14] Cullen (from 1751), Black and Hope held chairs in other branches of that Faculty along with the lectureship in chemistry : the two former were prominent practitioners as well. William Irvine, professionally a physician, was notable in his day for the degree to which he was " engrossed in chemical pursuits ":[15] on the other hand, Cleghorn was exceptional in the extent to which he accepted the primary purpose of the department.

For, at its beginning, Cullen nurtured and welcomed the general appeal of chemistry as a " new science " emerging impressively from the mists of an outmoded alchemical jargon. The nature of his emphasis and its effect are already evident in the reminiscence of Dr. Robert Wallace who had been among the first to enrol. " The number of students in the Physic Class and Materia Medica were very few, not above twenty. But in the Chemistry the number was considerable ; the lectures being calculated not only for the medical students, but for the general students of the University, and for gentlemen engaged in any business connected with chemistry."[16]

It was Cullen's breadth of interest and of mind which ensured the continuance of the lectureship in Chemistry. Black continued the original policy, drawing £20 in stipend but almost thrice as much in fees from the prosperous new class.[17] It survived Black's departure for Edinburgh, though his medical students trooped after him ; and there is significance in the succession, at this time, of John Robison, who was not a physician but an early type of professional scientist. Dr. Irvine, who had £30 per annum for conjoint lectureships in Chemistry and Materia Medica, maintained the profitable tradition. His lectures were advertised for 7 p.m. in the laboratory. The meagre research facilities were shared with promising devotees. Even Cleghorn, who was little given to experimental enquiry, maintained Irvine's device of a Chemical Club and discussed with its members the heady doctrines of Lavoisier.[18]

The new department also performed a public service in its guidance of municipal and private enterprise. The detailed picture is incomplete : enough remains to establish that the association with Chemistry at Glasgow of such as James Watt, Dr. William Couper,[19] Charles McIntosh and Josias Gamble was not an accident. A degree of active continuity had been assured by the foresightedness of Cullen, fructified by the fame of his immediate successor.

It is difficult still to appreciate the full significance of Joseph Black's achievement in his " Magnesia Alba ". Technically this paper records what John Ferguson has described as " a matter-of-fact examination of a matter of fact ",[20] and yet it spread from Edinburgh to become a bible to the following generation, a hermetic " Principia " to those for whom chemistry was indeed the " Black art ".

One thing seems certain. Black's international reputation had not been so rapidly established but for the reading of his thesis to the Philosophical Society of Edinburgh during the brief period when it undertook publication of a selection from presented papers. Such opportunities were rarely available to Scots scientists when Glasgow was as " far " from Edinburgh as from Paris of to-day, and when Edinburgh was more distant from London than from modern New York. Expounding Black's doctrine of latent heat, Reid tells a correspondent in 1766, " I cannot find that Cullen or any of the Edinburgh people know anything of this matter." A little earlier he had complained that " Our College Library is ten or twelve years behind in the Memoirs of the Royal Academy " of Paris.[21] The *Transactions of the Royal Society of Edinburgh* did not appear until 1788, and the first *Proceedings of the Philosophical Society of Glasgow* came only in 1841. Earlier exponents of chemistry in Scotland relied largely and of necessity on the criticisms of learned coteries, and on the pious memories of their students.[22]

Continued interest in " fixed air " and the carbonates of the calcium group was to be expected among Black's associates in Edinburgh and Glasgow. Although pneumatic chemistry in Glasgow saw no development to rank with Rutherford's recognition of nitrogen, some further progress was made : it seems curious that none extended Black's technique to similarly gas-productive solids like mercuric oxide. Bleaching-powder as a subject of general interest was emphasised by an expanding textile industry. Acid, alkali and glass had careful consideration. An unexpected degree of attention to agricultural chemistry is partly explained by the pairing of chemistry with botany in the training of physicians.

Heat, then widely held to be a form of matter, was the most sustained topic of enquiry, and knits the lecturers from Cullen to Thomson into one coherent group. Discussion and investigation had been revitalised by Fahrenheit's description of a handy, standardised thermometer in 1724 ; and were again intensified by Braun's achievement of alchemical ambition in his " fixation " of mercury, by a freezing-mixture, in the Russian winter of 1759. Black proposed to publish his course of chemistry as " Lectures on the effect of Heat and Mixture ": [23] courses generally comprised extensive review of laboratory furnaces and fuels ; they began with lengthy dissertations on the forms and properties of heat.

On this question Glasgow derived immediate benefit from the efforts of two St. Andrews men, George Martine and Alexander Wilson. As a former pupil of Boerhaave and graduate of Leyden (M.D., 1725), Dr. Martine explained the construction and calibration of Fahrenheit's new instrument in a series of articles which appeared in his *Essays Medical and Philosophical*. This publication in 1740, the year of the author's death on service before Cartagena, contains the observation that the new type of thermometers was " made no where in greater perfection or with greater exactness than by our own countryman Wilson in London ".[24]

Alexander Wilson settled down in Glasgow by 1744, and his earlier services to the University—he became its first professor of Astronomy in 1760—included the provision of his celebrated thermometers at prices ranging upwards from a guinea.[25] This was a most fortunate concatenation of circumstances for the young chemistry department. Cullen and Black were influenced by Martine, a modified edition of whose book was prepared for the use of Black's students in Edinburgh. The first scientific publication from the new department, Cullen's " On the Cold produced by Evaporating Fluids ", which immediately attracted the attention of Benjamin Franklin and Henry Cavendish,[26] was the precursor of Black's greater achievements and of a continued departmental interest in the subject of Heat which terminated only with the second edition of Thomas Thomson's text-book *Heat and Electricity* in 1840. By this date the substantial theory of Caloric which had seemed to be established by Black was fast losing ground ; but it is interesting to remember that William Thomson, Lord Kelvin, acknowledged the influence of his namesake on a career which capped the contributions of Glasgow University to the solution of an ancient enigma.[27]

In more practical matters there was an effective clash of personalities in the bustling Clydeside town. The dexterity of Wilson, the intuition of Black, the youthful enthusiasm of Robison, Irvine and others, all fanned the flame of James Watt's brooding, jealous genius. " Some people think," writes A. R. Ubbelohde, " that the stone circles which are found in the bleaker parts of Britain were built by men who worshipped fire. Britain's industrial cities were built by men who measured it, and are memorials of their triumphs as well as of their limitations."[28] The early chemistry department at Glasgow took a full share in the reduction of Fire to order and arithmetic : its lecturer's laboratory and the equipment for Professor Dick's class of natural philosophy were forcing grounds of the Industrial Revolution.

Events and interests in Glasgow University at this time had some suggestive parallels in the Imperial Academy of St. Petersburg, then subject to the impact of the peasant prodigy, Lomonósov—a Cullen writ large, a Slavonic compôte of Theophrastus Paracelsus, Samuel Johnson and Benjamin Franklin. Appointed the Academy's first professor of Chemistry in 1745, and as insistent as Cullen that his subject was not an art but a science, Lomonósov achieved the construction of a laboratory in 1748. A pupil of Christian Wolff, in the Cartesian rather than the Newtonian tradition, Lomonósov speculated daringly on the structure of matter, on the nature of combustion, and on heat as a dynamic phenomenon ensuing from the spinning impact of warty primary particles.

His *Reflections on the Cause of Heat and Cold* were published in 1747. Although he proposed and, single-handed, attempted a wide range of practical investigation, Lomonósov's ideas on this and other questions died with him in 1765, to be disinterred from unkind oblivion only in the present century.[29]

It is permissible to speculate on the possibilities of effective contact between the two youthful schools of chemistry in St. Petersburg and Glasgow. Black (who became an honorary member of this Academy at St. Petersburg in 1783) had Russian students from St. Petersburg in his class of 1764-5 : [22] Robison reached Kronstadt in 1770. Liaison between the minds of Black and Lomonósov might have affected the history of science, and but for the great, lone Russian's untimely death had been almost inevitable. In fairness it must be added that the Glasgow school, like others of that date, were influenced against kinetic theory by their failure to detect temperature changes in liquids subjected to friction : [30] this remained for Joule and more adequate instruments. Earlier scepticism was here a rational deduction from experience, and was confirmed, curiously enough, by the first interpretation of Herschel's work on radiant heat.[31]

These Georgian exponents had other than practical problems to attempt, and were already at grips with some which still deny accepted solution, such as the relationship of physical science to industry, to philosophy, to medicine and to education.

Science in later eighteenth-century Scotland moved in a propitious atmosphere. " The Scotland, and especially the Edinburgh of that time ", writes A. T. Pledge, " was, after Paris, the intellectual centre of the world," [32] and Scottish philosophers had been most receptive to Newtonian ideas : Hutcheson, Smith, Reid, Hume and Stewart were amateurs of physical science. " Jupiter " Carlyle has an amusing, characteristic tale of a dinner-party in 1759 where Wight, a dissenting minister and future professor of History, starts to dispute with William Cullen on chemistry in the presence of Benjamin Franklin and David Hume, and is held to have the best of it! [33]

" Bacon and Newton over and over were named as the masters they would follow ", writes Gladys Bryson, " Newton was science and science was the eighteenth century ideal." " The century really preferred to speak of philosophy instead of science." [34] Our rigid separation of the two disciplines was then unforeseen : interest lay in the mutual benefits of harmony, and this symbiosis meant a wealth of interest and association for the scientific, who had not yet, in Mumford's phrase, " lost the sense of the whole and failed to develop a method of dealing with wholes ".[35]

So we find the chemists, like so many Joseph Priestleys,[36] active and interested in almost every field—in almost every field save Scottish politics where the corrupt competence of my Lord Dundas dissuaded all but the most aggressive. The mighty international events of their time seldom affected their lives, though Robison saw action at first hand, while Cullen and Irvine each had a son who died on service.

Their general acceptance of mechanical philosophy influenced also their attitude to medicine : it is self-evident that they emphasised the significance thereunto of the advancing physical sciences, although they had certainly been surprised to find J. S. Haldane complaining that in the twentieth century, physiology— their Institutes of Medicine—" teaches that life is nothing but physical and chemical mechanism ".[37] In general education there was experiment in more than the academic use of native tongues and discussion clubs. In seeking a wider audience than medical undergraduates they approached what G. M. Trevelyan calls " the desire of mechanics for general knowledge " in which, as he holds, lay the inspiration of organised adult education.[38]

The lectureship established the clear status of chemistry in Scotland as a separate science : the Regius chair, it seems, was the earliest (1818) for chemistry, *tout simple*, in the country.[39] Thomas Thomson, its first occupant, fought a stern and success- ful battle to establish the parity of such appointments, in status and emolument, with the older scholastic foundations.[40] His text-books and the extant lectures of Cullen, Black and Hope, show careful planning and clear forethinking in educational method. Aware that, as John Read emphasises, " There is a chemical geography ; there is also a chemical history ",[41] they established a cultural tradition which Glasgow still maintains. Among students of the eighteenth-century class are some already mentioned—Black, Robison, Irvine, McLean of Princeton, Adair Crawford—Fellows of the Royal Society in Richard Chevenix and J. F. W. Johnston, and many such as William Ogilvie, humanist and chemist of Aberdeen. In later years names like those of Thomas Graham and John Stenhouse (both founder Fellows of the Chemical Society) were added to a still-lengthening roll, which has justified the prescient energy of those who sustained the early trials.

Of the seven Glasgow lecturers, only Irvine lacked extensive association with the University of Edinburgh : his, too, are the only lineaments unrecorded by famous artists like Raeburn or James Tassie. All, save Cleghorn, have their place in the *Dictionary of National Biography*. Black, of course, enjoyed an international repute and the honours of foreign Academies. Thomson became a Fellow of the Royal Society. All played some part in launching or sustaining the Royal Society of Edinburgh. Locally they were kenspeckle figures : a Glasgow versifier [42] wrote of the time when :

> " Cullen and Hunter here began
> Their first probations ;
> And Smith, frae Glasgow, form'd his plan,
> The Wealth o' Nations ! "

Thomson long presided over the (Royal) Philosophical Society of Glasgow : he, and all the others except the unqualified Robison, served one or more terms as president of the historic Royal Faculty of Physicians and Surgeons of Glasgow. They were men of mark in their day, in the social and scientific clubs of Glasgow and the capital.

Few students of these records in prose and illustration can fail to savour that variety in personality which may accompany one common interest. There is the noble simplicity of Cullen's character and ambitions : Black's pallid and seignorial grace : the energy of Robison, much-travelled, turbulent, tendentious : Irvine's shy, devoted competence : Hope's charm of person and his resplendence in exposition : the alertness of the egregious Cleghorn, his busy finger in every purse and every pie : Thomson's erudite enthusiasm, cool and tirelessly persistent. They are linked together, and with us, by their common devotion to science and its progress. They are divided from us more by their portentous variety of scholarly activity than by their general addiction to wigs and knee-breeches, to nepotism and neurasthenia. It is an interesting commentary that the polyhistor John Ferguson, following Thomas Thomson with the single intervention of Professor Thomas Anderson, should so soon have seemed an oddity in the chair.[43]

Chemists born and educated in the eighteenth century had advantage and handicap from their position in time. The few major ideas which inspired their criticism or research were less effective, less concise, and excitingly less impersonal than the few we use to-day. Their primitive apparatus did not so tax their patience and energy to appreciate its use. If they lacked our present range of accumulated experience, they needed not the rigours of specialisation to develop it : in the absence of intensive team-work they found time and courage to think for themselves.

They suffered on occasion from the difficulty of achieving scientific publication, but had acres less of it to read. Though they worked in relative isolation the age of the great solitaries was past : they enjoyed eventually, by personal contact or friendly report, the esteem not only of their academic associates but also of fellow-scientists at home, in western Europe and in America. Inclined by Galileo, Bacon, Newton, Boyle and Boerhaave to a more modern method, they yet retained a Greek delight in casual enquiry and care-free speculation. They were as blissfully inattentive to the ravages of material progress as we are unhappily ignorant of the remedies. This may not have been modern science ; but in some respects it was magnificent.

Supporting also the activities of the Dicks and John Anderson in natural philosophy, of the Hamiltons and Hunters in medicine, of the Wilsons in astronomy (this was an age of academic dynasties), science at Glasgow in the later eighteenth century had a notably close association with the University, and an influence by its encouragement of Watt on the economic and political history of mankind. The department of chemistry, now one of the largest in the country, has since enjoyed the leadership and services of many notable men : some indications of its more recent organisation and personnel appear in the following pages.

These indications are complementary to more detailed studies of various factors in its origin and early progress. The lectureship (1747-1818) spans an important period including, by modern definitions, the pre-scientific phase of chemistry. Here the school at Glasgow, in close conjunction with Edinburgh and in collaboration with other centres of physical philosophy, played a part of some distinction in bringing modern chemistry to birth, by developing new outlooks, new ideas and new facts. If transmutation were never taught, the Four Elements of Aristotle, the *Tria Prima* of Paracelsus, phlogiston, and the symbology of Alchemy underlay its first instructions. Its later history illustrates the effect of improved scientific method and instruments in creating a new tempo of progress. The young department was alert to the value of advances elsewhere, by Stahl, Boerhaave, Geoffroy, Lavoisier (perhaps Glasgow was first, outside France, to teach his doctrines) and others, in their turn.

It gained status and vitality from a Baconian attitude to the social potentialities of physical science, but combined this with pursuit of fundamental inquiries on the structure of matter and on its relationship with energy. It fostered the organised association of practical research with academic teaching—using University, not private apparatus—and the laboratory training of undergraduates. Incidentally it influenced for good the lingering monastic pattern of University education, revivified the medical curriculum, supported the town's new industries then struggling into life after the economic disaster of the American War.

Now that the department has behind it two centuries of such tradition, these early achievements, though they must be seen against the imposing background of scientific progress, still justify a retrospective, grateful glance. [44]

NOTES AND REFERENCES

[1] G. M. Trevelyan, *English Social History*, Longmans, Green and Co., London, 1944, p. 456.

[2] Andrew Dewar Gibb, *Scottish Empire*, Alexander MacLehose and Co., London, 1937, p. 11.

[3] Thomas Reid, *The Works of Thomas Reid, D.D.* (ed. Hamilton), MacLachlan and Stewart, Edinburgh, 1863, pp. 40, 43.

[4] D. A. Stauffer, *Universities Review*, 1947, *20*, 14.

[5] A. Duncan, *Memorials of the Faculty of Physicians and Surgeons of Glasgow*, 1896, pp. 111, 141.

[6] John Carrick, brother of the famous Glasgow banker Robert Carrick of Monfode, had previously assisted Professor Hamilton of Anatomy. He resumed teaching in other medical topics but died in 1750. Thomson (ref. 16), 29, and Duncan, 255.

[7] J. Frank, *Reise*, Vienna, 1804, p. 281.

[8] J. R. Partington, " The Early History of Strontium ", *Annals of Science*, 1942, *5*, 161, quotes T. C. Hope, " when I filled the chemical chair in the University of Glasgow ".

[9] Duncan, 172.

[10] It should be added, in fairness to Cullen, that he did not press for his full fees. Cf. Dr. Anderson, " Account of Dr. William Cullen ", *European Magazine*, 1803, *44*, 251, for this and many other attractive characteristics of Cullen as a teacher.

[11] Frank, 144, 146, 237.

[12] James Coutts, *History of the University of Glasgow*, MacLehose, Glasgow, 1909, pp. 233, 234.

[13] A. Findlay, *The Teaching of Chemistry in the Universities of Aberdeen*, University Press, Aberdeen, 1935, p. 2.

[14] A. Kent, " A Chemical Bicentenary ", *Nature*, 1947, *159*, 594.

[15] William Irvine, *Essays on Sicily*, Mawman, London, 1813, preface.

[16] John Thomson, *Life of Cullen*, Blackwood, Edinburgh, 1859, Vol. I, p. 25.

[17] Reid, 45.

[18] John Thomson, *loc. cit.*, prefatory notice (Vol. I), p. 8.

[19] Duncan, 262.

[20] John Ferguson, " On Some of the Constituents of the Atmosphere ", *Sanitary Journal of Scotland*, Jan. 1st, 1877.

[21] Reid, 43, 45

[22] J. P. Muirhead, *Mechanical Inventions of James Watt*, London, 1854, Vol. II, p. 119. Here, in a letter to Watt on a question of priority, Black adduces an interesting list of students.

[23] Joseph Black, *Lectures in the Elements of Chemistry* (ed. Robison), Longman and Rees, London, 1803, I, lxiv.

[24] George Martine, *Essays Medical and Philosophical*, Miller, London, 1740, p. 206. The form of the author's name may have caused some doubt as to his nationality. Preston's *Theory of Heat* refers to his book by its French title.

[25] Sir William Ramsay, *Life and Letters of Joseph Black, M.D.*, Constable and Co., London, 1918, p. 55 ; J. Leslie, *Dissertation Fourth*, Edinburgh, n.d., p. 643.

[26] William Cullen, *Essays and Observations*, 1770, *2*, 159. Cullen's is Article 7 ; the succeeding Article 8 is most appropriately Joseph Black's, " Experiments upon Magnesia Alba ", p. 172. Benjamin Franklin, *Complete Works*, Longman, Hurst, Rees, Orme and Brown, London, n.d., Vol. II, p. 75. Franklin in a letter dated 1757, quotes information from " Professor Simpson, of Glasgow ", on " some curious experiments of a physician of his acquaintance ". Cullen read his paper on May 1st, 1755. George Wilson, *Life of Cavendish*, Cavendish Society, London, 1851, p. 449.

[27] Andrew Gray, *Lord Kelvin*, Dent, London, 1908, p. 14.

[28] A. R. Ubbelohde, *Time and Thermodynamics*, Oxford University Press, 1947, p. 7.

[29] The first publications of B. N. Menshutkin on Lomonósov have led to an extensive number of later articles. The author is much indebted to G. A. Birkett, M.A., head of the Department of Russian in this University, for translations of items from some recent works in Russian, and from Lomonósov's original papers in that language.

[30] Cf. W. Irvine and W. Irvine, *Essays*, Mawman, London, 1805, p. 22. Here Dr. Irvine, Jr., comments, " Fluids however much agitated, do not become hot ".

[31] Cf. Thomas Thomson, in *Edinburgh Encyclopaedia*, Vol. 6, p. 32.

[32] A. T. Pledge, *Science since 1500*, H.M.S.O., London, 1939, p. 110.

[33] Alexander Carlyle, *Autobiography*, Blackwood and Sons, Edinburgh and London, 1860, p. 395.

[34] Gladys Bryson, *Man and Society* (*The Scottish Inquiry of the Eighteenth Century*), Princeton University Press, 1945, pp. 15, 18, 22.

[35] Lewis Mumford, *The Condition of Man*, Martin, Secker and Warburg, 1944, p. 246.

[36] Cf. A. Kent, " Joseph Priestley ", *Chemistry and Industry*, 1943, *62*, 71.

[37] J. S. Haldane, *Materialism*, Hodder and Stoughton, London, 1932, p. 14.

[38] Trevelyan, 479.

[39] A. Clow, *Nature*, 1945, *155*, 158.

[40] The Regius Professors of Chemistry and Materia Medica, *A Memorial* (*with Remarks by the Principal and Professors of Glasgow College*), *1835*, G. Richardson, Glasgow, 1841.

[41] John Read, " Specialisation and Culture in Chemistry ", 1948, p. 5.

[42] Senex, *Glasgow Past and Present*, Robertson and Co., Glasgow, 1884. John Mayne's poem is given in full (Vol. I).

[43] F. O. Bower and T. S. Patterson, *In Memoriam Professor John Ferguson, LL.D.*, Glasgow, 1917.

[44] Some further general information was provided, as part of the bi-centenary arrangements, in a broadcast, Scottish Home Service, by J. W. Cook (*Radio Times*, 9/5/47) : in articles by A. Kent (*Nature*, 3/5/47, *Chemical Age*, 17/5/47), J. C. Speakman (*Chemistry and Industry*, 26/4/47), T. S. Patterson (*Glasgow Herald*, 9/5/47) ; in announcements and reports of the lectures in this latter newspaper.

WILLIAM CULLEN'S
HISTORY OF CHEMISTRY

THE following is an extract from the bound manuscript of Cullen's *Lectures on Chemistry* compiled by Dr. John White of Paisley, presumably when he was an undergraduate at Edinburgh University.[1] His surgeon-apprentices, who used these notes, included Cullen's biographer John Thomson, son of a local weaver ; and the manuscript is now in the possession of the Public Library, Paisley.

The historical chapters are distributed irregularly throughout the text. This arrangement, their more careful caligraphy and their concise brevity suggest that they may be a transcript of the lecturer's own notes.[2] It was thought best to reprint the text as exactly as possible. Underlinings are apparently arbitrary and may be over-emphasised by the use of italics. " Borrichius ", " Corregius " and " Beeker " are the seventeenth century scholars Ole Borch, Hermann Conring and J. J. Becher (or Beccher). " Lues " is an archaic term for disease.

These notes manifest the extent to which Cullen, like others of his period, was indebted to Boerhaave's *Elementa Chemiae* : whole sentences, as in the description of Paracelsus, come directly from Shaw's translation : even the tributes to Dr. Daniel Cox and Dr. Frederick Slare of the Royal Society are of Dutch origin. Cullen has contributed a critical attitude, a cheerful scepticism which illustrates his personality. He nods rather than bows to ancient authorities ; and the long-established custom of praelection in Latin is here reduced to a single Horatian tag on the credulity of Appella the Jew.

ACCORDING TO the custom long established in this University, we shall begin with a history of Chemistry ; and though this was introduced only probably to fill up the time allotted for public Lectures, yet it is of great service to the young students, if properly attended to : It shews by what means the art has been brought to its present state of perfection, and by it the students become acquainted with the characters of the original writers in this science, for though in these, as in most other sciences, there are many systematic writers, yet every body knows how little any system is to be depended upon. And though these systems are compiled from former writers, and ought therefore to contain all the discoveries in the Science, yet they are in general performed so inaccurately as to omit many useful circumstances, or copy the faults of the writers from whom they compile, that a person who relies entirely upon them, without applying to the original writers, will acquire but a very scanty and superficial knowledge. We shall, therefore, give a few lectures upon the rise, progress, and improvements of Chemistry, and at the same time endeavor to point out to you the characters of the most considerable chemical writers.

Professors in every Science take a pride in endeavouring to prove that Science as ancient as possible, whether they think that this antiquity will make it be more esteemed, or that they will shew its great usefulness by the esteem in which it has been held for many ages : The Chemists have not been behind in this ; they have endeavoured to trace their art to the first ages of the world ; and indeed in every age many chemical processes have been made ; but it will appear upon further examination that it was not reduced into a distinct Science till many ages after. The first that can with justice claim the title of Chemist is Tubal Cain, who, as the Scripture tells us, was the first artificer in brass and Iron. This shews us that the branch of Chemistry called Metallurgy was at that time brought to some degree of perfection, otherwise Tubal Cain would not have been able to get metal from ores so hard to fuse, and so deeply buried in the bowels of the earth. And indeed when we consider what short time that men had lived on the Earth, we should scarce give credit to it, if it was related in any book but the Sacred Writings. The Second Chemical process we read of is Noah's making wine after the flood. From Asia Chemistry was carried into Egypt probably by Ham one of the sons of Noah, from whose name some derive the term Chamia or Chemia. Indeed Corrigius asserts that the Egyptians knew little of Chemistry and Borrichius asserts on the contrary that they understood it very well; but there is little credit to be given to either on account of their prejudice and partiality ; but comparing them both together, we may conclude that the Egyptians understood the manner of fusing ores and getting the metal from them:

and Moses, a man, as the Scripture expresses it, skilled in the wisdom of the Egyptians, knew how to calcine and powder gold, so as to mix it with water, a process that has puzzled many of our modern Chemists. It may be done by melting gold with Liver of Sulphur powdering the mass and throwing it into water.

Though the Egyptians understood the Metallurgy so well, yet they do not deserve the name of Chemists, in the present acceptation of the word, which signifies a peculiar kind of experimental philosophy, and which requires a knowledge not only of metals, but of all natural bodies in general. The Chemists however refer the origin of this art to Egypt, and sometimes they call it the Hermetic art, from Hermes Trismigistus whom they suppose was the first inventor. But it is ridiculous to refer the invention of any general art to one particular person ; it is always by the successive labors of Several that an art is brought to perfection, and instead of being able to refer the origin of any particular art to one particular person, we can scarce tell for certain who invented any particular art : who knows the discovery of the Mariner's Needle, and what disputes there have been about the Air pump, Barometers, Thermometers etc. The Case is, a second improves upon it, a third puts it in execution ; and all claim the honor of the invention.

But to proceed : From Egypt Chemistry travelled with the other Arts into Greece, and though the Greeks were not general Chemists, yet many Chemical writers conceive every Greek historian to be a profound Alchymist : Hence they explain the story of fetching the golden fleece to be only the discovery of Alchemy, or, the transmutation of the baser metals into gold. And honest Homer, who has escaped most others, is dragged in by the Chemists who say that by the story of Mars and Venus being caught in an Iron Net by Vulcan, he means to express in an allegorical manner the whole of their Grandwork of transmutation. There are many other passages which they explain in the same manner, but this is sufficient as an example ; for I shall observe once for all, that the baser metals were never changed into Gold, notwithstanding all the boasts of the Alchymists. However the Greeks studied Natural Philosophy very much, and consequently Chemistry as a branch of it, and some of their Philosophers, examining the structure of Natural bodies, asserted that they were made of certain Elements or Compound particles ; some, that all

B

bodies were made originally of water, (Thales) ; others, of fire (Heraclitus) and the Pythagoreans and Peripateticks assumed the four Elements of Fire, Air, Earth, and Water, which have been adopted by most of the Moderns. These, however, were but rude attempts, though we must own, that, notwithstanding all the modern discoveries, the Ancients made quicker progress than the Moderns have done ; and if we examine their doctrines in a favourable light, we shall find that they agree in many respects with the Moderns. Thus, Pericles considered all bodies in a state of Amity and discord in relation to each other, which, when fairly considered, we will find to be the same as the well received doctrine of Attraction and Repulsion.

Parmenides asserted that all bodies were composed of fire and earth ; by which he meant that in any body there is an Active and Passive principle. Heraclitus asserted that all bodies were composed of Fire, i.e. Different bodies are composed by different condensations and rarefactions of this element, Thus Earth when melted becomes Water, Water when rarified is called Air, Air still more rarified & divided becomes Fire, and condensed fire becomes Earth. But these were only bold assertions and rude conjectures ; whereas the modern philosophers, Bacon, Boyle etc. followed different but better methods : they began with experiments, and from Bases formed just & firm theories. The success of each method is apparent from the great progress Chemistry has lately made. However, though the Grecians in general were only intent upon Theory, without recourse to experiments ; yet Democritus was continually employed in making useful experiments : his works are indeed lost, but we can learn from Petronius Arbiter that he made Glass and Artificial gems.

Lect. 2. After Democritus had thus happily begun the method of making experiments, the study of Natural Philosophy was checked in Greece by Socrates, who turned their minds from Natural to Moral Philosophy. However the study of it was revived by Aristotle who wrote a history of animals etc. And after him came Theophrastus who had wrote treatises upon plants and Fossils : the latter is still remaining, and has been translated by Dr. Hill ; but although these knew some little of Chemical Arts, yet by their works at that time we may safely say that Chemistry was not brought to any degree of perfection, nor was even termed a distinct Science. Persons in endeavoring to find out the history of Chemistry would naturally examine the writings of Physicians of the several ages : And accordingly they will find that Hippocrates is dubbed a profound Alchymist by the Chemical historians upon the authority of one paragraph only, and which, when fairly examined, rather proves his ignorance in the Science ; and if we examine the medicines he made use of, we shall find that there were none properly called Chemical, and that seemed to have any alliance with it, that were made purposely for Physic but borrowed from other Arts.

From Greece Chemistry passed with the other Arts into Italy ; but we do not hear of any chemical process till the time of Tiberius, when Pliny mentions the making glass, and in the time of Caligula of Gold being obtained from Orpiment : Tho' the making of malliable glass is probably a fiction, yet these shew they were proficients in the Art of making glass, and the assaying Mercury was likewise at this time obtainable from Cinnabar, but yet it was no general Art, for in the time of Discorides and Galen they scarcely knew any thing of sublimation & distillation which are employed so much at present in Chemical experiments ; but the only instance of Distillation is that of distilling Tar per Descensum ; and the only method they had of getting Mercury from Cinnabar was by putting the Cinnabar over the fire in an earthen bowl and inverting another over it, the Mercury rose to the upper vessel, and they separated it by getting all their small particles together ; and to obtain an oil from pitch which we call fossileum they were obliged to having a fleece of wool in the steem of pitch to condense the vapour. These instances prove the ignorance of the Antients about the Art ; and indeed we find that there was no Pharmaceutical Chemistry till after the time of Galen and toward the decline of the Roman empire ; and the first time we hear of Alchymy was in the fifth century, and Chemistry was prosecuted by Dioclesion who ordered all the books relating to this Art to be burnt. Soon after the rise of Chemistry, came the Goths & Vandals who overrun the Roman Empire and put a stop to all the Arts. However there are more Greek manuscripts on Chemistry preserved in our Public Libraries, Said to be wrote during the general confusion, a list of them may be found in Boerhaave, and notwithstanding what these or any other writers may assert we may venture to affirm that Gold was never made from any of the baser metals, the only two instances when it is positively asserted

to be done the one by Helmont, the other by Helvetius, both of
whom say that they had a small quantity of powder given them by
persons they never saw afterwards which would change the other
metals into gold. *Credat Iudeas Appella—Non Ego.*

L. 3. There are many other chemical writers, but after examining all impartially, we may conclude, that though they pre-
tend to many secrets and arcana, yet in fact they had not any of
consequence. But to proceed—While the Goths were destroying
Europe, the East was ravaged by the Saracens, and learning was
quite stopped for a while, till it was revived by the Arabians under
the patronage of the Caliphs, who particularly encouraged
Medicine : and the effects soon appeared for Rhazes soon after
gives us the process for purifying quicksilver, subliming the
Mercurius Corrosives, making the Oleum philosophorum, and
this we may properly call the origin of Chemistry, since we find
that most of the terms of the Art are borrowed from the Arabians.
When the Saracens had firmly established their government,
there were several universities founded for Physic and its several
branches. But notwithstanding this, we do not hear of any great
inprovement till the 13th Century, when we find that they were
acquainted with most of the processes in Chemistry. They knew
how to distil inflammable spirit from Urine, they had Nitre which
was unknown to the Greeks & Romans, and they could extract
acid from this and the other Salts. They had the fossil, vegetable,
and Volatile alkalis, and knew how to make the Neutral Salts by a
combination of the several alkalis and acids. From this time we
may divide Chemistry into Alchemical and Pharmaceutical.
Among the Alchemical writers of the 14th Century were Friar
Bacon, Albertus Magnus, Arnoldus Devilla Nova and Raymond
Lully who said that Mercury can be converted into Water. After
these came a tribe of Alchemistical writers, who are enumerated in
Borrichius. Before we leave the tribe of Alchemists, we must
observe that it was through their means that Chemistry was first
advanced, as they were always employed in making experiments
to find out a substance to change all Metals into gold ; though they
missed the point aimed at, yet they hit upon numberless discoveries
in Chemistry : And others to find out a Panacea or universal
Medicine, by trying the effects of several preparations, discovered
many very efficacious Medicines.

Lect. 4th. We have now dispatched the first set of Chemists,

PLATE III

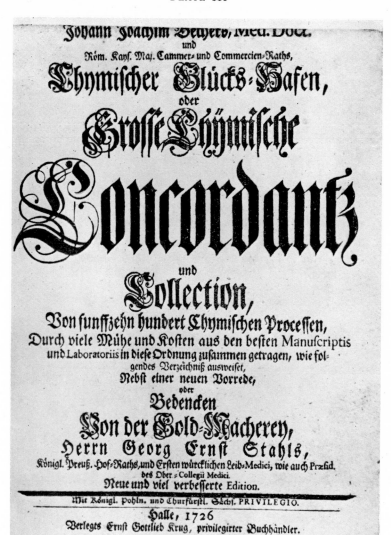

Becher's "Chemical Lottery", a manual typical of the early eighteenth century. Cullen, an exponent of Boerhaave's system, described it to his classes as "a heap of useless, insignificant experiments" (cf. p. 26). (Ferguson Collection, Glasgow University Library)

PLATE IV

A NEW METHOD OF CHEMISTRY;

INCLUDING THE

THEORY and PRACTICE of that *Art :*

Laid down on MECHANICAL PRINCIPLES, and accommodated to the *USES* of *LIFE.*

The whole making

A CLEAR and RATIONAL SYSTEM of

CHEMICAL PHILOSOPHY.

To which is prefix'd

A CRITICAL HISTORY of *CHEMISTRY* and *CHEMISTS, From the Origin of the Art to the present Time.*

Written by the very Learned

H. BOERHAAVE,

Professor of *Chemistry, Botany,* and *Medicine* in the University of *Leyden,* and Member of the Royal Academy of Sciences at *Paris.*

Translated from the Printed Edition, Collated with the best MANUSCRIPT COPIES.

By *P. SHAW,* M. D. and *E. CHAMBERS,* Gent.

With additional Notes and Sculptures.

LONDON :

Printed for J. OSBORN and T. LONGMAN, at the *Ship* in *Pater-noster-Row.* M.DCC.XXVII.

The first description, in English, of Boerhaave's system of chemistry. It is based on an unauthorised publication of 1724 which led Boerhaave to publish, in 1732, his celebrated *Elementa Chemiae* (cf. pp. 41, 78). (Ferguson Collection, Glasgow University Library) commonly known by the name of Alchemist, whose writings in general are false and affectedly obscure ; and the greatest use they have been of to Chemistry is that by their means the art was preserved and has since been applied to nobler purposes.

We now proceed to the second class of Chemists, Viz. those who cultivated the art with a view to Medicine and who have enriched it with so many powerful preparations. Medicine in the first ages of the world was chiefly Diatetick, however they soon discovered certain simple drugs, which, by repeated trials, they found had peculiar qualities, some would cause vomiting, others purging ; and by degrees these were increased in number ; and when particular persons came to study Physic and to cure diseases, they enquired into the virtues of more plants and added them to their Materia Medica, which vastly increased the number of Medicines. Pharmacy was hitherto very simple : even in the time of Hippocrates it consisted only in the mixing several simple drugs into Compounds ; and Sometimes of making decoctions & infusions, and, as we said before, Hippocrates used some minerals in Physic, yet these were only such as were made for other arts, and not purposely for Physic. They may therefore justly be looked upon as Simple medicines ; in the same manner as we do Camphor, Vitriol etc. at present.

The Materia Medica was greatly increased by Herophilus, who spent a great part of his time in examining the virtues of plants. Superstition has likewise from time to time increased the catalogue ; and we justly remark that in ignorant barbarous ages the bulk of the Materia Medica was always larger than in refined polite ages. Towards the declension of the Roman Empire the Materia Medica was greatly lessened by the Methodic Sect who endeavored to reduce all diseases to three or four different symptoms of Hot, Cold, Dry & Moist ; and accordingly only used a very few medicines to counteract such disorders. On the contrary the Dogmatical or Empirical Sect encreased it, and it is to these we owe those Farrages of drugs mixed together in the Mithridates and Theriac. This was the state of Pharmacy when Galen appeared, who greatly increased the number of drugs. After him Medicine received no improvement for a thousand years ; partly occasioned by the ignorance of the ages, and partly by the Reverance they paid to the father of Medicines. Nor do we hear of any Chemical preparations except Rose water. Chemistry as we before observed first appeared in Arabia, but Pharmacy did not then receive any great improvement from it, though the foundation was then laid for the improvements which it received in the succeeding centuries. The regular physicians of these times exclaimed against the violent Chemical preparations of Mercury and Lixivi Tartari etc. etc. The Empyreans, however, ventured to use them, and by their help performed great cures in the following age.

Learning was universally languid, and the arts were but little cultivated till the 15th Century, when learning again was revived, and was greatly forwarded by printing which was invented at this time. The discovery of America and the West Indies in the 15th Century furnished us with many noble drugs, and about this time Pharmaceutical Chemistry was greatly studied : Basil Valentine is the first author of this class of chemistry we know of ; he has given us the virtues of each preparation. Some say he lived sooner, but there are proofs to be brought to the contrary. By this time most of the present operations in Pharmaceutical Chemistry were known and some of the preparations to be used in Medicine, and Mercury, which was before only used in external applications, was now tried in the Lues Venerea, which had just appeared, and had been in vain attacked by common Gallenical Medicines. This gained great honour to the Chemists, and entirely baffled the Schools. At this time appeared Paracelsus, a strange unaccountable man, who caused great revolutions in all the parts of Medicine. He was born in Switzerland, and when he was of a proper age, was committed to a famous Chemist who taught him his Art. Not contented with that, he travelled through all Europe, and applied himself indifferently to Physicians, Barbors, Old Women, Conjurors, & Chemists, from whom he learned many secrets, and thus he encreased his stock of sure and approved remedies : he performed so many surprizing cures by daring to use mercury & opium, that the magistrates of Basil made him a Professor in their University : Here he read lectures, not, as was the common custom, from Galen, but from his own books, and in a solemn manner, when seated in his Professor's chair, he burnt the writings of Galen & Avicenna. By this means Physic was furnished with many noble Medicines : and though he was a ridiculous and impious fellow, yet we are obliged to him for breaking through the prejudiced reverence to Galen, and for opening the road for experiments and free reasoning. From this time Chemistry gained ground apace, except at Paris, where the Galenists assisted by the civil power, persecuted the Chemists, and forbid the use of Opium and Mercury in Medicine. However, they were countenanced in other places, particularly in England.

Lect. 5th. At the beginning of the 17th century the experiments of Galileo and the Theories of Gassendi & Descartes, assisted by Anatomy, shook the authority of Galen and the doctrine of the Peripateticks : and now Chemical Medicines were universally used, and even Chemical Theories of Physick came into Vogue ; though most physicians still kept the Galenic theory and used Chemical Medicines, even the faculty of Paris revoked the decree they had made, & vouchsafed to use Chemical preparations. Pharmaceutical Chemistry daily gained ground and new preparations were continually discovered. But not to dwell too long upon these, we shall only observe that the chemists before the last century were in general of weak judgments, illiterate, fond of Alchymy and of discovering a Panacea : they likewise mixed judicial Astrology with Physic. Their writings are affectedly obscure, and their experiments false ; and though a Proficient in Chemistry may pick out some useful hints from them, yet to a young student they will not be entertaining, and will likewise be apt to mislead him.—About the year 1650 Chemical preparations became very numerous, but from that time they have been gradually decreasing. The reason of their prodigious number was, that the Chemists upon their inventing any new medicine and finding it serviceable, never considered that its effects were similar to those of another Medicine ; thus we find that a few of the numerous distilled & essential oils will serve all the purposes of the great Farrage of them formerly used by Chemists. The Galenical infusion of many plants is preferable to the extracts which the Chemists had instituted in their place : the essential salts so much extolled by the Chemists are now entirely neglected, being found similar to some other salts got with less trouble : Salt of wormwood or Tartar is found to answer the purposes of all the different Lixivial Salts. There are likewise great alterations in the mineral preparations. The Chemists were formerly possessed with a foolish notion that all metals were of all value in Medicine in proportion to their intrinsic value : thus they reckoned Gold as the best etc. But we now find that Gold has little or no medical value, & that some other metals have poisonous and deliterious effects :

and even the preparations of Mercury & Antimony are now reduced to a very few and these are not all used. Mercury is found to be serviceable without any preparation. But notwithstanding all these reformations, there may be several things altered hereafter for the better. These improvements were first begun by the Edinburgh college of Physicians ; but the College of London, though difficult to rouse, has vastly exceeded them, as may be seen by an impartial view of their Dispensatory : and we may say with great truth that Britain has exceeded all other countries in the improvements of Pharmacy. France comes nearest her, but yet she is far behind, as is sufficiently proved by their distilled waters, which is ridiculous.

Before we proceed to philosophical Chemistry, I shall give you a short account of the application of Chemistry to Medicine. The Arabians, who, as we have often observed, were the first chemists, did not think of any improvements in the theory of Physic from Chemistry ; nor did any till Paracelsus, who was very daring in this, as well as in his other schemes ; he joins to it the absurd doctrine of Judicial Astrology and the Cabala. After him came Van Helmont with his ridiculous doctrine of an Archeus. When the Chemists had once begun a chemical theory, they would allow nothing else to have a share in it. They endeavored to account for every disease from this doctrine of acids & alkalies, and to this they said was owing all the process of Digestion & Chilifaction as is shewn in anatomical treatises. Afterwards the royal Society, Boyle & Newton, introduced the Mechanical Theories, which seemed diametrically opposite to the Chemists ; At last appeared the great Boerhaave, who, being learned in both, and not bigotted to either, has shewn that both theories are in part true, that to explain original diseases we have need of Mechanics, and that Chemistry alone can explain the doctrine of the fluids.

Lect. 6th. *Philosophical Chemistry*.

This, as well as other branches of Chemistry, was very imperfect, and but little cultivated by the Grecians, Romans, or Arabians; nor was there any considerable improvement till the 16th Century, when the Arts were thoroughly revived ; and it was then that Galileo, and Lord Bacon appeared and restored them. They laid the foundation of Natural Philosophy. Some have attempted a contrast between these two, but very unfairly, as they were employed in quite different pursuits. When Galileo was promoting mechanical philosophy, Bacon was laying the foundation of Chemical. For this purpose he used the best and safest methods, Reasoning, Viz. that by Induction : and while the whole world was subject to the Aristotelic Philosophy, Bacon boldly rejected it, and planned out the only sure way to Philosophy, Facts and Experiments, and tho' he was no favourer of the Alchymists, yet he justly observed that they were possessed of an infinite number of facts & secrets which, if properly applied, might prove a sure basis to true Chemistry. Some of Bacon's enemies have denied his being so great a man as he is generally esteemed : They say that he made no improvements in Chemistry, but they ought to consider that he planned out the road by which we have made so great discoveries. His continual avocations from Philosophy in his daily necessary business of state may well excuse his making experiments ; and upon this account we must not entirely rely upon those experiments which he mentions.

The improvement of experimental knowledge was left to Boyle, who took up Chemistry where Bacon left it, and by this example set all the Chemists in Europe to work in making experiments. With the advantage of an affluent fortune he spent a long life in making experiments upon every branch of Chemistry. The surprizing effects he met with every day in his experiments induced him to believe the transmutation of metals, which he often declared he believed and as he thought it might be his lot to make the happy discovery, he employed his interest at court, and procured a repeal of that law that forbad persons making gold from other metals. He spent a great deal of his time in contriving chemical medicines ; but as he was not a physician himself he was forced to trust the trial of them to his friends, who often by way of flattery, extolled them too much. This has made some people blame him for his credulity, and boasting of his Specific remedies and *Spt. Blood* in Pleuratic cases and *Ens. Veneris* in the Rickets. He was particularly versed in philosophical Chemistry, and has reformed the Chemical Experiments : Vid : Boyle's Sceptical Chemist.

Though he rather objects to other systems than proposes any of his own, he shewed us the use and importance of experiments ; he taught us that more Chemistry is to be learned in the shops of artizans than the laboured theories of Chemists : He likewise stript Chemistry of all its uncouth and mysterious language.

Some say that he is mysterious himself and affects to keep Chemical secrets : but an impartial enquirer will find that he only conceals some subtile poisons, and such secrets as had been communicated to him by Chemists with an obligation not to divulge them ; and it is to be feared that some of his manuscripts are fallen into hands that will not communicate them to the world.

Boyle is almost the first Chemist that is worth reading ; but after him, came many famous ones, particularly the great *Newton* who has left several folio Manuscripts upon Chemistry, which I fear will never be published. Before Boyle, indeed, lived two good metallurgists, Viz. Agricola and Erckern and contemporary with them were Kunkel, Glauber and Beeker. The first of these published a commentary on Neris's Art of Glass in high Dutch ; Observationes Chemicae, these are obscure by his absurd theory— Laboratorium Chymicum ; This is mysterious, though it is on the whole a useful work. Glawber was chiefly employed in the improvements of Arts : He published many works which are enumerated by Shaw in his translation of Boerhaave—Beeker was almost the first who applied Chemistry to Philosophy in general, and shewed its universal use. He was poor, and supported by Mr. Boyle, till he died in making experiments in the Cornish mines. He published many books, and amongst the rest his Concordantia Chemica, or, as the title is in high Dutch, the Chemical Lottery, which by the bye is a proper one for it is a heap of useless, insignificant experiments, where you will find many blanks to one prize. Since this time Chemistry has been chiefly improved by the several societies, as those of London, Paris. The royal society of London has not added much to the improvement of Chemistry : The only Chemical papers are those done by Dr. Cox and Slare ; but the Society of Paris, under the name of *Academie Royale de Sciences*, is much better regulated. Every one of the pensioners is obliged to deliver into the society annually an account of their several labors. Hence several ingenious persons are continually employed in Chemical pursuits.

Lect. 7. Among the first that have published any papers in this Society is *Homberg*, who being supported by the Duke of Orleans, tried an infinite number of experiments, which he has communicated to the world in the French Memoirs. His theory is the Corpuscularican, which is mere conjecture, for how can we fix the shape of the primary particles, which are to us invisible. After him followed the Lemerys, and Geoffrey who published his Lectures on the Materia Medica, a table of Elective Attractions, the great use of which will be fully explained in the following Lectures.—Reamure, who has left us a compleat treatise upon Iron, together with many other valuable writings. Duhamel ; Hellot ; Macquer, and several others. Germany has always been famous for Chemistry, which is, as it were, its natural science. The country being full of mines, the people have been naturally led to Metallurgy & other arts. Hence we have had *Stahl*, who is full of improvements, and was the first that gave us anything of Chemical system. He is, however, obscure, and cannot be understood by any but proficients.—*Juncker*, who has given us a collection of experiments in his Conspectus Chemicae, but he does not tell us the original authors, and the facts are strained to favor his Theory. *Hoffman*, who was both a great Physician and a Chemist, has given us an excellent book called his *Observationes Physico Chemicae*, and several treatises upon salt and mineral waters.— Kunkel's book of Pyristologia is of considerable value. John Andreas Cramer has given us a very elegant treatise on Metallurgy. In the *Memoires de l'Academie de Berlin* we have *Caspar Newmann*, who is chiefly a Pharmaceutical Chemist. Pott and Margraaff both very good writers, and the latter may serve as an example to young students. Lastly came *Boerhaave* a person of great learning. He is the chief reformer of the Method & Language of the Chemists. He is accurate in his description of the processes and has made great discoveries in Chemistry, particularly in fire, which, if it be not complete, yet is an excellent treatise for the first of that kind.

We have now finished the history of Chemistry, and have likewise pointed out to you some of its uses, so that it is needless to dwell any longer upon it.

NOTES AND REFERENCES

[1] The *Paisley Advertiser* for 16th January, 1830, records his death at the age of 75.

[2] Thomson believed these lectures on the History of Chemistry to date from 1756 and considered them to represent very faithfully the "manner of composition" employed by Cullen. John Thomson, *Life of William Cullen, M.D.*, Blackwood and Sons, Edinburgh, 1859, Vol. I, p. 99.

GLASGOW UNIVERSITY IN THE EIGHTEENTH CENTURY

J. D. Mackie

THERE IS a pleasing picture of our university in the *Journall* of an unknown Englishman who visited Scotland in 1704, and found, except in Edinburgh and Glasgow, very little to approve. Of Glasgow, which had then a population of about 12,500, he writes that it was "the second town in Scotland, and an university, which tho' perhaps is not so large as Edynburgh, nor are the buildings quite so high, nor is the town so populous, yett 'tis a more regular built and a cleaner town, and has more good streets in it then Edenburgh has, and the buildings are as handsome as those at Edenburgh, or are rather before them. . . . In the east streete of this town is the college belonging to this university, which is all in the town, and, I think, is a more regular building then the college at Edenburgh, tho' not so large. Here are 40 scholars that lodge in the college, but there are 200 or 300 that belong to it, and all wear red gowns, as do likewise those at Aberdeen and St Andrew's, the 2 other universities of this kingdom. In the ffront of this college, towards the streete, is a good library, and this college is about the middle of this streete." [1]

The College which excited the admiration of this unknown visitor had been erected during the seventeenth century, at a time when it might have been supposed that the religious disputes would have made building difficult. It was begun by Principal Strang in 1632, but its main architect was the zealous Patrick Gillespie, who, though he succeeded in getting in a surprising amount of money—even from some of the professors—left behind him a considerable debt and an ambitious programme which alarmed his cautious successor, Robert Baillie. Nevertheless the work went on, and it was completed under Principal Fall (1684-90), who surrounded the College with a wall, put a clock in the tower, and balusters on the stair leading to the Fore Hall, displaying the lion and the unicorn (the unicorn being given pride of place).

28

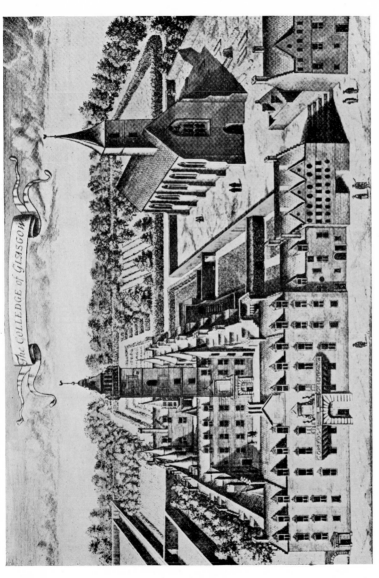

The COLLEDGE of GLASGOW

Glasgow University. (From the drawing by Slezer in the late seventeenth century) (cf. p. 29)

The College of the eighteenth century stood on the east side of the High Street, right on the line of the street. The main building consisted of two quadrangles, the first of eighty-three by forty-two feet—that is, about twice as broad as it was deep—and the second of seventy-nine by a hundred and three feet. These quadrangles were joined by a thoroughfare above which mounted the great tower. The drawing by Captain Slezer,[2] published in 1693 (but possibly made before 1670) shows the buildings as they stood towards the end of the seventeenth century. They were of three storeys, except for the east end of the inner quadrangle which was of two storeys only. From other evidence, we know that to the right hand, or south, of the main entrance was the lion and unicorn stair leading to the fore hall, which must have occupied most of the front of the building. To the left was the house of the janitor, or bedellus. This served as a sort of tavern where wine was supplied to both teachers and students—as the College claimed, without license—and as a " howff " where student societies could meet.

To the south of the main building and flush with its front was the Principal's house. South of that again a few steps led to the kirkyard and kirk of the Blackfriars, sometimes called the College, church. This church had been closely connected with the University from its first foundation ; [3] it had at one time actually belonged to the University, and in it the University worshipped until the year 1764. In that year the College resolved to establish a University chapel,[4] but, in fact, services were held in the common hall, and the University kept its sittings in the Blackfriars church until 1848.

North of the College was a garden, which during the course of the century was turned into a professors' court ; between 1722 and 1782 were erected a dozen handsome houses, which excited the jealousy of the civic community in which the occupation of a whole house by a single family—even a wealthy family—was extremely rare.

Beyond the second quadrangle were gardens which extended to the Molendinar, and open lands on the other side which, during the eighteenth century, were, by skilful purchase, extended south until the College property reached the Gallowgate. The gardens were famed for their beauty, though between 1732 and 1744 a small portion, close to the eastern side of the inner quadrangle (in which, in fact, the books had hitherto been housed) was used for the site of the new library.[5] Much later, between 1804 and 1807 another part of the garden disappeared to make way for the new Museum which was built to house the Hunterian treasures.[6]

Meanwhile, 1757-60, in the open fields beyond the Molendinar there had appeared a new observatory. The story of its foundation is instructive.[7] Alexander Macfarlane, brother to the laird of that name, who was a wealthy West-Indian merchant, had erected an observatory in Jamaica for his own use, and in 1756 it was announced that he had bequeathed to the University the instruments, which were the best then procurable. The University accepted the bequest, resolved to lay out £400 on the building of an observatory, used the pretext to acquire additional lands in Dovehill, appointed the young James Watt (who was a kinsman of Professor Muirhead) to help to look after the instruments when they did come, and conferred on the donor's brother the degree of LL.D. Even though the diploma for this degree was enclosed in a silver casket bearing the arms of Macfarlane and of the University, the incident may serve as an example of shrewd academic economy.

The mention of the observatory and of James Watt serves to call attention to the changes which took place in the University during the eighteenth century. It was a period of great, though rather unspectacular, expansion. There was development both in the curriculum itself and in the method of instruction.

When the century opened, the main purpose of the University was, as it had always been, the provision of clergy for the national church. Although, under Andrew Melville in the sixteenth century and at various times during the seventeenth century, attempts had been made to broaden the concept of teaching, which declared themselves, for example, in efforts to provide separate chairs in different subjects, none of these attempts had come to very much.

In the year 1700 there were only two professors—the Professor of Divinity, of old standing, and the Professor of Mathematics, whose chair dated only from 1691. For the rest, the teaching was still done by four regents, each of whom was supposed to take the entrants of one academic year through the whole of the four years' course in Arts—Greek in the first year, Logic in the second, Ethics in the third, and Physics in the fourth. This system though it was defended by some wise men, obviously became more and more difficult as the scope of the subjects spread more and more beyond the limits of the old Aristotle ; and it was already beginning to break down.

In 1704, a separate chair was founded for the teaching of Greek, and the establishment two years later of a chair of Humanity took cognisance of the facts that Latin was a subject worthy of study in itself, and that, were it regarded merely as a vehicle for the communication of learning, the average Bajan, or entrant, who was often a boy in his very early teens, came up insufficiently prepared. Even so, Latin had no regular place in the Arts curriculum, and Mathematics was somehow regarded as an " extra ". The Arts student did his Greek in his first year (though sometimes he was given a little Latin too), and his Philosophies in the succeeding years, under the same regent until 1727 when separate chairs were founded for Logic, Moral Philosophy, and Natural Philosophy.

Then he might go on to his Divinity ; the training in this subject had meanwhile been improved by the creation of chairs in Oriental Languages (1709) and Ecclesiastical History (1716). At the same time provision had been made for the teaching of what might be called professional subjects by the establishment of chairs of Civil Law (1713), Medicine (1716), and Anatomy (1718).

The only other chair founded in the eighteenth century was that of Astronomy (1760) ; but the curriculum was extended in other ways. In 1704, a small Botanic, or " Physic " garden was made in the College grounds, and there was created a lectureship in Botany, which, in 1720, was fused with the chair of Anatomy. In 1751, the able Cullen, who had already been teaching Medicine, Botany, Materia Medica, and Chemistry in the University, was given the chair of Medicine ; but it was in the field of chemistry that he and his successor Joseph Black were most distinguished. Later in the century, lectureships in Materia Medica (1766) and Midwifery (1790) were established. Just as, from the chair of Medicine there sprang the new subject of Chemistry, so from the old Natural Philosophy there arose new and virile shoots. Even before the Macfarlane bequest, Professor Dick had had a telescope and other instruments ; and though it was to recondition the astronomical instruments that James Watt first entered the College, he was afterwards much under the protection of the

32 A LECTURESHIP IN CHEMISTRY

professor of Natural Philosophy. Since, lacking a burgess ticket, he could not ply his craft of mathematical instrument-maker in the city, he was allowed to work, and even to open a shop, in the precincts of the College ; and it was within our walls that he developed his improvements on the Newcomen engine. It was not only among what we should now call the " science " subjects that expansion occurred. In the hands of Adam Smith, the teaching of Moral Philosophy developed into the teaching of Political Economy ; and at various times special arrangements were made for instruction in French and Italian.

It must not be supposed that with all these changes the University lost its ecclesiastical complexion. The Principal (until 1858) must always be a minister ; so also must the professor of Divinity, and, in effect, the professors of Oriental Languages and of Ecclesiastical History. Many other professors, too, were connected with the manse, and if some of them had served as tutors in great families before they obtained their chairs, it must be remembered that a tutorship was in those days a recognised road to a parish.[8] The University still sent its representatives to the General Assembly, and with its affairs the local ministers were closely connected ; the minister of Glasgow was one of the official Visitors ; other ministers served on the early Commissions of Visitation, and the Presbytery of Glasgow kept an eye on the orthodoxy of the teaching. John Simson, professor of Divinity, was attacked in 1714 and again in 1726, and eventually suspended by the General Assembly, in 1729 ;[9] even Leechman himself was attacked[10] on his appointment to the chair of Divinity in 1744.

None the less, the whole tendency of the age inside the church, as without it, was towards broad-mindedness and toleration.

There was abroad a feeling that the work of the University had been too much aloof from the needs of an expanding society. This feeling was loudly expressed by the Rev. William Thom, minister of Govan (1746-1790), who in his *Letter on the Defects of an University Education and its Unsuitableness to a Commercial People*,[11] advocated the creation of what we might call a commercial college ; and it was shared by John Anderson, Professor of Natural Philosophy from 1757-1796, who left his money (inadequate to the purpose) for the foundation of what we should call a technical college, though he called it Anderson's University. Certainly Anderson took his teaching outside the walls of the

University, but it is not true to say that he was the inaugurator of " night classes " or adult education. As early as 1743, Francis Hutcheson had opened a special class on Sunday evenings "to whoever chose to attend", and the lectures which he delivered "though learned and ingenious, were adapted to every capacity ".[12]

It must be remembered, too, that Adam Smith was in close contact with the civic community where Provost Andrew Cochrane was the exponent of sound economic ideas[13] and that the opinions of the *Wealth of Nations* were developed in lectures given in Glasgow before Smith had come into contact with the French Physiocrats.[14]

The " never to be forgotten " Hutcheson, as Adam Smith called him, was a supreme example of the new method and the new tone which began to pervade the teaching of " Philosophy " or, as we should say, Arts. Not only did he handle his subject with a wide tolerance, but he paid little heed to his notes, walked up and down (Thom called him the " ambulatory Professor "), and spoke in English.[15] Cullen taught in English too, and very soon the practice of lecturing in Latin ceased. It seems to have survived longest in the Faculty of Law.

Plainly the University was, in the eighteenth century, in a thriving way. From a little College of 400 students, concerned mainly with the study of Philosophy and Divinity, it had become, by 1800, a University boasting thirteen chairs, several lectureships, and at least 1,000 students, which concerned itself not only with the old Philosophy and the old Divinity, but with the study of Language, Literature, and Economics, as well as with Medicine and Science.

It must not be supposed that the expansion had always been peaceful. Indeed, the truth seems to be that the University in the eighteenth century was given over to violent disputes which sometimes degenerated into personal rows. The College had in fact, all the strength and all the weaknesses of a close corporation. Owing their places very often to patronage, interest, or kinship, the professors felt that they had a vested interest in their chairs. Often they clung to office when their powers were in decline ; when they ceased to teach, they sometimes still retained the title, the house, and a great part of the salary ; and if at last they were brought to consider retirement, they sometimes claimed the right to appoint a successor. That the personal factor should enter into

c

College disputes was inevitable, especially as the professors, taken all in all, did not lack character, and some of the controversies were the expressions of idiosyncracy. Others, however, turned on matters of principle, and were due to the faulty constitution of the University.

That there were difficulties inherent in the organisation of the University will appear from the very fact that Reid, writing after 1790, explained how the " modern constitution " was founded on the " new royal charter " (the *Nova Erectio*) of 1577.[16] By this, the whole revenues held of old or newly granted were given to the College then founded—not to the University—though an annual account was to be presented to the Visitors :—the Rector, the Dean of Faculty, and the minister of Glasgow. Of these officers, the first two, along with the purely honorific Chancellor, represented the University, which was maintained as the degree-giving institution. There were, therefore, two rival authorities, the Rector's Meeting (representing the University), and the Principal's Meeting (representing the College, or Faculty as it came to be called) ; and as the questions at issue often touched finance, it is easy to understand how frequent were the disputes. Feeling ran high, and on one occasion (1766) Principal Leechman " admonished " his opponents though they constituted the majority of the Faculty.[17] Decisions of the Court of Session (1771-2) proved that he was in the right, in claiming that property was vested in the " College ", but the controversies continued throughout the century. In so far as any governing motive can be detected, it is the complaint that the Principal, with the aid of a few supporters and of the factor, exercised too much power in University finance.

At the beginning of the century, there was a bitter struggle about the election of the rector. According to the practice of the earliest times, which had not been altered save in detail, the rector should be chosen by all the members of the University voting in their four nations. At the time of the Revolution Settlement, however, perhaps on the pretext that a popular election might lead to tumults, which could be used by the Jacobites, the Principal virtually took the nomination into his own hands though there was some pretence of an annual election. Sir John Maxwell of Nether Pollok held the office from 1691-1717. When, on his retiral, the students, the masters and even some of the teachers tried to assert their rights, Principal Stirling moved the Chancellor, the Duke of

Montrose, to appoint two successive royal commissions which gave him his own way. In 1718, four professors and the three regents—the majority of the teaching staff—were suspended from any share in University administration, and it was not until 1727 that the rights of the University to choose its own rector were restored.[18]

The election of rectors may have led occasionally to acts of disorder, but these were not serious ; more remarkable were cases of individual misconduct, which were due to the uncertain system of discipline which obtained. As originally founded, the College had a strict discipline which was quasi-monastic. This had gradually become looser, and during the eighteenth century it was very much relaxed because the residential system disappeared. By 1700 the common table had already vanished, and though forty students still " lived in ", their numbers steadily decreased. Occasionally, as in 1760, the College seems to have proposed to take in more students ;[19] but it seems that the students did not particularly want to come, and that the University was glad to have the rooms to house not only new classes and collections of instruments, but James Watt's shop, the Foulis' printing press, and even the Foulis' Academy of Art (founded soon after 1750). The University gave to the students of this Academy a room under the north part of the new library, and even permitted an open-air exhibition to be held annually " upon every return of his Majesty's birthday ", until 1775, within the inner quadrangle.[20]

In these circumstances, it was impossible to maintain the old control over the students. Even the keeping of terms had become very casual. At the beginning of the century, the session began on October 10th, but the students drifted in so casually that teachers had to mark time for two or three weeks, and the only remedy found was to postpone the real opening to November 1st. That the students should be compelled to come in time does not appear to have occurred to anyone. Once embarked upon his career, the student was subject, in the first place, to the discipline of his professor, then to the *jurisdictio ordinaria* wielded by the Principal and the professors of the five " gown classes " ;[21] serious cases might be taken thence to the Faculty, and the gravest cases of all to the Rector's Court, in which all the professors and the Principal sat as assessors. The jurisdictions of these authorities were not quite clearly delimited, and the cases of individual students were sometimes affected by the fact that they were boarders with professors. When it is added that the student of the eighteenth century might, on occasion, assert that he had renounced his studentship and warn the professor to expect to " hear from him as a gentleman ", it is plain that difficulties must inevitably arise.

From our records may be culled some remarkable cases. In 1766, Semen Desnizkoy, one of two Russian students sent to study Law under the patronage of the enlightened Prince Shuvalov, felt himself insulted by Professor John Anderson, who had refused him a place in the College " band " or choir. After consultation with a Law student, Alexander Ferguson,[22] the Russian assaulted the professor in the quadrangle. So grave a breach of discipline demanded a trial by the Rector's Court, at which the Earl of Selkirk presided. The offender was sentenced to make public apology—actually he seems to have made many apologies, including one to Ferguson, who was sent to prison for his part in the affair.[23] A little later David Woodburn, underwent a nine days' trial before the Rector's Court[24] for remarking that " more good was to be got by attending the theatre, than the drowsy shops of Logic and Metaphysics ". He was eventually dismissed with an admonition ; but soon afterwards was expelled for a scuffle in the quadrangle with John Robison, who succeeded Black as lecturer in Chemistry in 1766. Robison, who was a choleric man and had served in the navy, was fined for his share in the affair.[25]

In 1773, James Moor, the one-eyed professor of Greek, was censured for having struck a student, who construed badly, with a heavy wooden candlestick ; [26] and in the following year he resigned when a fresh complaint was made against him by Anderson, with whom he had a permanent quarrel,—there had at one time been talk of a duel, and both the professors had been fined.

Anderson, who seems to have had a gift for quarrelling, was concerned in very many disputes. In 1773, he assaulted an Irish student, James Prossor, and when the victim spoke of demanding satisfaction, had him haled through the streets to prison. Conscious, probably, that the Faculty would not support him, he managed to get a not very honourable absolution from the Court of Session. Ten years later he denounced, probably with reason, the conduct of the Hon. Mr. Fitzroy, a boarder with Professor Macleod ; and when Macleod replied to the accusation with a flood of invective, Anderson gave him the lie direct, shaking his cane at him across the table. A couple of months later, the shoe was on the other foot. One of Anderson's boarders was detected in a small delinquency, and his defence of his pupil was so intemperate that the pupil found himself expelled for defying the College jurisdiction, and Anderson himself was censured. In 1784 he was temporarily suspended from the exercise of academic discipline for his arbitrary conduct towards a student ; it was about this time that, he threatened to proclaim to his students the folly of the Faculty in the institution of certain prizes. Next year, his instigation of abusive papers against the Principal on the matter of College finance led to the degrading and expulsion of two of his *protégés*, and his own condemnation—in £250—by the Court of Session.[27]

But, in spite of these unworthy squabbles, College life was a pleasant and not ungracious thing. The pages of " Jupiter " Carlyle[28] show us a society where young men were well taught, taught themselves in well-run literary clubs, enjoyed good society, and had opportunities of social and intellectual intercourse with their teachers. The teachers, too, kept abreast of the times. The informal club of the eccentric but able Robert Simson, professor of Mathematics, was evidently a nursery of right thinking and wise conversation, and the Literary Society of Glasgow College, (founded 1752) which included most of the professors and many other distinguished citizens received from its members valuable papers on the most recent books and the most recent discoveries. Black, for example, told the Society about his discovery of latent heat ; and Reid, a year before his death at the age of 86, contributed an objective study of the alteration of muscular movement as the frame deteriorated.

Dr. Johnson, it is true, was not very favourably impressed with the Glasgow professors. He seems to have found some of the local big guns silent before his heavy artillery, but as he concluded his stay with an evening at the house of Professor Anderson, there may have been another reason for his irritated patronage.

Taken all in all, the professors were not a bad lot. Simson was a great mathematician, Leechman a great theologian, Hutcheson and Adam Smith great philosophers. Moor in Greek, Ross and Richardson in Latin, were excellent scholars. Forbes and Millar were eminent in Law, Cullen and Black in Chemistry. Both the

Dicks were competent teachers of Natural Philosophy, and more competent still was John Anderson, despite his habit of quarrelling with everybody. When Lord Brougham, who had been Rector in 1825, visited Glasgow in 1860 as President of the National Association for the promotion of Social Science, he was eighty-two years of age. His address, like the sermons of the ageing Mr. Micah Balwhidder, was something too long, yet it soared at times with the eloquence which, even then, belonged to a past age, and his tribute to the University of Glasgow is worthy of repetition :

" It was here that Black made those discoveries which have changed the face of Natural Science more than any since the days of Newton ; that Watt gave the great invention to the world which has made such an alteration in its aspect, and such a revolution in its fortunes ; that Stewart learnt and Simson taught the ancient geometry which he restored ; that Reid placed the philosophy of mind upon its firm foundations, and freed it from sceptical cavils ; that Millar traced that history of the constitution upon principle, freed from the vulgar errors, empirical as well as absolutist ; that Smith established those sound doctrines, now happily become the faith of practical statesmen, as they had long been of the learned, connecting the commercial gains of all nations with the improvement of each, and making their mutual intercourse a mutual and equal benefit, and the bond of peace ".[29]

NOTES AND REFERENCES

[1] *Tour in Scotland, Etc.*, 1704, Blackwood, Edinburgh, 1818, pp. 47-9.

[2] *Theatrum Scotiae*, ed. 1874, no. 18.

[3] At the time of the foundation of the University many of the friars had been incorporated, and within the walls of the priory lectures had been given and congregations had met. After the Reformation, the University obtained a gift of the kirk and its pertinents on condition that the University regents read prayers there ; but in 1636 the college eased itself of necessary repairs, and gained 1,000 marks for the building fund, by surrendering the kirk to the city, reserving to themselves the best place after that of the Town Council, and the right to use the church for graduation. After the building had been destroyed by fire in 1670 it was reopened in 1702, the University contributing one sixth of the cost of repair. (See Murray, 407 *et seq.*).

[4] This project was the subject of a most amusing diatribe by the Rev. William Thom, minister of Govan (1764-90). (*Works*, 1799, 231). Under the old charter of the *Nova Erectio*, 1577, the University

enjoyed the teinds of Govan, the Principal of the College being obliged to preach every Sunday. In 1621, the Visitors of the College relieved the Principal of this duty on condition that the University should give to the minister of Govan manse and glebe, five chalders of victual or 500 marks of money. In 1630, this arrangement was confirmed by a charter of Charles I. After an increase granted in 1762, the stipend was 500 marks, plus two chalders each of meal and bear. On the valuation of 1777 the victual was worth £42 8s. sterling, and in 1783, £50 13 4. (Comm. 1831, ii, 323). As 500 marks Scots was worth at this time only about £28 sterling, the original stipend had been appreciably increased ; and the value of the glebe, which was of seven acres, must now have been considerable. Thom, who had been presented to the living by the College in 1746, seems to have thought that the stipend was too small. His grievance may have been real, but it must be remembered that he was apt to tilt against other institutions besides the University. He criticised nearly everybody. When the city showed no interest in his scheme for a commercial college he trounced the citizens as Philistines in a pamphlet *Showing the Scheme for Erecting An Academy in its own Proper Colours,* and in *The Happiness of Dead Clergymen* his attack on his own cloth was astonishing.

[5] David Murray, *Memories of the Old College of Glasgow,* Jackson, Wylie & Co., Glasgow, 1927, pp. 272-3.

[6] Murray, 347 *et seq.*

[7] J. Coutts, *History of the University of Glasgow,* MacLehose and Sons, Glasgow, 1909, p. 229.

[8] (Rev.) Alexander Carlyle, *Autobiography,* Blackwood, Edinburgh, 1860, p. 55.

[9] Coutts, 210 *et seq.*

[10] Coutts, 238. Carlyle (p. 70) points out that the attack on this professor only served to establish his " superior character ".

[11] W. Thom, *The Works of the Rev. William Thom,* Cf. also pp. 263 *et seq.*

[12] Carlyle, 70.

[13] Carlyle, 73-4.

[14] W. R. Scott, *Adam Smith as Student and Professor,* p. 319.

[15] Murray, 144.

[16] *The Statistical Account of Scotland.* 1799. XXI, Appendix, p. 21. The account of the University in this volume is generally attributed to Thomas Reid, Professor of Moral Philosophy, 1764-96.

[17] Coutts, 273.

[18] *Ibid.,* 200-1. *Report of the Royal Commission on Scottish Universities,* 1831, p. 220. The Commissioners doubted the wisdom of a system whereby boys in their early teens exercised a power as great as their teachers.

[19] *Ibid.*, 334.

[20] MacLehose, *The Glasgow University Press*, 1638-1931, G. U. Press, 1931, pp. 186, 188.

[21] These were Greek, Humanity and the three Philosophies, on the ground that they represented the original teachers under the *Nova Erectio, plus* two professors added by the College itself. It is difficult to see why, if Humanity were included, Mathematics was excluded ; and the Commissioners thought that the claim rested on " very questionable grounds ". *Report of the Royal Commission*, 1831, pp. 240, 264.

[22] Son of the Laird of Craigdarroch ; himself the Craigdarroch of Burns' *Whistle*, " Craigdarroch, so famous for wit, worth, and law ".

[23] Coutts, 322.

[24] Duly pilloried in Thom, (374 *et seq.*) : *The Trial of a Student at the College of Clutha, in the Kingdom of Oceana.*

[25] Murray, 186.

[26] Coutts, 310-11.

[27] Coutts, 284 *et seq.*

[28] Son of the minister of Prestonpans, he was a student of Divinity at Glasgow, 1743-45.

[29] Murray, 314.

HERMANN BOERHAAVE AND SCOTTISH CHEMISTRY

Archibald Clow

THERE WAS a strong alchemical tradition in Scotland, we learn, but naturally the cryptic nature of alchemical operation did not lead to public instruction. The roots of chemical teaching in Scotland are to be found rather in pharmacy and medicine. Indeed, when in the last decade of the seventeenth century the surgeons of Edinburgh acquired a new Hall, Alexander Monteith of Auldcathie equipped a laboratory where apprentice apothecaries might receive some training in the arts of chemistry. Not only did Monteith see to the furnishing of his department . . . three rooms furnished with four hundred *gally pigs* . . . but he took steps to see that it was adequately supplied with funds.

After the surgeons' laboratory had been set up, it is not long before we hear of the teaching of chemistry in Edinburgh and in 1702 it was announced that a " course of chemistrie " would be given in the surgeon apothecaries' hall. So right at the beginning of the eighteenth century the teaching of chemistry was started.

The next development is one of great importance from at least two points of view. In the first place it established the active teaching of chemistry in a Scottish University, and in the second, by the appointment of Dr. James Crawford, an already formed connection between the Universities of Edinburgh and Leyden was further developed. This Continental connection is of the utmost significance to Scottish chemistry, so it is necessary to say a little more about it.

The University of Leyden was founded in 1574. Ostensibly Protestant in outlook it was willing to admit students of all faiths at a time when the only other foundation in the Low Countries was the Catholic University of Louvain. In the course of time Leyden became famous as a medical school, its reputation being built up by the teaching of Boerhaave, Albinus, Gaubius, Ostendyk and Van Royen. While Hermann Boerhaave (1668-1738) lectured on chemistry there, his eminence was perhaps its chief attraction.

" For a student, therefore, to possess every advantage for improving himself in his medical studies, it was deemed necessary to repair to Leyden and attend Boerhaave's lectures on Chemistry." [1]

From our point of view it is important that Boerhaave was the pupil of the Fife-born Dr. Archibald Pitcairne (1652-1713).

Pitcairne studied Arts and Divinity at Edinburgh and Medicine at Rheims, where he graduated in 1675. He returned to Scotland to practise, and became a founder Fellow of the Royal College of Physicians. A man of great spirits and jovial habits he soon built up an international reputation and in 1692 he was invited to go to Leyden to occupy the chair of medicine. In this way a vital link between Leyden and Edinburgh was established which persisted throughout the greater part of the eighteenth century.

Pitcairne did not stay long at Leyden but while he was there he had the good fortune to have Hermann Boerhaave as a student. Boerhaave followed Pitcairne as professor at Leyden and helped to build up the reputation of the Leyden medical school.

Boerhaave's influence on European science was immense. Stahl (1660-1734), the propounder of the phlogiston theory, was influenced by his teaching. Others are to be found among the founders of celebrated faculties throughout Europe, particularly at Vienna and Edinburgh. We can trace his influence on John Dalton (1766-1844), and on the early chemists in Ireland, but perhaps nowhere was it of greater significance than in Scotland. The first two holders of the chair of chemistry at Edinburgh attended his lectures, as also did Francis Home who helped to establish the chemical industry of Scotland although he was actually professor of Materia Medica.

After Boerhaave's death in 1738 his influence at Leyden was carried on by his pupil, Hieronymus David Gaubius (1705-1780), and the close connection with Scotland was kept up, till during the course of the eighteenth century no less than forty holders of Scottish academic chairs had studied at Leyden.

While we are primarily interested in the origins of the teaching of chemistry in Scotland, we cannot leave the subject of Leyden without commenting on the effect which Leyden alumni must have had on the course of Scottish intellectual development as a whole.

Every member of the faculty of medicine founded at Edinburgh in 1726 had studied at Leyden under the celebrated Boerhaave and the following examples are but a few instances of those occupying cardinal positions in science or medicine who had done likewise.

Of the holders of chairs in the Universities of Aberdeen there were Pat. Chalmers (d. 1727), James Gregory (1674-1733), James Gordon (d. 1755) and James Gregory (1707-1755). To Glasgow went Thomas Brisbain (1684-1742), John Johnstoun (1685-1762), Robert Dick (1722-1757). Thomas Simson, who was first professor of medicine at St. Andrews, was also at Leyden. Further afield we have the Percivals of Warrington and Manchester, Wm. Stephens and Brian Higgins of Dublin. Then there were the chemical entrepreneurs of Edinburgh who continued their studies on the Continent, namely Dr. John Roebuck and Dr. James Hutton.

Leyden was in fact the focus of Continental learning for Scotland during several generations, son following father in the lecture halls, till they returned to take up academic appointments in the Universities of Scotland.

But to return to the development of chemical teaching. In the year of Pitcairne's death the Town Council of Edinburgh decided to appoint a professor of Chemistry and at the end of the year Boerhaave's student, James Crawford, was appointed professor of Chemistry and Physic. Crawford's appointment to Edinburgh is noteworthy since it gave professorial status to a teacher of chemistry before even the first text on the subject was printed, viz. Boerhaave's *Elementa Chemiae* (1732).

Of Crawford's students or influence we know little and there is some evidence that he did not attract many students. At any rate in 1724 four fellows of the Royal College of Physicians purchased a house for a chemical laboratory and announced that they proposed to lecture extramurally on chemistry and materia medica. They were John Rutherford (1695-1779), Andrew Plummer (d. 1756), John Innes (d. 1733), and Andrew St. Clair. After a year or two they established themselves in the University of Edinburgh where for a time there were four " professors of chemistry ".

Of the four, Rutherford and Plummer are the most important. Like his predecessor Rutherford was a pupil of Boerhaave.

" Having studied under Boerhaave, he had formed a strong predilection for chemistry ; and, in the plan which he and his associates had projected, that department of medical science was assigned to him as his province . . . The science of chemistry was then in its infancy, and possessed but few of the allurements which now accompany the study of it." [2]

None of the four " professors " made any memorable contribution to the advance of chemistry but they numbered among their students several chemists whose contributions were noteworthy. Three prominent industrialists studied under Plummer, John Roebuck (1718-1794) to whose credit goes the founding of the first sulphuric acid works in both England and Scotland, and of perhaps even greater moment, the founding of Carron Iron Works. Another of Plummer's students was James Keir who succeeded in establishing the manufacture of soda at Tipton several decades before the start of the Leblanc Process in this country. The third of Plummer's students who calls for mention here is James Hutton (1726-1797) who derived a considerable income from the manufacture of sal ammoniac and thus had the leisure to devote his energies to geology. Both Roebuck and Hutton completed their education at Leyden, most probably reading under Gaubius who taught there till 1775.

On the academic side Plummer had two brilliant students, William Cullen (1710-1790), whose fame is celebrated in this volume, and Joseph Black, both of whom followed their master in the chair of chemistry at Edinburgh.

Plummer continued to lecture till 1755 when he was succeeded by Cullen, the first of a series of men who came from the expanding industrial centre in the west to infuse the University of Edinburgh with a new vitality. It is indeed not without social significance that from Cullen's appointment to Edinburgh in 1755 the chair of chemistry there was held for over a hundred years by chemists whose training and initial teaching experience was obtained in the industrial west of Scotland. If Edinburgh during the later eighteenth century was considered next to Paris as the intellectual centre of Europe, it should not be forgotten that in the chemical field at least its reputation was founded on imported personnel and that one of the chief centres from which it imported personnel was Glasgow.

Of Cullen's achievements we need not speak at length here. He marks the beginning of a new era. He lectured in English and as soon as he had established himself he printed and distributed *The Plan of a Course of Chemical Lectures and Experiments directed chiefly to the improvements of Arts and Manufactures* to be given in the laboratory of the College of Glasgow during the session 1748. The objective of Cullen's lectures should be noted since he was one of the first chemists to appreciate that chemistry was a discipline standing on its own, subservient neither to medicine nor to pharmacy. He recognised the importance of the application of scientific chemistry to industry, but that must not suggest a narrow outlook.

" He was a great master in the scientific branches of husbandry; a consummate botanist, and possessed a correct taste in the fine arts. In the year 1758, after finishing off chemistry, he delivered to a number of particular friends, and favourite pupils, more lectures on the subject of agriculture. In these few lectures, he, for the first time, laid open the true principle concerning the nature of soils, and the operations of manures." [3]

Yet Adam Smith, who was professor of Logic and Moral Philosophy at Glasgow from 1750-63, and as such a colleague of Cullen, could say that Universities were " sanctuaries in which exploded systems and obsolete prejudices found shelter and protection after they had been hounded out of every other corner of the world ". Either Adam Smith was not referring to the Scottish universities, or he was unfamiliar with developments co-extensive with his own.

For five years during his tenure of office in Glasgow Cullen had as a pupil Joseph Black (1728-1799) who succeeded him in Glasgow and later in Edinburgh when Cullen was translated to another chair. Black was an outstanding figure but he was by no means Cullen's only notable student. Others included Dr. Withering of the Lunar Society, Dr. George Fordyce of Harley Street, William Hunter, and most important from the point of view of the teaching of chemistry in Scotland, George French who established the teaching of chemistry in Aberdeen. As a student of Cullen the non-medical approach to chemistry which characterised French's teaching is significant.

In 1756 Cullen was succeeded by his pupil and friend, Joseph Black, who during his occupancy of the new lectureship made important provisions for improving the facilities for teaching chemistry there. In 1763 he persuaded the University to equip a new laboratory and lecture room. This was done at the then very considerable expense of five hundred pounds.

In 1766 Black followed Cullen to Edinburgh and for thirty years he occupied the chair of chemistry during one of the greatest formative periods through which both theoretical and practical chemistry has gone. In everything Black laid great emphasis on accurate quantitative work and so influenced the generation of men who were his students at Edinburgh.

In the late eighteenth century Black was to Edinburgh what Boerhaave had been to Leyden. Not only did his pupils Robison, Irvine, Hope, Cleghorn and Thomson succeed to the lectureship at Glasgow or chair at Edinburgh but several of his other pupils founded chemical schools throughout the world. Smithson Tennant developed the backward Cambridge school, Thomas Beddoes stayed for a time in Oxford : J. Morgan and B. Rush founded the chemical school at Philadelphia, Ogilvie went to Aberdeen, Garnett to the new Anderson's Institution of Glasgow. Wm. Henry, the Manchester chemist studied under him. Sir Humphry Davy regretted that it had not been his good fortune to study under Black.

And so the succession went on. At Glasgow, Black was succeeded by John Robison (1739-1805) and he in turn by William Irvine (1743-1787). Irvine died in office and was succeeded by Thomas Charles Hope (1766-1844), son of the professor of botany at Edinburgh. Hope only occupied the lectureship for four years before transferring to the chair of medicine but his interest in research maintained the reputation of the Glasgow school established by Cullen and Black.

When Hope was appointed professor of medicine he was succeeded by Dr. R. Cleghorn (1755-1821) and for a time, under pressure of extramural activities, original chemical work in Glasgow was discontinued. Cleghorn had not the leisure to engage in original research but is said to have been a lucid and interesting lecturer. He continued to lecture with acceptance till succeeded by Thomas Thomson in 1817 but it was a great misfortune for Glasgow that she was unable to attract and hold a teacher of chemistry who would have more ably followed the experimental tradition of Black and Cullen, especially as the social context was one to which a practical scientist should have responded with enthusiasm.

When the weight of the years began to fall on Black, Hope, then professor of medicine at Glasgow, was appointed joint professor of " chemistry and physic ". In 1799 he became sole professor, the third of Glasgow's lecturers to hold the chair in the capital. Under Hope's influence the development of chemistry was rapid and of increasing economic importance. In some ways Hope, on account of his contacts, occupies a place of equal importance with Black, because more and more industrialists, of the Macintosh and Tennant concerns for example, were in a position to benefit by contact with the universities. The popularity of chemistry with all classes in Edinburgh became so great that Hope sometimes had five hundred students attending his lectures while outside the university interest was every bit as great. Hope continued to lecture till 1844 when he was succeeded by Dr. William Gregory as independent professor of chemistry fully quarter of a century later than the foundation of an independent chair in the more highly industrialised city of Glasgow.

Contemporaneously with the period of academic brilliance which coincided with Cullen's and Black's occupancy of the chair at Edinburgh, a group of men in England laid some of the corner-stones of the industrial revolution. Some were English by birth and education ; some were Scots, but the intellectual power behind their achievements was the direct offshoot of the cultural renais-sance in eighteenth century Scotland. Taken *en masse* this group probably represents the highest concentration of fellows of the Royal Societies that has ever been associated at one time with any industrial undertaking. The social context of this industrial group was Birmingham industrialism, and for convenience it may be referred to as the Lunar Society. For a period of years when the Royal Society of London and the Universities of Oxford and Cambridge were characterised by their lethargy, and the Royal Society of Edinburgh was struggling with the millstone of polite learning which was attached to its neck from birth, the Lunar Society, a small, unofficial, private colloquium of philosophers, did much to bring into greater prominence the application of chemistry to arts and manufactures.

Never before in history was there such a fruitful coming together of pure science and advancing industry as in the Lunar Society. Matthew Boulton, the prince of industrial capitalists, put his table at their disposal. Phlogistians and anti-phlogistians dined together : James Watt and Joseph Priestley vied with Cavendish and Lavoisier over the discovery of the composition of water :

James Keir achieved the manufacture of alkali where Watt, Black, and Roebuck had failed : William Murdock's gas-light illuminated the mills powered by Boulton and Watt's engines : Josiah Wedgwood supplied chemical utensils for Priestley's experiments : Priestley in turn analysed minerals of possible utility in pottery : a leaven of wit and philosophy was added by Erasmus Darwin and Richard Lovell Edgeworth. Indeed there was not an individual, institution, or industry with pretensions of contact with advancing technology throughout the length and breadth of the land, but some member of the Lunar Society had connections therewith. Behind many of them was the inspiration of the environment in which they had passed the formative years of their adolescence, the Scotland of Cullen, Black, and Hope, faithful guardians of embryonic science who remained in the north while their pupils moved south to plant and nurture in English soil the seeds of the industrial revolution . . . and reap their often rich reward.

NOTES AND REFERENCES

[1] A. Bower, *History of University of Edinburgh*, Edinburgh, 1817, Vol. II, p. 126.

[2] *Ibid.*, 216.

[3] *Ibid.*, 392.

Further information on topics just touched on in the preceeding essay will be found particularly in

A. Clow, *Scotland's Contribution to Industrial Development through the Application of Chemical Science since the Seventeenth Century.* (Blackwell Prize Essay—MS.—Aberdeen University Library).

A. Clow, " Chemistry at the Older Universities of Great Britain During the Eighteenth Century", *Nature* 1945, *155*, 158.

J. D. Comrie, *History of Scottish Medicine* (2 vols.), London, 1932.

A. Duncan, *Memoirs of the Faculty of Physicians and Surgeons of Glasgow* (1599-1850), Glasgow, 1896.

R. W. I. Smith, *Students of Medicine at Leyden*, Edinburgh, 1932.

H. C. Bolton, " The Lunar Society, ", *Transactions of the New York Academy of Science*, 1887, 7, No. 8.

Alex. Findlay, *The Teaching of Chemistry in the Universities of Aberdeen*, (Aberdeen, 1935).

WILLIAM CULLEN, M.D., AND HIS TIMES

Born, 15th April, 1710 : died, 5th February, 1790. Edcn : Grammar School, Hamilton, Universities of Edinburgh and Glasgow (M.D., 1740). Lecturer in Chemistry, 1747-55. Professor, successively, of Medicine (Glasgow, 1751-5), Chemistry and Physic, Institutes of Medicine, Practice of Physic (Edinburgh, 1755-89).

Douglas Guthrie

IN JANUARY 1747, the University of Glasgow decided to expend the sum of fifty-two pounds upon the equipment of a chemical laboratory and to appoint a lecturer to teach chemistry.

The first lecturer was Dr. William Cullen, one of the most eminent physicians of a century which was singularly rich in masters of medicine. Second only to Hermann Boerhaave of Leyden, who was the foremost figure of his day in chemistry and in medicine, Cullen is remembered as one of the most efficient and successful teachers in the whole history of science and medicine.

To William Cullen, Glasgow owes a deep debt of gratitude, and it is fitting that his name should stand first among those pioneers who are to be honoured in this series of lectures. Not only did he initiate the teaching of Chemistry in Glasgow ; he actually was the founder of the Glasgow Medical School.

The Rise of the Glasgow Medical School

When Glasgow University was founded in 1451, no provision was made for the teaching of medicine. There may have been efforts to introduce it into the curriculum ; indeed, Andrew Boorde, that adventurous English traveller who could " trust no Skott ", wrote in 1536—" I am now at a little unyversite named Glasco, where I study and practyse physyk for the sustentacyon of my lyving ". Our information becomes much more clear and

D

definite towards the end of that century, when the worthy Master
Peter Lowe, after spending 22 years as a surgeon with the armies
of France, returned to his native town of Glasgow, wrote his
famous text book of " Chirurgerie " in 1597, and founded the
Faculty of Physicians and Surgeons of Glasgow in 1599. The
Faculty retained full control of medical and surgical practice in
Glasgow and neighbourhood for many years, but it was not a
teaching body. In 1637 Robert Mayne was appointed " ane
Professoure of Medicine " but little is known of his activities.
He died in 1646 and apparently the " Chair " died with him!

Early in the eighteenth century several medical appointments
were made by Glasgow University. In 1714, John Johnstoun was
elected professor of Medicine ; in 1720, Thomas Brisbane became
professor of Anatomy and Botany. Neither of those gentlemen
appears to have taken his duties seriously, and one historian refers
to them as " the inert professors ".

William Cullen's Apprenticeship and Training

Into this rather unattractive academic atmosphere William
Cullen entered in 1744. He had undergone a careful training and
was well prepared for his task. Born at Hamilton in 1710, the
son of the factor to the Duke of Hamilton, young Cullen attended
the local school and afterwards some of the Arts classes at
Glasgow University. At the same time he acted as apprentice to
Mr. John Paisley, a surgeon and general practitioner, the apprenticeship system being the normal means of entry to the
medical profession when there was no clinical teaching in hospitals.
The Town's Hospital at Glasgow Green was opened in 1733, but
it was not used for teaching purposes, and the Royal Infirmary
was not founded until the last decade of the century (1794).

After completing his apprenticeship, Cullen made a voyage to
the West Indies as ship's surgeon. Next, he was employed as
assistant to an apothecary in Henrietta Street, London, where he
perfected his knowledge of Materia Medica. Then he returned to
Scotland, as his father had died and he was responsible for the
education of his younger brothers and sisters. He therefore
commenced practice at Auchinlee, near Shotts. There, by a
happy chance, he met the Duke of Argyll who was paying a visit
in the neighbourhood. The Duke was interested in chemistry
and, being in need of some apparatus, he had the want supplied by

Dr. Cullen. He was much impressed by the young man's ability, and this patronage from the leading peer of Scotland was naturally of advantage to Cullen. A few years later, when in practice at Hamilton, Cullen became the medical adviser to the Duke of Hamilton, who held him in high esteem. The family of Hamilton, the Douglases, has always been characterised by frankness of manner and love of learning, and the Duke was quick to appreciate similar virtues in his young medical attendant. Useful though such contacts naturally were, Cullen had no need to depend upon distinguished patients for his advancement. He possessed not only sound knowledge, but in high degree that indefinable aptitude for the art of medicine which is found in all great physicians. As one of his successors, Thomas Thomson, tells us in his " History of Chemistry ", Cullen " became the friend and companion of every family he visited, and no one who employed him could dispense thereafter with his attendance or his intimacy ".

In 1736 Cullen joined forces with his friend William Hunter, another Lanarkshire man, eight years his junior, and the two began practice in the town of Hamilton. It was arranged that for a period of each year one of them should go away to continue his studies while the other attended to the practice. Cullen spent the first winter in Edinburgh, the medical school there being at the height of its fame under the leadership of Professor Alexander Monro (primus), who was virtually its founder. Next year, it was Hunter's turn, and he went to London. Finding there an attractive field, he decided to stay, residing at first with Dr. William Smellie, who had recently gone from Lanark to London and was soon to become the leader of British midwifery. William Hunter, though less famous than his younger brother John, attained eminence as an anatomist and obstetrician. His bequest of his museum and library to Glasgow University has made his name a household word there. Although there is no record of Cullen and Hunter having ever met again, they remained life-long friends and frequently corresponded. Hunter is reported to have referred to Cullen as " the man to whom I owe most, and love most of all men in the world ".

The house at Hamilton in which Cullen and Hunter commenced practice has long since disappeared, but on the wall of the Old Tolbooth there a metal tablet has been fixed, bearing the following inscription :

" Opposite this building stood the house in which from 1737 to 1740 medical practice was carried on by the celebrated physicians

William Cullen, M.D. 1710-1790

William Hunter, M.D., F.R.S. 1718-1783

Erected by the Hamilton and District Civic Society."

The partnership being thus dissolved by mutual consent, Cullen was obliged to find a new assistant, but at this time also he contracted a more permanent union by marrying Miss Anna Johnstone, daughter of the minister of Kilbarchan, who became the mother of his seven sons and four daughters. She was a lady of great charm and intelligence, and, during a long and happy married life, she contributed in no small degree to her husband's success.

Dr. Cullen found time to interest himself in civic affairs and he assumed the office of senior magistrate at Hamilton. But a genius and energy so great as his demanded a wider outlet. To be the founder of a Medical School at Glasgow, similar to the schools of Leyden and of Edinburgh, was his supreme ambition, and with this object in view he removed to Glasgow in 1744.

Cullen comes to Glasgow

He had already taken the M.D. degree of Glasgow in 1740. The Medical Faculty in 1744 consisted only of the " inert " Professor Johnstoun and his colleague Professor Robert Hamilton who had recently succeeded Thomas Brisbane in the chair of Anatomy and Botany. Cullen began to lecture on Medicine in a semi-official capacity, although no doubt there were some interruptions of academic activity during the troublous " '45 ". He was lecturing on Medicine in 1746 when he became convinced of the need for the teaching of chemistry within the University, or " College " as it was then called. Now it so happened that the newly-appointed professor of Oriental Languages, Alexander Dunlop, had been allowed to defer his duties for a time in order that he might act as tutor to a nobleman in Geneva. Dunlop proposed that the £30 saved by the University owing to his delay in assuming office should be applied to equip a chemical laboratory. To this sum the University added £22, and with the £52 thus raised the laboratory was established, while its lecturer was to be paid the handsome allowance of £20 per annum. Cullen was the first lecturer, assisted by John Carrick, who was also assistant in Anatomy to Professor Hamilton.

Unfortunately Carrick fell ill and was unable to fulfil his part of the bargain, so that Cullen was obliged to continue alone. With characteristic modesty, he explained to his first class of students that the course was " not offered by us as experienced masters, but as an attempt, for want of more able performers, to supply the rudiments of a useful and necessary branch of knowledge " and he added, " we desire and expect a good deal of indulgence and favour ". He went on to explain the attractions offered by a study of chemistry. " If a young man delights to have his hands employed in experiment, Chemistry will furnish him sufficient exercise. If his imagination must be amused with uncommon and curious appearances, Chemistry will constantly present them to him. If a man aims at gain and the improvement of the useful Arts, it is chemistry that must feed his hopes and give him assistance. Or if, more liberal still, he aims at the study of causes, Chemistry will gratify him in explaining the most curious phenomena of the natural world."

At a later stage of this lecture I hope to discuss in full detail Cullen's services to Chemistry in general. In the meantime, with your kind indulgence, I propose to complete the brief sketch of his life, and then I shall attempt to trace the progress of chemistry to the position in which Cullen found it. Cullen was an admirable teacher of chemistry, as he was of other medical subjects. Not only was he a good teacher who inspired enthusiasm in his students, but he took a deep personal interest in their welfare, and he placed at their disposal not merely his vast knowledge, but also his library and on many occasions his purse. Many a student was grateful to him for advice regarding the choice of a career and many found a second home in the hospitable house of Professor and Mrs. Cullen.

Cullen's philosophy is shown in his letters, many of which have been fortunately preserved. To a former student he writes, in 1759, " Everybody needs the corrections of his friends and should consult them before he appears in public. Show your Essay to some persons of patience, judgment and candour before you decide to publish it ". To his son, in 1765, he gives the following advice : " Study your trade eagerly, decline no labour, bear hardship with patience, be obliging to everybody above or below you, and hold your head up in a literal and figurative sense."

Cullen was not content to confine his teaching to chemistry ; he lectured also on botany, on materia medica, on the practice of physic as well as the theory or, as we now call it, physiology. As Dr. Alexander Duncan writes in his admirable " Memorials of the Faculty ", Cullen " was, in fact, a medical faculty in himself ". In addition to all this he conducted a busy practice, so that his leisure moments must have been few indeed. In 1751 he assumed a fresh responsibility when he was promoted to the Chair of Medicine on the resignation of Johnstoun, and it is not surprising that when the chair of Chemistry fell vacant in Edinburgh, he welcomed this opportunity of making a change which would allow him more time for private study.

Cullen in Edinburgh

This happened in 1755, when he succeeded Andrew Plummer as professor of Chemistry and Physic. Chemistry had been included in the Edinburgh curriculum for some years. The first professor of the subject, appointed in 1713, was James Crauford, who was at the same time professor of Hebrew—truly, a strange combination. Edinburgh, however, was not the first British University in which Chemistry was taught. That honour appears to belong to Cambridge where John Francis Vigani, a native of Verona, who had been giving lectures on the subject since 1683, was appointed professor of Chemistry in 1703. Incidentally, it is interesting to note that the first to teach Chemistry in Paris, at the Jardin des Plantes, in 1642, was a native of Aberdeen, William Davisson (ingeniously Gallicised as D'Avissonne) (1593-1669). Professor Plummer, Cullen's predecessor in Edinburgh, had confined his teaching for the most part to pharmacy, but Cullen, as we shall see, interpreted the subject in a much more liberal fashion.

The class of Chemistry prospered greatly in Cullen's hands. In his first session he had 17 students, in his second 59, and eventually the class numbered 145. Among his students were many who became eminent. One of them, Benjamin Rush, whose name is perpetuated in Rush Medical College, Philadelphia, wrote to Cullen after returning to America, " If I have been in any degree useful or successful in my profession, I owe all these things to you ".

Cullen's interest in Clinical Medicine led him to commence lecturing on that subject in the Royal Infirmary of Edinburgh, after the fashion of Leyden which had been introduced by Dr. John Rutherford, the grandfather of Sir Walter Scott. Meanwhile he continued his lectures on Chemistry.

In 1766 Cullen resigned from the chair of Chemistry in order to become professor of the Institutes of Medicine (physiology) in succession to Robert Whytt. He himself was succeeded by his brilliant Glasgow pupil, Joseph Black, of whose career we are to hear in the next lecture. I shall therefore refer to Black merely by name and shall pursue in no great detail the story of Cullen's later career in Edinburgh, as it has no direct bearing upon Chemistry. Edinburgh owes to Cullen a debt quite equal to that owed by Glasgow. He was one of the founders of the Royal Society of Edinburgh ; he was President of the Royal College of Physicians and laid the foundation stone of the new building in 1775. After having lectured for some years as joint-professor with John Gregory, he became sole professor, on the retirement of Gregory in 1773. Cullen was then 63 years of age, nevertheless he applied himself with energy to the duties of the new office, besides con- ducting a large consulting practice. Gradually, however, his mental faculties deteriorated. His last years were clouded by the death of his wife, and by a difference of opinion with his former assistant, John Brown, whose " Brunonian " doctrine of diseases aroused his strong antipathy. Although Cullen was a man of mild and equable temper, he would never allow that medicine should be a slave to such " systems ". Yet he was wont to remark, slyly, that " there must be a tub to amuse the whale ". He resigned his chair in 1789, and two months later at his country house of Ormiston, nine miles east of Edinburgh, his strenuous life reached a peaceful end.

Before I complete the story by attempting to assess the value of Cullen's services to Chemistry, here is a brief sketch of preceding developments in the subject, from the time of the Renaissance to that of Cullen.

Paracelsus changes the Theme

The Renaissance was no sudden upheaval but rather a steady change spread over a number of centuries. It is not surprising that chemistry was one of the earliest of the sciences to be affected. Clearly, alchemy could not live in the new atmosphere which was then created. Early in the fifteenth century, more than a decade before Vesalius published his " Fabrica ", and a century before Harvey wrote " De Motu Cordis ", there had lived a man who was determined that chemistry should be applied to medicine. Paracelsus (his many other names need not concern us) was born at Einseideln, near Zurich in 1493, the son of a country doctor, and he led a roving and adventurous life, dying in poverty at the age of 48. To this day he is a subject of controversy, lauded by some and decried by others. Certainly his methods were unconventional and his manners crude even for that time. The professor at Basle who prefaced his lectures by publicly burning the works of Galen and Avicenna as a gesture of his contempt for them, could not hope to be popular with everyone. " I pleased no one," he writes, " except the sick whom I healed." Nevertheless, Paracelsus was the herald of a new outlook in medicine and chemistry. He introduced simplicity in prescribing, using simple chemical remedies in place of the mixtures of numerous animal and vege-table products which had been favoured, and he showed how chemistry could be applied to the service of medicine. Of course he retained much of the medieval philosophy. To the two funda-mental substances, sulphur and mercury, he added a third, salt. " What burns is sulphur, what smokes is mercury, the ashes are salt ", the inflammable, the volatile, and the fixed principles. Paracelsus regarded disease as a maladjustment or lack of these three components of the body, and it was to be cured by supplying the deficient substance. His extensive works, written in a mixture of old German and Latin, are difficult to understand. But one fact is clear : Paracelsus changed the trend of alchemy. The ob-ject of alchemy, in his view, was not to make gold, but to make chemicals which might be directed against disease. He was, in fact, the founder of Iatrochemistry or medical chemistry, although it cannot be said that he contributed much to the existing chemical knowledge. His search for pure and simple extracts from minerals and plants, the quintessence or " arcana " as he called it, led eventually to the " active principles " in use to-day. Paracelsus showed how essential chemistry was to medicine and since his day chemistry has occupied a prominent place in every medical school.

Meanwhile the old alchemy degenerated into a cult of erudite nonsense and mysticism, a doctrine of such sects as the Rosi-crucians, a quasi-science approved only by cranks and misguided persons.

Perhaps the most important chemist to follow Paracelsus was Van Helmont (1577-1644), a nobleman of Brussels, who devoted his time and fortune to the study of chemistry. His doctrine of the life force, or " archaeus ", which he called " Blas ", is long since forgotten, but he was on surer ground when he coined the word " Gas ", and applied it to his " gas sylvestre ", or carbon dioxide, which he recognised as a product of fermenting wine and which he distinguished from vapours or air. " I call this spirit," he wrote, " by the new name of gas, which can neither be retained in vessels nor reduced to a visible form." Van Helmont is further remembered for his accurate, if misguided, experiment of estimating the gain in weight of a willow tree during five years, which, he concluded, was entirely due to water. He thus reverted to the ancient theory of Thales that water was the elemental source of all. Van Helmont recognised air, as well as water, as an element, but curiously enough failed to recognise the significance to plant growth of his newly discovered carbon dioxide. Nevertheless, Van Helmont is one of the great figures of chemical history. His views on fermentation as a significant factor in digestion and other processes were elaborated by Sylvius of Leyden and by Willis of Oxford, both of whom developed the ideas of the Iatro-chemical school. In their view the human body was a sort of wine-vat or brewery, with the physician standing by to regulate the actions of the ferments. It was a meddlesome type of medicine and if the patients recovered, they did so " in spite of " the treatment. But the dawning of a much more significant era in chemistry was at hand.

Robert Boyle and his Influence

The seventeenth century was a period of intense activity in every branch of art and science. There was a thirst for the new knowledge and a general desire to discard argument and to rely upon experiment, to get rid of medieval superstition and to seek for new truths.

Francis Bacon and Descartes provided a solid philosophical background to the scientific advances of their time. Galileo laid stress upon the value of measurement in science and Gilbert explained magnetism and was the first to use the word " electricity ", although it was not until 1687 that Newton revolutionised Physics by the publication of his " Principia ".

Harvey changed the entire outlook of medical science by his discovery of the circulation, made public in 1628 but only very slowly adapted to practice. The pioneers of microscopy revealed more and more fresh wonders to the eye, and the Royal Society was founded in 1663.

It was most natural that Chemistry should share in the general advance of learning, under the able guidance of Robert Boyle (1627-1691) whose influence on science was little short of that of Isaac Newton. This remarkable man, the Father of Modern Chemistry, was born in Ireland in 1627, the seventh son and the fourteenth child of the Earl of Cork, and he passed most of his life in Oxford and London.

Boyle, like Paracelsus, infused new life into Chemistry. Moreover, his methods were more dignified than those of the Swiss reformer. At last, Chemistry was to be studied for its own sake, and not merely as an aid to Alchemy and Medicine. Boyle's principal work appeared in 1661 and it was appropriately entitled " The Sceptical Chymist ". The writer appears to have been the first to question the ancient doctrine of elements and principles. Aristotle's four elements did not appeal to Boyle ; nor did the Salt, Sulphur and Mercury of Paracelsus. According to Boyle, an element was " something which has not been decomposed ", a view which remained current until quite recently. " I mean by Elements—Simple Unmingled Bodies, which not being made of other Bodies or of one another, are the ingredients of which all perfectly mixed Bodies are compounded and into which they are ultimately resolved." Unfortunately Boyle drew up no list of elements, a task accomplished by the next great reformer of chemistry, Lavoisier, more than a century later. Many of Boyle's numerous experiments were carried out with the aid of the air pump which he perfected. Some of them were physical rather than chemical, as the two sciences were still as one, and physiology was also involved when Boyle investigated respiration in small animals.

He followed previous observers in proving that Nature did not " abhor a vacuum ", and he showed that air was a material substance having weight and also explained satisfactorily what he called " The Spring and Weight of Air ", but its composition puzzled him. " There is some use of the Air which we do not understand," he wrote, this " vital quintessence which seems to refresh and restore our vital Spirits." . . . " Air is not a simple body but a confused aggregate of effluviums." He suspected the presence of " some odd substance on whose account the Air is so necessary to the subsistence of Flame ". Apparently he was on the verge of discovering oxygen, but chemistry had still to pass through " the phlogiston period " before the problem was solved. Nevertheless Boyle's achievement was a great advance and he clarified much of the obscurity which surrounded the relation of air to combustion and respiration. It is not surprising that Samuel Pepys referred to him in his Diary under the date April 28th 1667 —" Mightily pleased with my reading of Boyle's book, and only troubled that I am not able to understand it all for want of study. I understand enough to see that he is a most excellent man." The work of Robert Boyle focussed attention upon the mystery of air, which became still more mysterious when Stahl introduced his theory of phlogiston.

The Mystery of Phlogiston

George Ernst Stahl of Halle (1660-1734), " the sour metaphysician " as Boerhaave called him, was not gifted with an engaging personality. Nevertheless he rendered good service, not only by reaffirming the existence of man's soul in an age of materialism, but by suggesting a theory of combustion based upon common-sense observation. It was obvious that an inflammable substance, reduced to ashes, had lost something, and this something was called " phlogiston ". The fact that a metal, when calcined, might actually gain in weight, did not upset the theory, as it was argued that the presence of phlogiston made a substance lighter by conferring negative weight. Boyle's suggestion, that the air might play a part, appeared to   be forgotten, and the phlogiston controversy dragged on for a century or so. The phlogiston theory, although it delayed the recognition of the elements, was the first plausible explanation of the phenomena of oxidation and reduction. Just as the alchemists, in their search for gold, discovered new facts in chemistry, so also did the " phlogistonists " add to the chemical knowledge of their time.

Now the eighteenth century arrived, bringing many distinguished chemists. Only one need be mentioned, as he serves as an essential link with William Cullen to whom we shall presently return.

Hermann Boerhaave of Leyden (1668-1738), who has been called the most celebrated physician of all time, was also a prominent chemist. He did not concern himself with the phlogiston theory, but his great text book " Elementa Chemiae ", contains a prodigious amount of information, and is a collection of all the known facts and processes. Boerhaave stripped chemistry of all mystery and produced the most luminous treatise yet written. Of course the subject was still well within the compass of a single mind. Organic chemistry did not exist, far less bio-chemistry and bio-physics. Seven metals, five acids, half a dozen " salts ", the sulphates or " vitriols ", sulphur, arsenic and a few other substances supplied the stock, but Boerhaave made the most of it. As a chemist, a botanist and a physician his career strongly resembles that of Cullen. Boerhaave conferred upon Leyden a distinction similar to that which Cullen brought to Glasgow.

Cullen's Service to Chemistry

Now, in conclusion, one must attempt to assess the value of the work of William Cullen in the field of chemistry. He wrote very little on the subject, and in many histories of chemistry his name is not even mentioned. Cullen, like Boerhaave, took a wide view of chemistry, viewing it as a science useful not only to medicine but to mankind in general. Before his time it had been taught upon a very narrow plan. Cullen took it out of the hands of the metallurgists and pharmacists, and portrayed it as a study for every man of good education. Eighteen years of his life, eight in Glasgow and ten in Edinburgh were devoted largely to the teaching of chemistry, and his last thirty years were very fully occupied in the practice and teaching of medicine. His fame and reputation as a physician were perpetuated by several publications his " First lines in the Practice of Physic ", his " Treatise of the Materia Medica " and above all by his " Nosology ", a method of classifying diseases after the manner of Linnaeus which was followed for a number of years. His single published paper on chemistry, or rather on physics, was " On the Cold produced by Evaporating Fluids ", a paper which influenced the trend of investigation which afterwards led to Black's discovery of latent heat.

Although he made no discovery in chemistry and contributed little to its literature, Cullen exercised a great influence by his teaching, which was clear, interesting and infinitely painstaking.

He constantly urged the claim of chemistry as a subject of what was called " philosophical study ", and also as a valuable aid to various industrial arts. Of course the chemistry of Cullen's day was not very profound. Oxygen had not been discovered and the changes involved in combustion and respiration were not understood. The investigation of gaseous substances other than the air had scarcely begun. There was no clear distinction between " fossil alkali ", related to compounds of soda, and " vegetable alkali " as the salts of potash were called. Among the few known compounds related to these two alkalis were rock or sea salt, borax, and nitre. In contradistinction to the fossil and vegetable alkalis which were described as " fixed " or non-volatile, ammonia was known as the " volatile " alkali. During the time of Cullen, about 1753, the difference between the " mild " and " caustic " alkalis was clearly demonstrated by Joseph Black, Cullen's brilliant pupil who may be regarded as his chief " discovery ".

It would be a great mistake to suppose that Cullen confined his attention to teaching and that he was devoid of originality. There were two subjects to which he paid particular attention and to which he applied his vast store of chemical knowledge, namely agriculture, and the bleaching of linen. Cullen's researches in these directions were admirably described by Dr. Leonard Dobbin in his Sir James Walker Memorial Lecture of 1939, and Dr. Dobbin has very kindly permitted me to make use of the unpublished manuscript of that lecture. The original information is contained in a number of manuscripts by Cullen, preserved in the library of the Royal College of Physicians of Edinburgh, and in other libraries, consisting of lecture notes, memoranda, and voluminous correspondence which has all been carefully sifted by Dr. Dobbin.

Agricultural Chemistry

Cullen's extensive researches in agricultural chemistry are the subject of correspondence which passed in 1750 between him and Lord Kames, who was also most enthusiastic regarding this experimental enquiry concerning the principles of agriculture. Henry Home, Lord Kames, was a Scottish judge who acquired considerable reputation as an amateur agriculturist at his estates of Kames in Berwickshire, and Blair Drummond in Perthshire.

Cullen expressed the view that " the matter fit for the nourishment of plants is the same that is fit for yielding nitre or saltpeter ". This matter, which Cullen called " mucilage ", was more generally known as " humus " and consisted of decaying organic material. Cullen conceived the idea that " by examining soils for the proportion of nitre they contained, he could obtain knowledge regarding their respective suitabilities for the nourishment of plants ". To this end he devised an elaborate series of experiments to determine the relation between the fertility of various soils and their chemical composition. He proposed to note the effect of different manurial substances for the same soil and to determine the effect of air in the process of nitrification. It was an ambitious plan, and Cullen concludes the description by wondering where he is to find the necessary materials, assistance and funds. It is doubtful whether the investigation was ever carried out.

Another of the Cullen manuscripts examined by Dr. Dobbin is a synopsis of seven lectures on Agriculture. It would appear from these lectures, that Cullen followed Van Helmont in regarding water as the sole source of nourishment of plants. In his view the texture of the soil was of great importance, while nitre and manures acted, not as foods, but as stimulants to growth. In spite of such now obvious errors, Cullen had made a praiseworthy effort to apply chemistry to agriculture.

The Chemistry of Bleaching

Whatever may have been Cullen's influence upon agriculture, there can be no doubt that he met with greater success in his second subject of research, namely, the application of chemistry to the linen-bleaching industry. Then, as now, linen was bleached by exposure to sunlight, air and rain ; by boiling it with alkaline liquids, and by various other means. Chlorine had not been discovered, and the use of hypochlorites and of other oxidising agents to hasten the bleaching process, was unknown. Incidentally, however, there was complete absence of the early appearance of holes during wear in the household and table linen, the result of over-oxidation of the linen cellulose sometimes caused by modern methods of bleaching.

Cullen was concerned chiefly with the preparation of the alkaline solutions in which the linen was boiled. The solutions were prepared from wood ashes which contained salts of potash and soda, including carbonates and sulphates, as well as calcareous and siliceous matters ; all in varying quantity. The ashes were imported from a number of European countries and often the supply was inconstant owing to unsettled conditions and difficulty of transport. Furthermore, there was little attempt to standardise the solution or to draw any distinction between potash and soda salts, which were simply grouped as alkalis. The strength of the solution, or lye was estimated by weighing, by the use of what was called a " proof-ball ", a form of hydrometer, or even, sometimes, by tasting the fluid, a crude and rather risky method.

Cullen conceived the idea of preparing the bleaching ashes in Scotland, in order to ensure a constant supply and also to save the expense of importing ashes from abroad. In 1762 he arranged for a large-scale experiment in the Rannoch district of Perthshire where workers were hired to cut down birch trees, to burn the wood and to collect the ashes. Brushwood and bracken were collected and burned by women workers. The ash was lixiviated with water, then boiled down to dryness, and the product was passed on to the bleachers for trial and comparison with foreign ashes. Although the reports were favourable, there was no considerable saving of expense, and this notwithstanding the fact that the workers were paid at the rate of sixpence per day. The experiment was therefore not continued beyond the year.

Among Cullen's papers, Dr. Dobbin found a number of letters to a bleacher at Ormiston named Chrystie. In them, Cullen suggests various improvements in bleaching and refers to a number of experiments, both completed and projected. There can be no doubt that by the application of his knowledge of chemistry, Cullen advanced the progress of the bleaching industry.

William Cullen's Place in History

It was Cullen's practice, not only in his lectures on Chemistry, but in those on Materia Medica, and the Practice of Physic, to introduce the subject by a series of lectures devoted to its history.

He held very strongly that only by studying the past could one hope to understand the present. His lectures on history, which have survived in manuscript, although unfortunately not in print, are no mere account of the curiosities of alchemy, but rather a reasoned statement of the trends and influences which had caused chemistry to become one of the important sciences. Thus William Cullen, one of the most eminent physicians of all time, was also a leading pioneer of Chemistry and, in particular, of the teaching of Chemistry. Two hundred years have passed since he delivered his first lecture on Chemistry in the University of Glasgow. It is only natural that we should recall his achievement and honour his memory.

BIBLIOGRAPHY

J. Coutts, *History of the University of Glasgow*, Glasgow, 1909.

The First Boke of the Introduction of Knowledge, A Boorde, Ed., Early Eng. Text Soc., London, 1870.

A. F. Fergus, *The Origin and Development of the Glasgow School of Medicine*, Glasgow, 1911.

A. Duncan, *Memorials of the Faculty of Physicians and Surgeons of Glasgow*, Glasgow, 1896.

" Cursory Hints and Anecdotes of Dr. William Cullen ", *The Bee*, Vol. I, 1791.

J. Thomson, *Life of William Cullen* (2 vols.), Edinburgh, 1879.

J. Ferguson, *Recent Inquiries into the Early History of Chemistry*, read before the Philosophical Society of Glasgow, Glasgow, 1877.

Lu-Chiang Wu & T. L. Davis, " An Ancient Chinese Treatise on Alchemy ", *Isis*, Vol. 18, 1932.

J. Read, *A Prelude to Chemistry*, London, 1936.

G. Rodwell, *The Birth of Chemistry*, London, 1874.

Thomas Thomson, *History of Chemistry*, London, 1813.

M. Berthelot, *La Chemie du Moyen Age* (3 vols.), Paris, 1893.

A. Campbell Brown, *History of Chemistry*, London, 1913.

J. R. Partington, *A Short History of Chemistry*, London, 1937.

F. J. Moore, *A History of Chemistry*, 3rd ed., New York (London), 1939.

E. M. Holmyard, " Jabir ibn Hayyan ", *Proc. Roy. Soc. Med.*, Vol. 26, 1933.

E. G. Browne, *Arabian Medicine*, Cambridge, 1921.

Chas. Singer, *From Magic to Medicine*, Oxford, 1928.

A. E. Waite, *Lives of the Alchemical Philosophers*, London, 1888.

H. Redgrove, *Alchemy, Ancient and Modern*, 2nd ed., London, 1911.

H. Jennings, *The Rosicrucians, their Rites and Mysteries*, London, 1887.

L. Thorndyke, *A History of Magic and Experimental Science* (6 vols.), New York, 1923-41.

Anna M. Stoddart, *Life of Paracelsus*, London, 1911.

K. Sudhoff, *Paracelsus, ein deutsches Lebensbild*, Leipzig, 1936.

H. Sigerist, *Paracelsus in the Light of Four Hundred Years*, New York, 1941.

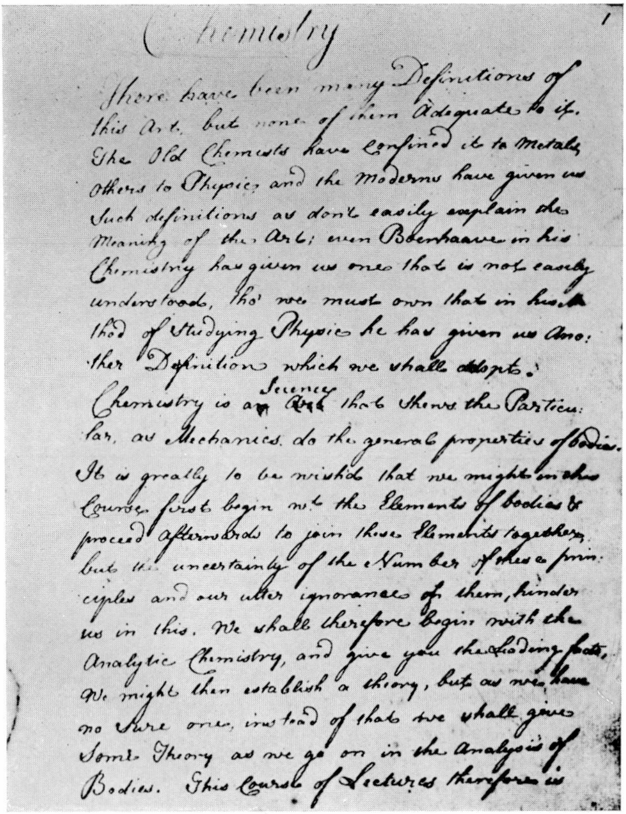

PLATE VI

The eighteenth-century student often compiled and bound his own
text-book (cf. pp. 15, 88). This page from John White's MSS. has
an interesting allusion to Boerhaave, a suggestive correction (" science "
for " art ") and a recognition of " our utter ignorance " of the
chemical elements.

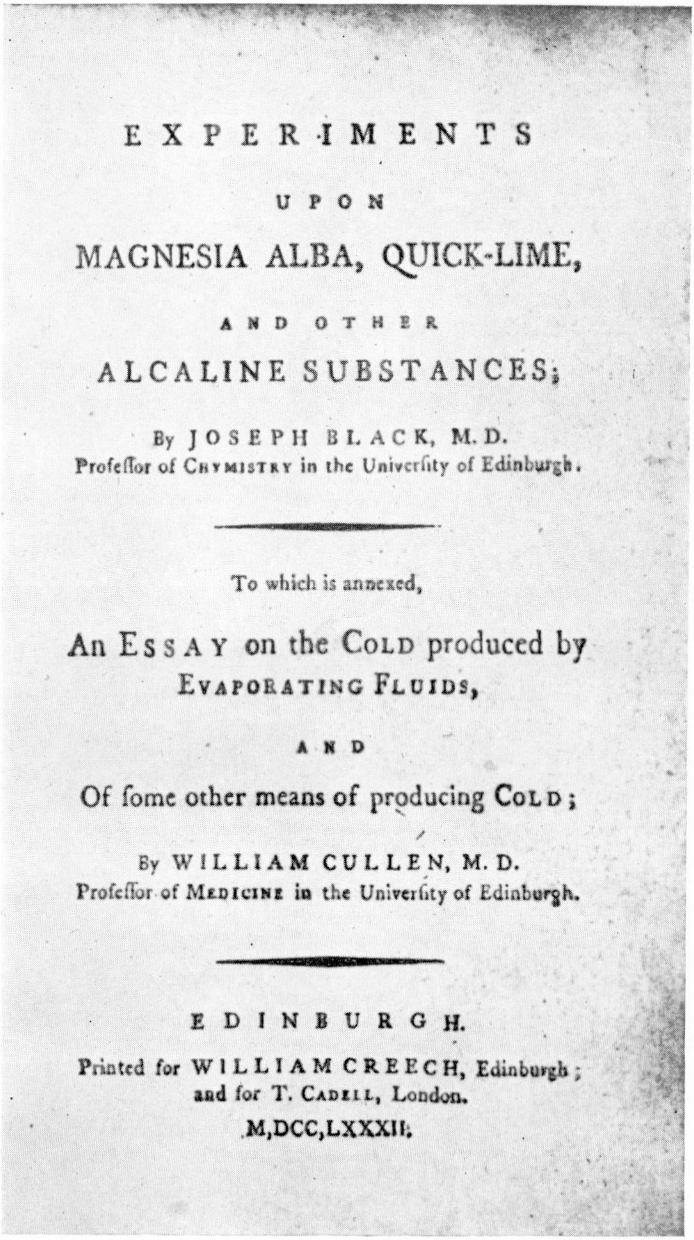

PLATE VII

EXPERIMENTS

UPON

MAGNESIA ALBA, QUICK-LIME,

AND OTHER

ALCALINE SUBSTANCES;

By JOSEPH BLACK, M. D.
Profeffor of CHYMISTRY in the Univerfity of Edinburgh.

To which is annexed,

An ESSAY on the COLD produced by
EVAPORATING FLUIDS,

AND

Of fome other means of producing COLD;

By WILLIAM CULLEN, M. D.
Profeffor of MEDICINE in the Univerfity of Edinburgh.

EDINBURGH.

Printed for WILLIAM CREECH, Edinburgh;
and for T. CADELL, London.
M,DCC,LXXXII.

The second book reporting, in Cullen's reprinted memoir, research
work in the Chemistry Department at Glasgow (cf. pp. 6, 60, 114).
(Ferguson Collection, Glasgow University Library)

Flora Masson, *Robert Boyle, a Biography*, Edinburgh, 1914.

L. T. More, *The Life and Works of the Honourable Robert Boyle*, London, 1944.

T. S. Patterson, " John Mayow in Contemporary Setting ", *Isis*, Vol. 15, 1931.

L. Dobbin, " A Cullen Manuscript of 1753 ", *Annals of Science*, Vol. I, April, 1936.

Sherwood Taylor, *Science, Past and Present*, London, 1945.

E

PHLOGISTON, CALORIC AND HEAT

J. C. Gregory

PHLOGISTON IS now a favourite example of a discredited notion. Though the phlogiston theory, roughly, covers the whole eighteenth century, its period of dominance and fall fits neatly into the last half without too much forcing into a chronological Procrustes' Bed. There is a little stretching, but not too much.

Dr. Joseph Priestley published *The Doctrine of Phlogiston Established*, with gratifying chronological neatness, in 1800—exactly at the end of the century. This can be reasonably called the last serious defence of phlogistic chemistry. Priestley himself recognises that he is one of a very small minority, and that the phlogiston theory may well be, or is even likely to be, superseded. Phlogiston, of course, did not die outright as Priestley dropped his pen, for it had penetrated science too completely to die any other than a lingering death. The lingering is visible in William Nicholson, in 1795. The greater simplicity of anti-phlogistic chemistry seems to Nicholson to make it more probable than the phlogistic, but he speaks of " phlogisticated air ", for instance, and, to avoid any anticipation of the public choice, does not adopt the anti-phlogistic nomenclature.

Though, according to Nicholson, most chemists in England and Germany still think of phlogiston disengaged during combustion, they are steadily disengaging phlogiston from their science. Lavoisier had converted his French *confrères*—vigorously when necessary if Thomson rightly compares his treatment of the recalcitrant Guyton de Morveau to " . . a political intrigue, rather than a philosophical inquiry ". Nicholson himself notes in his own country the defection of the Irish Richard Kirwan. In 1792, Thomson records, Klaproth made the Berlin Academicians into antiphlogistians by the more philosophical method of " requisite experiments ". In 1796, Dr. Girtanner reports, only a small handful of German chemists defend phlogiston, and, according to Van Mons, a little later, there are no unqualified phlogistians in Germany. In 1800 Priestley admits the smallness of the phlogistian minority.

Chemists had thought phlogiston too inveterately into chemical constitutions to think it out very easily. In 1794, when he was 61, Priestley had fixed component phlogiston firmly for years in such compounds as " alkaline air " (gaseous ammonia), and in 1800 he is virtually unable to think the phlogiston out of them. This seems to explain the sceptical Priestley whom Sir Philip Hartog detects in 1800, for Priestley plainly *intends* to defend phlogiston, though he is compelled to recognise its highly hypothetical status. Remnants of phlogistic chemistry persisted into the nineteenth century, but Priestley's defence in 1800 ends the vogue of phlogiston decisively enough to give the aesthetic satisfaction of the terminal century date.[1]

Stahl, who organised Becher's chemistry into the phlogistic, was professor at Halle from 1694 till his death in 1734—with a short period at Berlin. Since Boerhaave was professor at Leyden and his influential *Elementa Chemiae*, 1732, does not mention the phlogistic theory, Stahl had not yet conquered Germany. The *Nouveau Cours de Chimie suivant les principes de Newton et de Stahl* does not seem to have convinced France in 1723. Baron repudiated Senac's alleged authorship of this anonymous " mauvais livre ",[2] and, according to Voltaire, Stahl's doctrine was unknown in 1740 when essays on the nature of fire were read before the French Academy.[3] Berkeley's *Siris* reflects the vogues of chemical notions in 1744. It refers to the loss by burning bodies of fire, as Boerhaave thought, or of " sulphur ", as English and other non-phlogistic chemists usually called the principle of combustion, but it says nothing of phlogiston.[4] Stahl had conquered when Cavendish isolated and examined the inflammable air from metals in 1766. Phlogiston was conquering when Macquer published his *Élémens de Chymie Théorique* in 1749, and his *Élémens de Chymie Pratique* in 1751. Macquer got education from France, " Mac " from his Scots ancestry and phlogiston from Stahl. Then phlogiston invaded chemistry effectively through the popularity of his text books. So far as any single event or year can date the rise of phlogistic chemistry to predominance, 1750, midway between Macquer's two years of publication, conveniently dates it.[5] This gives the aesthetic

satisfaction of the precise mid-century date without too Pro-
crustean a chronology.

By a curious chronological chance an important event in 1775
divides the exact half-century, from 1750 to 1800, precisely into two
halves. Hartog may be too ruthless in proposing to strip the text
books of the statement that Priestley discovered oxygen on
August 1, 1774, but Priestley himself, as Hartog notes, did date
his *discovery* of " dephlogisticated air " by March 1, 1775, though
he had handled the gas at the earlier time,[6] but without under-
standing its real nature. When Lavoisier had used Priestley's
dephlogisticated air to depose phlogiston he called it oxygen. Clio
can concede the aesthetic satisfaction of a period beginning
exactly in 1750, ending precisely in 1800, and equally divided
by 1775, without seriously prejudicing truth or misleading
anybody.

As Berkeley ascribes many virtues to tar-water in the *Siris*,
including cures for small-pox and indigestion, he recognises the
legitimate suspicion that a substance reputedly good for so much
is actually good for nothing. Lavoisier, later on, accuses phlogiston of having too many roles. His famous research, from 1772
to 1789, makes phlogiston intelligibly a myth ; phlogiston's
ancestry makes equally intelligible why it did get into science to
play its many parts.

Charcoal, according to one favoured phlogistic constitution, is
phlogiston and earth, or ashes. *Carbo*, according to Rabanus
Maurus in the ninth century, is fire incorporated with earthly
matter, and united with it. The flame leaping from the burning
log is the recognisable prototype of the combustive process implied by Rabanus and the phlogistian. The original notion of
combustion, the dismembering escape of fire from the residual
ash, is still visible in Rabanus, and has its perceptible analogue in
the escape of previously combined phlogiston from the remaining
" earth " when charcoal burns.

Some phlogistians constituted charcoal of " earth ", phlogiston
and aerial acid—otherwise fixed air (carbon dioxide). This con-
formed to the production of aerial acid, or fixed air, by burning
charcoal. The original prototype is still discernible in the residual
dismembered ash of burning charcoal, the emitted aerial acid and
the fugitive phlogiston. There were further complications as
phlogistic chemistry struggled with increasing experimental data,

but the essential combustive escape of phlogiston, parallel to the original escape of fire, persisted.

St. Augustine notes how lime, " whitened by the fire ", keeps some of the fire secret within itself from sense, for the cold lump, when moistened, gives up its secretly detained fire and warms the water. He interprets the strange burning of lime in water, as he calls it, by material fire, combined as insensible heat and manifesting without flame or light.

This fifth century notion has been elaborately reconstructed by Boerhaave in 1732. Elementary fire in his chemistry consists of minute, solid, globular, smooth and immutable particles (atoms). This fire constantly tries to stretch itself out, as air strives to expand, because its particles repel one another. It dilates bodies by lurking in their pores and forcing their mutually attracting particles more apart ; the bodies contract when the pulls between their particles reduce the distending power of the contained fire. This elementary fire, which throbs in all spaces or pores, also passes to and fro between bodies through spaces. Boerhaave distinguishes the fire supported by combustible matter from the elementary fire itself, which, though corporeal, is *weightless*.[7]

In 1749 Macquer introduces phlogiston as the matter of fire, combined in combustible bodies and quietened by its detention in them. Inflammable substances obviously contain the very small particles of fire, as actual combustion shows, though the how of their fixing in the substances is a puzzle, and the fixed fire is not active like free fire. Macquer, who changed his notions later on, in 1749 identifies phlogiston with the element of fire combined with a basis into a kind of secondary principle. This phlogiston is also known as the inflammable matter or the sulphureous principle.[8]

A familiar association had gripped tradition when St. Augustine called hell a lake of fire and brimstone. By the seventeenth century, through the long traditional connexion between burning brimstone and fire, the principle of combustion, which was presumed to escape from all burning bodies, was usually called " sulphur " or the sulphureous principle, or by some equivalent name. Boyle notes the ambiguity of " sulphur "—brimstone itself or the principle of combustion. Nicholas Lemery can call sulphur a kind of bitumen because both can burn ; inversely, combustible substances, such as oils or fats, were sometimes called

" sulphurs " or sulphureous bodies. The principle of combustion
was sometimes called the oily or fatty principle through its association with oils or fats, just as it was called the sulphureous principle
through its connexion with brimstone. The inflammable principle,
the analogue of fire itself, came to Stahl through the oily or fatty
route. It might have been called phlogiston at almost any time,
for the word is apparently derived from the Greek " phlogistos ",
meaning burnt. In 1606 Hapelius did call the essence of the
sulphur ingrafted in all things " the phlogiston " (in Greek).[9]
Thus in phlogistic chemistry the sulphureous principle conquers
under the name of phlogiston. Macquer himself recognises this
equivalence, and whatever the relations presumed in the past, or
by Stahl himself, between fire and the inflammable principle, he
virtually identifies phlogiston with fire.

The conviction of centuries, based on the leaping flame and
nourished on principles of combustion, lay behind the presumed
escape of phlogiston from the burning body. Its inveteracy
powerfully protected the Achilles' Heel of the phlogiston theory
until Lavoisier pierced it. Phlogiston was presumed to escape
from the calcining metal, as from the burning wood. The calx,
however, is *heavier* than the original metal, and heavier because
the metal has combined with oxygen into the oxide. Lavoisier's
deposition of phlogiston through this disclosure is a familiar tale
often told. Phlogistians could, and did defend their chemistry
effectively until Lavoisier systematised chemistry on combining
oxygen, but the clue of the augmented calx was finally fatal to
phlogiston.

Boyle, in the seventeenth century, connected a practical joke
with the nature of heat. An artist, who was turning great guns
very swiftly, made merry by telling spectators to pick up the
detached bits of metal. They snatched their fingers away, it
seemed to Boyle, because the boring, by increasing the tumultuous
agitation of their small parts, made the fragments *hot*. Anything,
Boyle notes, that agitates the small parts of a body sufficiently,
heats it, as a hammer hits heat into a nail.[10] The fifth Query of
Newton's *Opticks* identifies heat with the vibrating parts of bodies.
When Benjamin Martin reviews the " Present State of Experi-
mented Physiology, or Natural Philosophy " in 1738 he explains
that " a great Agitation of the Particles of the hot Body " excites
the sensation of Heat " in the Mind ".[11] When phlogiston

escapes from the inflammable heated by a candle, the heat produced seems to Priestley, in 1775, probably to be a vibratory motion excited in the separated principles.[12]

Electricity still seems to Sir Oliver Lodge in 1887 to be transferred like a substance, as it had seemed to Franklin in the later eighteenth century.[13] Heat also behaves, or appears to behave, too much *as if* it is a transferable substance not to be regarded as one. Dr. Joseph Black, in Franklin's days, calls heat the most *communicable* of all properties. Nicholson contrasts the two rival theories of heat in 1795. One attributes heat to a peculiar motion, or vibration, of parts in bodies ; for the other heat is a substance or fluid. The temperature is higher or lower as the vibrations are stronger or weaker on the first supposition ; it varies with the quantity of heat according to the second.[14] Black speaks for many of his day when he calls heat the chief *material* principle of activity in nature.

The scientific activities of Black (1728-99) from about 1750 to his last course of lectures in 1796-7, closely coincided with the heyday and fall of phlogiston. In 1803 Robison published Black's Edinburgh Lectures on the elements of chemistry from the original manuscripts. The text faithfully presents Black's sentiments or opinions, and, as far as possible, in his own words.[15]

In 1672 the heat of bodies seems to Rohault to be easily regarded as movements of their parts, and, in Cartesian vein, as circular movements ; [16] particles of solids moving among themselves seem to Black to be unimaginable. If heat is a tremulous motion, Black also objects, denser bodies should communicate it more powerfully, and they do not.[17] Black's own researches, especially on latent and specific heats, seemed to disfavour the internal movement theory and to favour the material substance notion. Nicholson notes that if heat is merely internal motion, then, since water at 32° F. contains more heat than ice at the same temperature, the extra motion must be preposterously supposed to be latent or incommunicable.[18]

Boyle speaks of the " spring " of air. Newton, in Queries 18 and 21 of his *Opticks*, speculatively imagines an Aether much rarer than air, much more highly " elastick " because its very small particles " recede from one another " with great " force ", and thus it is still more able than air to " press upon Bodies " in its effort to expand. Newton also presumes this elastic aether to

" pervade all Bodies " readily. Boerhaave's fire is an analogue of
Newton's Aether. So is the subtle penetrating fluid of Black's
pages, that is highly elastic because its particles repel one another.
Cleghorn, Black notes, credits heat with an attraction for the
particles of other bodies. This is evidently to explain why heat
can remain fixed, or combined, in substances. The latent heat of
water, the heat absorbed by the melting ice and concealed by the
constant temperature, seemed to offer a way of settling the vexed
question of ponderable or imponderable heat. Boerhaave had
found heat imponderable, though not to Muschenbroeck's
satisfaction ; heat makes bodies heavier according to Buffon ;
Fordyce, avoiding the effect of heated air, discovered a slight
increase of weight by loss of heat. If heat is matter, Black assesses,
it has no perceptible weight.[19]

Substances intelligibly get bigger as they get hotter if more
heat pulls their particles more apart by its own elastic effort to
expand. Quicksilver intelligibly requires less heat to raise its
temperature X degrees than the same weight of water does if its
capacity for heat is less. In melted ice the latent heat may be combined in a special way with the water. The air itself, Black
observes, is now considered to be elastic because its heat makes it
so. Thus heat is intelligibly the efficient cause of fluidity.[20]

According to the eighteenth Query in Newton's *Opticks* hotter
bodies communicate their stronger heat vibrations to the weaker
of colder bodies by intermediary vibrations in an aetherial
medium. On the material version heat itself flows from the hotter
to the colder body. If heat flows into the colder finger from the
fire or the hotter handled plate, there is a sensation of warmth ;
there is a sensation of cold if heat flows from the hotter finger
towards or directly into anything less hot. This dispenses with a
medium to carry radiant heat between substances, and reduces
cold to a less degree of heat. Frigorific particles had been presumed to pass from colder bodies, and frigorific atoms to entangle
the round smooth particles of water in their angular, pointed and
wedge-like selves. This had probably already become what Black
calls it—a groundless imagination.[21]

The connexions between phlogiston, fire, heat and light
troubled interpretation. Black notes the *motus vorticillaris*—the
swift whirling motion of Stahl's phlogiston which moves fire
round in circles. Stahl also identifies the sulphureous principle,

or phlogiston, with the matter of fire itself—heat being finely divided fire.[22]   Macquer at first also identifies the sulphureous principle with phlogiston, this with fire, or fixed fire, and the sun with its main reservoir.   Black contemplates air made elastic by heat ; Macquer contemplates it made elastic by fire : if the air lost all its fire, he suggests, it might become solid.[8]   Later on, Macquer, who regarded heat as the movements of particles in the body, virtually identifies phlogiston with the matter of light.[23] Oxygen finally killed phlogiston, but it had some curious consequences for the inflammable principle and heat before the final kill.   It had some in Scheele's chemistry.

When Scheele (1742-86) discovered oxygen he called it fire air. This seemed to Scheele to contain a " subtle acid matter ", because, amongst other data, plants convert it into aerial acid (carbon dioxide).   The fire air, a *dulcified* elastic fluid, also contains some phlogiston which the plants remove to leave the (undulcified) aerial acid.   Phlogiston plus acid matter seems a curious oxygen, but, as consequences follow one another, the constitutions become still more curious.

During combustion the phlogiston of the burning body unites with the fire air to produce an " extremely subtle, elastic substance ".   This " newly generated " compound of subtle acid matter with more phlogiston than in fire air is *heat*.   The augmented calx also seems to Scheele to correspond to *ponderable* heat, because this, in effect, combines with the metal to form the calx.   Either the calcining metal attracts fire air directly by its phlogiston, or it first loses phlogiston and then combines with the heat from the combination between this fugitive phlogiston and fire air.   Lime indicates that the calx must contain much heat, for when it is watered its superabundant heat makes it soluble. Scheele probably did not know what St. Augustine thought about lime.   Heat or fire was often presumed to make air elastic ; for Scheele, fire air and heat are made elastic by phlogiston.

A little more phlogiston, according to Scheele, converts heat into radiant heat ; a little more converts this into violet light, and successive small additions of phlogiston result in the variously coloured lights of the spectrum—red having the most phlogiston. This curious array of phlogiston compounds has a still stranger ending, for inflammable air (hydrogen) is fire air combined with still more phlogiston than in light, Scheele has to face an anomaly, for, though the phlogiston in heat and light makes them subtle enough to pass through glass, inflammable air, which contains still more phlogiston, can be kept in a bottle.

Scheele died too soon to surrender phlogiston, and he might have been unable to revise it out of his complex phlogistic chemistry. He did alter the constitution of fire air to a " non-elastic, fundamental or saline principle " combined with some water and a little phlogiston, but he always regarded fire as an aggregation of heat and light with their less and greater proportions of phlogiston.[24]

Scheele's system, which, as Lavoisier notes, breaks harshly with tradition by making heat and light into compounds, is an extreme instance of a phlogistic chemistry under the impact of oxygen, though other phlogistians were driven into similar complexities. The simplest phlogistic response to Lavoisier and oxygen identified phlogiston with hydrogen. The phlogiston of the calcining metal combines with oxygen to form *water*, and this combines with the dephlogisticated part of the metal to form the calx, or oxide—returning the phlogiston to the metal and adding the oxygen to it. This, Cavendish notes in 1784, conforms to the quantitative data.[25] Phlogiston makes Scheele's inflammable and fire airs elastic ; in 1784 Kirwan's dephlogisticated air (oxygen) and the phlogiston of his inflammable air are made elastic by elementary fire. The two combining gases lose fire and form water.[26]

" At the end of the eighteenth century Lavoisier banished the fictitious phlogiston and caloric " : the eminent philosopher who wrote thus had either forgotten Lavoisier's new list of elements or had never seen it. The list contains no phlogiston, but it names *lumière* first and then *calorique*. Lavoisier specifies five earlier equivalent names for caloric : heat, the principle of heat, igneous fluid, fire, and the matter of fire and heat. These significantly indicate the ancestry and nature of the caloric which is destined to a long expository role, and to a place, with light, magnetism and electricity, among the four imponderables.

In Lavoisier's *Traité Élémentaire de Chimie*, 1789, oxygen gas is oxygen base combined with caloric. This is an obvious parallel to Kirwan's dephlogisticated air, which contains fire, and to Black's air made elastic by heat. Lavoisier had hesitated over the relations between heat and light before including them separately in his list of elements. Light, he suggests, may be present in oxygen gas as well as caloric, and help to keep the oxygen gaseous. Caloric is Lavoisier's substitute for phlogiston, or its analogue, in his system. Light shares the role of caloric, but much more tentatively. The perceptible burning of iron wire in oxygen clearly illustrates the combustive roles of caloric and light in Lavoisier's chemistry. When the iron unites with the *oxygen base* to form the oxide the caloric escapes to manifest as heat felt by its impact on human sense-organs, and the light also escapes in the visible glow, as it does in the flame of burning wood, though Lavoisier is less explicit about the light than about the caloric. Since the caloric is weightless the weight of the oxide equals the combined weights of the participating iron and oxygen gas, as experiment requires.

Lavoisier's caloric is obviously related to fire, especially as Boerhaave conceives it, and to heat as Black discusses it—the two had always been closely connected, both before and after St. Augustine. All natural bodies are immersed in caloric, like fish in the sea or birds in the air. *Free* caloric surrounds them, penetrates them, and fills the spaces between their molecules (small parts). Attraction, Lavoisier presumes, holds *combined* caloric in bodies as part of their substance, even of their solidity. The molecules of caloric, or heat, tend to separate, and, by their repulsive force, to press the molecules of substances apart. Thus solvent caloric liquefies solids, and maintains gases as aeriform fluids—in effect solids dissolved in caloric. Lavoisier suggests that *calorique spécifique* depends on the distances between molecules and on the degree in which caloric adheres to them.

Caloric, Lavoisier recognises, may be a convenient concept and no real substance. Almost any hypothesis, Black remarks, can be fitted to facts to please the imagination without advancing knowledge. Imagination, self-confidence and *amour-propre*, Lavoisier warns the reader, mislead us. In practical life pain and pleasure constantly check false judgments, but science can only avoid error by a constant appeal to facts, by refusing authoritative control, and by reducing reasoning to the simplest operations, as the mathematicians do. In caloric Lavoisier recognises the provisional hypothesis ; in phlogiston he recognises the discarded theory. His shade would not be surprised today to discover neither phlogiston nor caloric in the list of elements.[27]

NOTES AND REFERENCES

[1] William Nicholson, *A Dictionary of Chemistry*, printed for G. G. & J. Robinson, London, 1795, vol. 1, pp. 2f, 8off, 269, vol. 2, p. 641 ; Thomas Thomson, *History of Chemistry*, Colburn & Bentley, London, Ed. 2, 1830-1, vol. 2, pp. 130f, 136 ; *Phil. Mag.*, 1798, 2, 328ff ; Joseph Priestley, *Heads of Lectures, etc.*, Johnson, London, 1794 ; Sir Philip Hartog, *Annals of Science*, 1941, 5, 43ff.

[2] Hélène Metzger, *Newton, Stahl, Boerhaave et la Doctrine Chimique*, Alcan, Paris, 1930, p. 94.

[3] Voltaire, *Œuvres Complètes*, Paris, vol. 31, 1784, p. 304.

[4] Fraser, *The Works of George Berkeley*, Clarendon Press, Oxford, 1871, vol. 2, Siris.

[5] Coleby, *The Chemical Studies of P. J. Macquer*, George Allen & Unwin, London, 1938.

[6] Hartog, *Nature*, 1933, *132*, 25 ; *Annals of Science*, 1941, 5, 30f.

[7] Shaw, *A New Method of Chemistry etc.*, transl. Boerhaave's *Elementa Chemiae*, Longman, London, 1741, vol. 1, pp. 206ff.

[8] Macquer, *Elements of the Theory and Practice of Chemistry*, transl. Andrew Reid, Millar & Nourse, London, 1758, vol. 1, pp. 7ff.

[9] G. H. White, *The Phlogiston Theory*, Arnold, London, 1932, p. 51.

[10] Thomas Birch, *The Works of the Hon. Robert Boyle*, Rivington, London, 1772, vol. 5, p. 3, vol. 1, p. 116, vol. 4, pp. 249, 287.

[11] Benj. Martin, *The Philosophical Grammar etc.*, Noon, London, 1738, p. 114.

[12] Priestley, *Experiments and Observations on Different Kinds of Air*, Ed. 2, corrected, Johnson, London, 1775, pp. 260f.

[13] Oliver Lodge, *Nature*, 1887, *36*, pp. 532ff.

[14] Nicholson, *l.c.*, vol. 1, p. 372.

[15] Joseph Black, *Lectures on the Elements of Chemistry*, Ed. Robison, Longman & Rees, London, Creech, Edinburgh, 1803, vol. 1, pp. 12, 22ff.

[16] Jacques Rohault, *Traité de Physique*, Paris, 1672, vol. 1, pp. 221f.

[17] Black, *l.c.*, vol. 1, pp. 262, 83.

[18] Nicholson, *An Introduction to Natural Philosophy*, Ed. 4, London, 1796, vol. 2, p. 121.

[19] Black, *l.c.*, vol. 1, pp. 34, 47f, 119ff.

[20] Black, *l.c.*, vol. 1, pp. 77ff, 106, 133ff, 201ff.

[21] Black, *l.c.*, vol. 1, pp. 22ff.

[22] Metzger, *l.c.*, p. 165.

[23] Coleby, *l.c.*, pp. 35ff.

[24] C. W. Scheele, *Collected Papers*, transl. Dobbin, Bell, London, 1931, pp. 106-45, 161-75, 286f.

[25] Cavendish, *Phil. Trans.*, 1784, 74, 179ff.

[26] Kirwan, *Phil. Trans.*, 1784, 74, 154ff.

[27] *Œuvres de Lavoisier*, Paris Ed., 1864-68, vol. 1, pp. 1ff.

JOSEPH BLACK, M.D.
THE TEACHER AND THE MAN

Born, 1728 : died, 6th December, 1799. Edcn : Grammar School, Belfast, Universities of Glasgow (matriculated 1746) and Edinburgh (M.D., 1754). Lecturer in Chemistry, 1756-66. Professor, successively, of Anatomy and Botany, Medicine (Glasgow, 1756-66), Chemistry and Physic (Edinburgh, 1766-99).

John Read

Prologue

AT ABOUT the time of Joseph Black's birth the erudite Herman Boerhaave was concerning himself at Leyden with an experiment which he described in his famous *Elementa Chemiae*,[1] published in 1732. Like all chemists of his day, he was completely baffled by the key problem of early chemistry : the nature of combustion. Boerhaave did not subscribe to the contemporary theory of phlogiston ; but he held an allied conception that all combustible bodies contained a so-called *pabulum ignis*, " a matter feeding fire, and converted by the same into the very substance of elementary fire." He sought to isolate this *pabulum ignis* from purified alcohol, which he supposed to contain it in a concentrated form. " How great was my disappointment," he wrote, describing the burning of this alcohol in a special apparatus, " upon finding that alcohol, by passing through fire, becomes vapour . . . The pabulum of fire, consumed by it, leaves water ; and itself becomes so light, as to dissipate into the chaos of air, and thus eludes all further pursuit."

Boerhaave declared that this experiment " shews us some fix'd limits of science." The infant Joseph Black became the pioneer who first found a passage beyond those " fix'd limits " and thereby opened a way into the illimitable realms of modern chemistry.

Career

Joseph Black was born beside the historic Garonne, near Bordeaux, in 1728. His father, John Black, a Belfast man of

Scots descent, married the daughter of an Aberdeenshire man, who, like himself, was engaged in the French wine trade. John Black was liberal, warm-hearted and well-informed ; in Joseph Black's words, he was also " industrious and prudent in business, of the strictest probity and honour, very temperate and regular in his manner of life." Some of these characteristics were inherited by his famous son. This Scots family of eight sons and five daughters formed a microcosm of domestic felicity in the sunny southern clime, and President Montesquieu, the philosophical historian of La Brède, wrote of the tranquil hours which he enjoyed in their midst, " contemplating their happiness and their virtues."

Joseph, who with the other children had been taught to read English by his mother, was sent to Belfast at the age of twelve, in 1740, to attend a grammar school. In 1746 he continued his education in the University of Glasgow ; and here, during his medical course, he came strongly under the influence of Dr. William Cullen, the newly appointed lecturer in chemistry, who has been described[2] as " the first in Great Britain to raise the science to its true dignity."

About the year 1751 Black went to Edinburgh to finish his medical studies, and he took his M.D. degree there in 1754. Two years after this he succeeded his old master, Cullen, as professor of anatomy and lecturer in chemistry, in the University of Glasgow, and later he exchanged chairs with the professor of medicine. Finally, in 1766, Black once more succeeded Cullen, this time in the chair of chemistry and physic in the University of Edinburgh.[3] He held this appointment until his death, in 1799. In 1795, owing to Black's failing health, Thomas Hope was appointed joint professor of chemistry, and Black delivered his last course of lectures in the winter of 1796-97.

Researches

Black qualified for the medical profession. His famous researches on " fixed air " (carbon dioxide) arose indeed out of efforts to find a more efficacious " lithontriptic medicine," or solvent for urinary calculi, than the contemporary alkaline remedies. These included not only lime-water, but also more dangerous remedies having, as Thomas Thomson observed, " a greater or less resemblance to caustic potash or soda." Black conceived the idea of trying to prepare an alkaline solvent of a milder type, starting from Epsom salt.

For this purpose he prepared " mild magnesia," or *magnesia alba* (basic magnesium carbonate) by precipitating Epsom salt solution with pearl-ashes (potassium carbonate). This magnesia alba effervesced with acids, and changed by ignition into a white powder devoid of this property, losing seven-twelfths of its weight in the ignition. Here, as Sir William Ramsay[4] observed, Black had " made an enormous stride ; he had weighed a gas in combination." As Black showed, the property of effervescing with acids could be restored to the white powder by dissolving it in dilute spirit of vitriol and adding pearl-ashes to the solution.

Black's work dispelled the former idea that causticity was due to an igneous matter gained from fire, as in the preparation of quicklime from limestone or chalk. Such calcinations, he showed, were accompanied by a loss of weight, due to a " fixed air " quitting the calcined material.

Black concluded " that magnesia alba is a compound of a peculiar earth and fixed air. When this substance is mixed with lime-water," he continued, " the lime shews a stronger attraction for fixed air than that of the earth of magnesia ; the air leaves this powder to join itself to the lime. And as neither the lime when saturated with air (calcium carbonate), nor the magnesia when deprived of it (magnesium hydroxide), are soluble in water, the lime-water becomes perfectly pure and insipid, the lime which it contained being mixed with the magnesia. But if the magnesia be deprived of air by calcination (magnesium oxide) before it is mixed with the lime-water, this fluid suffers no alteration. If quicklime be mixed with a dissolved alkali (pearl-ashes or potassium carbonate), it likeways shews an attraction for fixed air superior to that of the alkali. It robs this salt of its air, and thereby becomes mild itself (calcium carbonate), while the alkali is consequently rendered more corrosive (potassium hydroxide)."

This extract, showing the trend of Black's work and his way of expressing the results of his observations, is taken from a paper[5] dated 5 June 1755, containing the chemical material recorded in his Latin thesis[6] presented for the degree of M.D. at Edinburgh on 11 June 1754. It has been remarked[2] that " there is, perhaps, no other instance of a graduation thesis so weighted with significant novelty."

PLATE VIII

JOSEPH BLACK

Writing in 1803, after Black's death, John Robison, professor of natural philosophy in the University of Edinburgh and one of Black's close colleagues, in the course of a biographical notice,[7] considered " that excepting the optics of Newton, there is not a finer model for philosophical investigation, than the essay on magnesia and quicklime." In the same contemporary judgment of this work it is pointed out that Black " had discovered that a cubic inch of marble consisted of about half its weight of pure lime, and as much air as would fill a vessel holding six wine gallons . . . What could be more singular than to find so subtle a substance as air existing in the form of a hard stone, and its presence accompanied by such a change in the properties of that stone? . . . What bounds could reasonably be set to the imagination, in supposing that other aereal fluids, as remarkable in their properties, might exist in a solid form in many other bodies? " Black's first series of researches, indeed, may be said to have fired that astonishing train of chemical investigations leading through Scheele, Priestley and Cavendish to Lavoisier and modern chemistry.

In the course of his second period in Glasgow, lasting from 1756 to 1766, Black maintained a large medical practice as well as discharging the duties of the professorship of medicine and the chemical lectureship in the University. It was during this period that he developed his ideas on latent heat and specific heat, in the second remarkable series of researches associated with his name. In December 1761 he was able to show that when a quantity of water froze it gave up an amount of heat equal to the amount absorbed or rendered latent during the liquefaction. He gave his first connected account of these investigations, and the views which he based upon them, on 23 April 1762, " to a literary society which met every Friday in the Faculty-room of the college consisting of the members of the University, and several gentlemen of the city, who had a relish for philosophy and literature ; " but according to Robison it was not until the summer of 1764 that he had satisfied himself concerning " the precise quantity of the heat latent in steam." [8] It is remarkable that Black never published this work, although he discussed it with his classes. Consequently the only printed account appeared posthumously in the version of his lectures edited by Robison.

Robison tells us that at this time (1764) Dr. Black " had now gotten a pupil who was as keenly interested in this scientific

F

question as the Professor. This was Mr. James Watt, then employed in fitting up the instruments in the M'Farlane Observatory of the University." Watt happened to be repairing a model of Newcomen's steam engine, used for demonstrations to the students of natural philosophy. By applying Black's new ideas on ebullition he prosecuted experiments, as Robison relates, " in a most happy train of success, and did not stop, till his steam engine was rendered more like the most docile of animals than a frame of lifeless matter."

With Black's encouragement and generous help,[9] Watt developed his idea of economising power by means of a separate condenser, and in 1769 patented the celebrated Watt steam engine which was afterwards manufactured by Boulton and Watt at the Soho Ironworks, Birmingham ; so that Watt, in Robison's words, " by his judicious application of Dr. Black's instructions . . . was now in the straight road to riches and fame."

Black's researches in physics led to results no less important and far-reaching than those which followed his chemical work. In both of these branches of physical science Black's advances were fundamental and of such a nature as to exert a trigger-action upon future progress. His studies in latent heat led immediately to Watt's improvement of the steam engine, with inestimable industrial and social consequences ; more remotely, these same studies opened the way to constantly widening fields, until, to quote some words of Sir William Ramsay,[4] spoken in the University of Glasgow in 1904, " in the hands of the masters— Joule, Clerk-Maxwell, Rankine, James Thomson, and Kelvin, on the physical side, and of Willard Gibbs, the American, on the chemical side—they form the very ground-work of the sister sciences, physics and chemistry."

Black's chemical researches were carried out during his first Edinburgh period, his physical ones during his second Glasgow period. With his departure from Glasgow to Edinburgh for the second time, in 1766, at the age of thirty-eight, his researches virtually came to an end. Henceforward, except for an occasional excursion into applied chemistry[10] and a light medical practice maintained among his friends, he devoted himself for the next thirty years exclusively to his teaching duties. Throughout this long period we see Black acting as a spectator of chemical developments following logically and inevitably from his own revolutionary discovery that an " air," or gas, could be " fixed " and weighed in the form of a solid combination. The question naturally arises why some at least of these further fundamental discoveries did not fall to Black himself.

Robison, in referring to " the remarkable fact " that Black " did not immediately engage with ardour and perseverance in this race of discovery and honour," remarks that " nothing can more clearly show Dr. Black's calm and unambitious character." He seeks a more convincing explanation in Black's intense preoccupation with his teaching and particularly in the fragility of his constitution. The slightest ailment, or indulgence " in any intense thinking, or puzzling research," induced a feverish condition culminating in a spitting of blood. Indeed, it was only through rigid dieting and regular exercise of a gentle kind, and the general observance of a calm and unruffled existence that Black was able to attain the allotted span of threescore years and ten. These facts are not in doubt; but according to a later and more critical opinion[2] " his mind was so nicely balanced as to be deficient in motive power. He had all the faculties of invention, but lacked fervour to keep them at work." In considering such a judgment, however, the sensitive interplay between mind and body must not be underestimated ; and there can be no doubt that Black's physical condition, especially in his later years, was one of excessive delicacy. Thomson[11] refers to his languor and listlessness, and as an example of " his carelessness of his own reputation " quotes the first demonstration of a hydrogen balloon, which Black gave to a party of friends in 1767, without making any further reference to it, even among his own pupils.

The Teacher

Since Black stood upon the threshold of modern chemistry, the substance of his chemistry lectures is of peculiar interest. Fortunately, we are able from contemporary records to gain a close acquaintance not only with the nature of these lectures, but also with the style and idiosyncrasies of the lecturer. In the days of Black's infancy, Boerhaave was lecturing on chemistry in Latin at Leyden. In Edinburgh it was Black's predecessor, Cullen, who brought with him from Glasgow his practice—which Black followed—of lecturing in English instead of in Latin.

Robison tell us that Black's " personal appearance and manner were those of a gentleman, and peculiarly pleasing. His voice in lecturing was low, but fine ; and his articulation so distinct that he was perfectly well heard by an audience consisting of several hundreds." Thomas Thomson,[11] who attended Black's last course of lectures, described him as the most perfect chemical lecturer in his whole experience.

Black illustrated his lectures with experiments. He was an expert manipulator, and Robison records that his practical demonstrations were " ingeniously and judiciously contrived, clearly establishing the point in view, and never more than sufficed for this purpose. While he scorned the quackery of a showman the simplicity, neatness, and elegance, with which they were performed, were truly admirable."

His aim was to make the teaching as plain and convincing as possible. Many of his students had, in Robison's words, " a very scanty stock of previous learning. He had many from the workshop of the manufacturer, who had none at all ; and he saw that the number of such hearers must increase with the increasing activity and prosperity of the country : And these appeared to him as by no means the least important part of his auditory." The lectures aroused so much interest and indeed enthusiasm that Black's student-audiences were eventually swollen by the attendance of intelligent outsiders wishing to gain an acquaintance with Black's own discoveries and to learn something of the general character of the intriguing branch of science upon which he discoursed so attractively. In Robison's quaint words, chemistry —at least in Edinburgh—" became a fashionable part of the accomplishment of a gentleman."

One of Black's last classes (probably the last of all) included the future Lord Brougham, who became Lord Chancellor of England. Many years afterwards Brougham[12] wrote in his memoirs that " the gratification of attending one of Black's last lecture courses exceeded all I have ever enjoyed. I have heard the greatest understandings of the age giving forth their efforts in their most eloquent tongues—have heard the commanding periods of Pitt's majestic oratory—the vehemence of Fox's burning declamation . . . but I would without hesitation prefer, for mere intellectual gratification . . . to be once more allowed the privilege . . . of being present, while the first philosopher of his age was the historian of his own discoveries, and be an eyewitness of those experiments by which he had formerly made them, once more performed by his own hands."

According to Brougham, these experiments " were often like Franklin's, performed with the simplest apparatus—indeed with nothing that could be called apparatus at all ... I remember his pouring fixed air from a vessel in which sulphuric acid had been poured upon chalk, and showing us how this air poured on a candle extinguished the light. He never failed to remark on the great use of simple experiments within every one's reach ; and liked to dwell on the manner in which discoveries are made, and the practical effect resulting from them in changing the condition of men and things."

The simple nature of his lecture demonstrations and some of his marked personal characteristics are admirably portrayed in one of the clever caricatures drawn by John Kay[13] in 1787. This depicts Black in position behind his lecture table, his mouth showing the ghost of that pleasing smile which according to Robison " began to form on his countenance, when he was about to exhibit or relate anything that he considered as peculiarly interesting."

Black's enterprise in teaching and his interest in the members of his class are shown by his foundation of a chemical society, which, according to the researches of Professor Kendall,[14] was the earliest of all chemical societies ; in 1785 it numbered no fewer than fifty-nine members. The earliest chemical society in America—the Chemical Society of Philadelphia, founded by James Woodhouse in 1792—may also have owed its inception indirectly to Black, since Benjamin Rush, one of Black's earlier pupils, had been appointed in 1769 to the first American chair of chemistry, in the medical school of the University of Pennsylvania.

It is appropriate to end this short account of Black as a teacher with a first-hand description of a student making his acquaintance, in the days when a professor's stipend was derived largely from fees paid to him by members of his class.

" I remember the first time I was ever in his society," wrote Lord Brougham. " When I went to take a ticket for his class, there stood upon his table a small brass instrument for weighing the guineas given. On learning who I was, he entered into conversation in a most kind manner ... When I was going away he said : ' You must have been surprised at my using this instrument to weigh your guineas, but it was before I knew who you were. I am obliged to weigh them when strange students come, there being a very large number who bring light guineas ; so that I should be defrauded of many pounds every year if I did not act in self-defence against that class of students.' "

No doubt, Black weighed the light guineas with much less satisfaction than he had weighed fixed air in combination ; but Brougham justly commented that " there was certainly no reason why he should pay a sum of forty or fifty pounds yearly out of his income " because of the easy morals of a section of his students.

The Lectures

Black had an aversion to appearing as an author, and his printed publications are astonishingly scanty, consisting according to Thomson[11] of only three papers.[15] The communication on his chemical researches[5] was the chief of these ; as already mentioned, he refrained from publishing any account whatsoever of his physical researches on latent heat, although he discussed them freely with his classes. In spite of this marked reticence Black achieved a wide reputation during his lifetime, and Fourcroy termed him " the Nestor of the chemistry of the eighteenth century." [16]

Even Black's lectures, so universally acclaimed, were not published until about four years after his death, in 1803. For this purpose his own manuscript notes, supplemented by others taken down by some of his hearers, were edited by John Robison and issued under the title, *Lectures on the Elements of Chemistry*,[7] in two large quarto volumes. Robison dedicated the work to James Watt, whom he described as " Dr. Black's most illustrious Pupil." Besides affording a permanent record of Black's lectures, this work gives a striking picture of the uncertain position of chemistry between the acceptance of Lavoisier's views and the advent of Dalton's atomic theory.

A great deal of the first volume is devoted to an account, mainly physical in character, of the " General Effects of Heat." In this section of his lectures Black naturally attached due emphasis to his own doctrine of latent heat. In discussing the nature of combustion, Black refers to the new theory, the opposite of the theory of phlogiston, which he observes " is fast gaining ground, especially on the Continent." He points out that the fundamental experiments and the leading inferences concerning " the nature

and qualities of atmospherical air, and of a number of other elastic
fluids ". were first made by Priestley, Cavendish and Watt ; but
that " it was chiefly in France that they were repeated, with proper
attention to all the circumstances that would affect the result, and
this result was made the foundation of a new theory of combustion,"
Lavoisier being its chief author.

These French experiments, in Black's opinion, showed conclusively " that a considerable quantity of air is really absorbed,
and combined with the matter of the burning body, so as to form,
in many cases, a dense compound in which the air so absorbed is
totally deprived of its usual form of an elastic fluid : And the
additional weight which the matter of the burning body acquires,
has been found to correspond exactly to the weight of the air
which has been absorbed by it." Unlike Priestley, Black sustained
no brief for phlogiston ; but, on the other hand, his habitual
restraint and reserve kept him from evincing any marked
enthusiasm for Lavoisier's views.

Black's lengthy discourse on heat is followed by a brief account
of the " General Effects of Mixture." Here he treats of " theories
of chemical mixture and combination " and also of " elective
attractions," which he explains as cases " in which a third body
frequently acts on a compound of two ingredients, so as to separate
these from one another, and join itself to one of the two."

The next section of the printed lectures deals with chemical
apparatus, and here a special reference is made to the use of con-
cave mirrors and convex lenses in producing effects " that appeared
astonishing when they were new; such as melting in a moment many
earths and stones, which were reckoned before perfectly unfusible."

The rest of the first volume and the whole of the second volume
deals with " The Chemical History of Bodies." Here it is natural
to find an arbitrary arrangement of the material, owing to the
uncertainty in Black's time about the number and nature of the
elementary bodies. *Faute de mieux*, the classification is made
under the heads of Salts, Earths, Inflammable Substances, Metals,
and Waters. Alkalies and acids are included with the compound
or neutral salts, so-called, under the first head. Oxygen is mentioned under nitre ; fixed air is treated with the alkaline earths ;
and dephlogisticated muriatic acid (chlorine), which Black terms
" one of the most remarkable objects in chemistry," is described
under manganese.

Inflammable substances appear in a kind of chemical menagerie, including "inflammable air," phosphorus, sulphur, charcoal, Bolognan phosphorus, spirit of wine, sugar, oils, soot, soap, tar, and pit-coal.

Fifteen metals are discussed, in the following sequence : arsenic, magnesium (manganese), iron, mercury, antimony, zinc or spelter, bismuth or tinglass, cobalt, nickel, lead, tin, copper, silver, gold, and platina or platinum. Iron receives most attention, and under this head Black describes Prussian blue, writing ink, green vitriol, cast iron and steel, and refers to the medicinal qualities of iron. Mercury also takes up a good deal of space, partly because the description includes roving commentaries on "nitrous air," "eudiometry," and "various oxyds of azote."

The last section of the work, dealing with "Waters," gives a somewhat slight account of natural waters and of their examination. Black quotes the "lately formed" opinion "that water is not a simple elementary substance but a compound," an idea which he attributes to Watt; he adds that "Mr. Cavendish, however, was the first who gave it solid foundation and credibility." [17]

During Black's lifetime many manuscript versions of his lectures were made by students and other members of his audiences, and these commanded a ready sale. They were often beautifully written and bound in several volumes. The Beaufoy copy, in the St. Andrews collection, consists of six handsome volumes, bound in tree-calf with gilt edges. It contains a record of 106 lectures, the first of which is dated "Octr. 29th, 1771." The first volume contains a folding inset, seven feet in length, bearing a large drawing of a Fahrenheit thermometer, numbered from 1,100 above zero to 450 below. To some extent these copies offer verbatim reports of parts of Black's lectures, and are thus of unusual interest. Black's own description of a lecture experiment* which he was carrying out in order to illustrate some of his original work is given in Lecture 63 as follows : " Into this Glass Syphon, I shall pour a quantity of Lime Water . . . I now apply my mouth to the pipe, and suck in the common air through it ; The fluid bubbles a little, but is not altered in its transparency . . . But I now blow through it, and it becomes instantly muddy, the

---

* This experiment was repeated in Prof. Read's lecture, with Black's original descriptive remarks.

fixed air from the Lungs being attracted by the Lime, it loses its solubility and is precipitated."

A second manuscript copy of Black's lectures, also in the St. Andrews collection,[18] consists of two volumes, dating from about 1775 and bearing the bookplate of William Herbert ; these cover only the first 44 lectures, to the end of the section on " Salts."

In the preliminary view of chemistry which he gives in the inaugural lecture of this manuscript, Black mentions that " a Century is not yet elapsed since it wore a garb which rendered it disgustful. Cultivated in ages of Barbarity and Superstition it made its appearance void of all ornaments of polite Literature and Taste, but tainted with all the folly and Credulity of the times, loaded with a barbarous jargon of terms and art, and confined in its views. But it is now simple and familiar in its language, more extensive in its views, and dedicated to the Improvement of the essential and ornamental arts of life. Now there is no occasion to learn the uncouth and barbarous terms of art. The best books are quite free from these, and the whole can be explained and acquired by means of plain and ordinary language, so that there is no study more worthy the attention of an ingenious and cultivated mind. It will be found agreeable and entertaining in the first attempts, and to those who have begun to think for themselves it will prove a fund of the highest enjoyment and satisfaction."

Black then proceeds to emphasise the experimental nature of chemistry. " It is remarkable in being more experimental than any other Science and it is upon this account that the study of Chemistry has proved a source of useful inventions and surprizing discoveries. To the Chemist things frequently turn out upon trial quite different from what was expected from mere speculation." It must not be imagined, however, interposes Black at this juncture, that chemistry is deficient in principles and reasoning. " The Chemical philosopher reasons as well as others, only he never trusts to it when the point can be proved by Experiment."

Even at this early date Black treated the theory of phlogiston with a studied reserve. He described it in the Herbert manuscript as " an opinion or Theory in Chemistry " according to which " the quality of Inflammability depends upon the presence of a particular principle or Ingredient abounding in Inflammable substances to which they give a name of Phlogiston." He ends his allusion to the theory by remarking that the gain in weight undergone by phosphorus and other bodies in burning " will probably make many of you reject the whole opinion of the existence of a Common principle of Inflammability."

The Man

The Herbert manuscript shows that Black's opening lecture consisted largely of a kind of moral exhortation to his hearers, addressed to them, as he says, " from zeal to your Improvement, not only in this study but in the other branches of your Education." He pictures the difficulties confronting beginners who set out with enthusiasm, " but by the multiplicity and extent of the Science to which they aspire, they are discharged, their ardour cools, and they seek relief from the disagreeable object which the loss of their time occasions, in amusement and dissipation." As an encouragement, Black goes on to remind them of " the difficulties and labours the greatest men have struggled thro' in their first advances." These difficulties he attributes to " the nature and constitution of the human mind, which is more or less slow in the apprehension of Ideas and things, and requires a repetition of them to fix them in the memory."

" What pleasure," he exclaims, " does an Anatomist receive from any discovery in his branch, or Chemists from a new interesting Experiment, or Botanists upon seeing a new plant! To these whose minds are already stored with Ideas of the same kind, they are precious acquisitions, as by them perhaps they are able to explain innumerable other particulars. Thus an uncommon Structure of some organ in one animal may serve to explain the functions of that organ in another animal where it is more complicated."

Once more, however, Black cautions " the ingenious and modest against being discouraged, assuring them that knowledge is not to be acquired without some study and attention, yet some progress being made it will prove an invaluable fund of entertainment and satisfaction."

" But diffidence," he continues, " is not perhaps the most general cause of the want of success. Many are reduced from their resolution to study and attention by the allurement of pleasure and amusement. There are so many snares in the way, and the loss of time and opportunity they occasion is not to be relieved. Besides by a little negligence and procrastination, business multiplies and the labour of understanding it becomes too great to be surrounded, and the mind is enervated by trifling amusements, so that it cannot give the necessary application."

At the same time, Black lays stress upon the necessity of a reasonable amount of recreation, " exercise of the Limbs, and the enjoyment of the fresh air after which the mind and body returns to study with constancy and alacrity."

Towards the end of the lecture Black stresses the importance of common-sense to the chemist. If doubts or difficulties of a chemical nature should arise, they should be referred to a " sensible chemist." " I say a Sensible Chemist," he goes on, " as it may be justly objected that the Chemists have run into the wildest extravagancies. So one of them who had thought so much upon acids, as almost to have lost the faculty of thinking upon any other Subject, thought that all fevers depended upon acidity, and thought of a method of Curing them accordingly, and others who thought that metals depended [upon] and were composed of Salt, Sulphur Mercury and Earth saw these in the composition of every body, and could neither think nor speak upon any thing else. But all this is the fault of the men not of the senses, and a Sensible Chemist can only clearly show that there is no acidity in the blood in such cases as it has been supposed, and that the principles of Salt, Sulphur Mercury and Earth are absurd."

A glance at this introductory lecture of the Herbert manuscript makes it clear that although Black was primarily concerned with a systematic presentation of a specialised field of science, yet his discourses were by no means devoid of humanism.

Physically, Black was above the average height, of slender build, and of a gentle and pleasing countenance. He was clearly a man of distinctive personality, possessing an attractive and sympathetic temperament combined with many intriguing traits of character. Contemporary accounts dwell upon his sweetness of manner, his calm and unruffled air, his freedom from passion or prejudice, his readiness to enter into conversation, and his complete lack of affectation. Adam Smith used to say that " no man had less nonsense in his head than Dr. Black." Robison regarded him as a keen judge of human character, endowed with a striking power of expressing his opinion in a trenchant phrase abiding long in the memory.

" My acquaintance with him," wrote Robison, " began at

Glasgow in 1758, I being then a student in that University ; and it began in a way which marked the distinguished amiableness of his disposition and behaviour. It was at the house of one of the Professors, to whom I was telling the great entertainment I had received from the lectures of Dr. Robert Dick, Professor of Natural Philosophy, and how much I admired him as a lecturer. Dr. Black joined in the commendation, and then, addressing himself to me, questioned me a good deal about Natural Philosophy, so as to perceive what were the peculiar objects of my attention. His advices relative to my favourite study were so impressive, and given in a manner so unaffectedly serious and kind, that they are still as fresh in my mind as if of yesterday's date. I was a stranger to him, and not even his pupil ; and he was prompted to take that pains with me, solely by the way in which he heard me speak of the lectures of one whom he loved and esteemed. Gently and gracefully checking my disposition to form theories, he warned me to suspect all theories whatsoever, pressed on me the necessity of improving in mathematical knowledge, and gave me Newton's Optics to read, advising me to make that book the model of all my studies, and to reject, even without examination, every hypothetical explanation, as a mere waste of time and ingenuity.[19] I am conscious that it was to these advices, so impressively, because so kindly bestowed, that I owe any ability that I may now possess for scientific attainments : For he set me into a path which I fear I should never have chosen for myself."

Black mingled freely in society until his activities were curtailed by declining health. Robison remarks that he was " a most welcome visitor in every family." A learned doctor and an eminent man of science, he was also responsive to music and art, being " a stranger to none of the elegant accomplishments of life . . . He performed on the flute, with great taste and feeling ; and could sing a plain air at sight." Apparently considering further explanation unnecessary, Robison adds : "I speak of Dr. Black as I knew him at Glasgow : After his coming to Edinburgh, he gave up most of these amusements."

Moreover, Black had considerable skill as an amateur artist, and Robison comments on his appreciation of form and figure. " Even a retort, or a crucible, was to his eye an example of beauty or deformity . . . These are not indifferent things ; they are features of an elegant mind."

I have mentioned Black's reference in his opening lecture to the slow apprehension of ideas and things by a process of repetition. The succeeding remarks betoken his interest in art. " To illustrate this," he says, " we imagine we have a distinct Idea of the outlines of the human figure of trees and other objects, and in consequence of seeing them often, we can judge whether they are justly imitated or not. But in the mind of a painter, their Idea is more compleat for he has viewed them again and again in all their parts till their Ideas are fixed so distinctly in his mind that he is not only a nice Critic of their Imitation by others, but is enabled to imitate and express them himself."

Black remained unmarried, although apparently not from lack of opportunity. It is said that he was a particular favourite with the ladies, who valued his approbation of their artistic tastes and regarded themselves as honoured by his attentions ; " for these," says Robison, " were not indiscriminately bestowed, but exclusively paid to those who evinced a superiority in mental accomplishments, or propriety of demeanour, and in grace and elegance of manners."

Those who knew him said that Black never lost a friend. Among his close companions in the days of his Edinburgh professoriate were Adam Smith, David Hume, Adam Ferguson, John Home, Alexander Carlyle, and other intellectual and social ornaments of Edinburgh in the last three decades of the eighteenth century. He was particularly intimate with Dr. James Hutton, who, according to Kay's *Portraits*,[13] shared Black's " remarkable simplicity of character, and almost total ignorance of what was daily passing around them in the world." On one occasion, when looking around Edinburgh for a suitable meeting-place for a club of " highly respectable literary gentlemen," these two bachelor cronies are said to have settled innocently upon a house of dubious fame. On another occasion, the two philosophers took part in a practical experiment designed to refute what they considered to be a popular prejudice against the eating of stewed snails. The test, according to Kay, ended abruptly as Dr. Hutton viewed the experimental material with a look of extreme distaste, started to his feet, and exclaimed : " Tak' them awa'! Tak' them awa'! " at the same time " giving full vent to his feelings of abhorrence."

Black's neatness and manipulative dexterity have already been mentioned. According to Brougham, his lecture table was as spotless at the end of his discourse as when he began : " not a drop of liquid, not a grain of dust remained." This love of orderliness and precision was one of Black's leading traits. It could be seen in his neat experiments, correct attire, precise speech, and orderly routine. Dr. Adam Ferguson[7] tells us that " his chambers were never seen lumbered with books and papers, or specimens of mineralogy, &c. or the apparatus of experiments . . . Every thing being done in its proper season and place, he seemed to have leisure in store."

Even the death of this great philosopher took a calm and orderly form, in keeping with the whole tenour of his life. Dr. Adam Ferguson, a relative and close friend, described his end in the following graphic words : " On the 26th Nov. 1799,[20] and in the seventy-first year of his age, he expired, without any convulsion, shock, or stupor, to announce or retard the approach of death. Being at table, with his usual fare, some bread, a few prunes, and a measured quantity of milk, diluted with water, and having the cup in his hand when the last stroke of his pulse was to be given, he had set it down on his knees, which were joined together, and kept it steady with his hand in the manner of a person perfectly at ease ; and in this attitude expired, without spilling a drop, and without a writhe in his countenance ; as if an experiment had been required to shew to his friends the facility with which he departed." [7]

In his last will and testament Black gave further evidence of his quantitative exactitude ; for he parcelled his considerable fortune, " in a most accurate and satisfactory manner," into 10,000 shares, distributed, as Robison observes, " according to the degree in which each individual was the object of his care and solicitude."

Epilogue

Even the barest sketch of Joseph Black's life and character cannot fail to assign to this calm and gentle savant of the golden age of Edinburgh society a place in the foremost rank of those who have brought renown to Scotland in the realm of science. While his purely physical investigations were of deep significance, in chemistry Black was a morning-star, a herald of that scientific dawn which ushered in the nineteenth century. The ripples from two small stones, which this mild unworldly philosopher cast carelessly into the pool of knowledge some two centuries since, have spread in ever-widening circles across a shining sea the farthest bounds of which no man can compass.

In chemistry, Black was the forerunner of a little band of ardent workers upon whose labours Lavoisier based his revolutionary views, so incalculably fruitful, concerning the nature of combustion. Black individualised " fixed air," showing that it was a distinctive kind of " air," or gas, which could not be dismissed as a mere variety of atmospheric air. To this " airy nothing " he gave, in the most literal sense, " a local habitation and a name." This epoch-making accomplishment, aided by Priestley's technique of pneumatic chemistry, opened the way to the isolation of other distinctive gases. The isolation and examination of these gases soon led in turn to the recognition of the compound nature of water, a discovery with which the name of James Watt, Black's most famous pupil, is inseparably linked.

Black's discovery that " fixed air " could be held in a solid combination and weighed in that state contained not only the germ of Lavoisier's later theory of combustion ; beyond this, Black's use of the balance in following chemical changes inaugurated another profound advance, this time in the development of quantitative chemistry.

The establishment of " fixed air " as an oxide of carbon by Lavoisier in 1783 extended in still another direction the ramifications of Black's key research ; for carbon dioxide, together with water, is an invariable product of the combustion of organic matter, and Black himself had shown, in 1757, the production of " fixed air " in the burning of charcoal.

" The pabulum of fire, consumed by it, leaves water," lamented Boerhaave, describing his experiment on the burning of alcohol, in the days of Black's infancy ; " and itself becomes so light, as to dissipate into the chaos of air, and thus eludes all further pursuit." The solution of this fundamental riddle of chemistry pivoted upon Black's researches of some twenty years later. Without the pioneering work of Black, followed by the labours of Scheele, Cavendish and Priestley, Lavoisier the chemist would have lived in vain ; for it would have been impossible for him to pass beyond the " fix'd limits of science " which baffled Boerhaave and his contemporaries and called a halt to the progress of chemistry throughout that dark night of the phlogiston era which foreran the dazzling dawn of the modern science.

NOTES AND REFERENCES

[1] Herman Boerhaave, *Elementa Chemiae*, 2 vols., Lugduni Batavorum, 1732.

[2] *Dictionary of National Biography*, London, 1886, 5, *sub voce*.

[3] For an account of the academic succession at Edinburgh in which Cullen and Black formed successive links, see Mackenzie, John E., " The Chair of Chemistry in the University of Edinburgh in the XVIIIth and XIXth Centuries," *Journal of Chemical Education*, 1935, *12*, 503.

[4] Sir William Ramsay, *Joseph Black, M.D. A Discourse delivered in the University of Glasgow on Commemoration Day, 19th April, 1904*. Glasgow, 1904.

[5] Black's paper was entitled : " Experiments upon Magnesia alba, Quicklime, and some other Alcaline Substances ; by Joseph Black, M.D." This paper occupies pp. 157-225 in : *Essays and Observations, Physical and Literary*. Read before a Society in Edinburgh, and published by them. Vol. II, 1756. The copy of this volume in the St. Andrews collection bears the autograph of Bishop Richard Watson, professor of chemistry at Cambridge (1764-71), with the Calgarth Park bookplate.

[6] Black's M.D. thesis was entitled : " De humore acido a cibis orto, et Magnesia alba." A translation of the opening paragraph by Dr. L. Dobbin runs as follows : " As I was thinking of this, my first little inaugural work, Magnesia Alba spontaneously presented itself, and the subject pleased me, chiefly because its simplicity makes it more easily adaptable to the prescribed limits, and more suited to my powers. But when I considered what I had written on it, it did not seem to have such a relation to Medicine as the motive of the work required, and I accordingly decided to preface it with some notes, as short as possible, on the acid humour derived from food, for which alone magnesia serves as a remedy."

[7] Joseph Black, *Lectures on the Elements of Chemistry, delivered in the University of Edinburgh ; by the late Joseph Black, M.D.*, 2 vols., Edinburgh, 1803. Edited, with a preface containing biographical details, by John Robison.

[8] Black's early value (determined with the help of Irvine) of 810 Fahrenheit units was low, the true value being 971 ; in later experiments (with Watt) the value 850 was obtained. Black's result for the latent heat of fusion of ice was more accurate, being 140, instead of 143.

[9] For a reference to a considerable loan of £1200 made by Black to Watt, see Clow, Nan L. and Clow, Archibald, *Chemistry and Industry*, 1942, *61*, 497.

[10] Thus, in 1771, Black was interested in attempts to manufacture alkali ; and his abiding recognition of the importance of industrial and economic chemistry is illustrated, for example, by his visits to Culross to look into the details of the coal-tar works established there by the Earl of Dundonald in 1782 : see the preceding reference ; also Clow, Archibald and Clow, Nan L., *The Economic History Review*, 1942, *12*, 47, and Kent, Andrew, *Chemistry and Industry*, 1942, *61*, 530.

[11] Thomas Thomson, *The History of Chemistry*, 2 vols., London, 1830-31. For other views of Black's character and circumstances see Cranston, John A., *Proc. Roy. Phil. Soc. Glasgow*, 1929, *57*, 83, and Kent, Andrew, preceding reference.

[12] Henry (Lord) Brougham, *Lives of Men of Letters and Science, who flourished in the time of George III*, 2 vols., London, 1845-46 ; also *The Life and Times of Henry Lord Brougham*, 3 vols., Edinburgh and London, 1871.

[13] John Kay, *A Series of Original Portraits and Caricature Etchings*, 2 vols., Edinburgh, 2nd edn., 1877.

[14] James Kendall, " Some Eighteenth-century Chemical Societies," *Endeavour*, 1942, *1*, 106 : *Nature*, 1947, *159*, 867.

[15] Besides the celebrated paper on magnesia alba (Note 5), Black communicated two relatively unimportant papers to the Royal Society of London and the Royal Society of Edinburgh. These bore the respective titles : " On the supposed Effect of Boiling upon Water in disposing it to freeze more readily, ascertained by Experiment" (*Phil. Trans.*, 1775, *65*, 124) ; and " An Analysis of the Waters of some Hot Springs in Iceland " (*Trans. Roy. Soc. Edin.*, 1794, *3*, 95).

[16] Ferdinand Hoefer, *Histoire de la Chimie*, 2 vols., Paris, 2nd edn., 1866-69, *2*, 344. It is remarkable that Black, unlike Cavendish, Priestley and Watt, did not become a Fellow of the Royal Society of London.

[17] For a discussion of rival claims concerning the discovery of the composition of water see the lecture on James Watt in Sir (T.) E. Thorpe's *Essays in Historical Chemistry*, London, 1923. For later evidence, settling the Water Controversy in favour of Watt, see Edelstein, Sidney M., *Chymia*, 1948, *1*, 123.

[18] For a fuller account of these two manuscript versions of Black's lectures, see the writer's *Humour and Humanism in Chemistry*, London, 1947 (chap. viii). Another version, in the possession of Prof. R. C. Gale, F.R.I.C., consists of 118 lectures on 1277 pp. in three quarto volumes ; the last lecture is dated 2 May 1774, and the original owner was Joseph Fryer of Rastrick. The notes on waters end with sea-water in lecture 110. The last eight lectures deal with vegetable and animal bodies and pharmacy, and lecture 118 ends thus : " . . . But you'll immediatly perceive that this plan is by far too extensive for us to prosecute at present. I shall therefore not proceed any farther but take leave of you and I must

beg leave to assure you that nothing will give me greater pleasure than to hear of your prosperity & reputat[n] in the several employments to which you are destined.

FINIS."

[19] Newton showed a reluctance to propound theories. His method, which evidently appealed strongly to Black, was first to establish the properties of things, as he said, " by experiment, and then to proceed more slowly to Hypotheses for their explanation. For Hypotheses should be adapted only to explain the properties of things, and not be misused to determine them, except so far as they may furnish experiments."

[20] This date is incorrect ; Black died on 6 December, 1799.

BLACK'S INFLUENCE ON CHEMISTRY

John A. Cranston

AN ASSESSMENT of Black's influence on Chemistry cannot be made merely on his published work, but must, to a peculiar degree be valued against the background of the times in which he lived. He was one of the pioneers of scientific method, and his work was remarkable, not only for its thoroughness, but also for the logical reasoning shown which enabled him with great economy to choose crucial experiments to test his theories. It would be difficult to claim for him that he discovered carbon dioxide, because many observations were made on this substance a hundred years before by van Helmont, who indeed in describing it as *gas silvestre* coined the generic name of " gas " ; or to claim for him to be the first to use the balance, because Rey in 1630 and others had observed the increase in weight of metals during calcination. Similarly, if it were said about Black that he showed that different kinds of air existed, claims of priority for such a demonstration might be put forward for Leonardo da Vinci (1500) and for Mayow (1674). The justification for the pre-eminence in which Black was placed by his contemporaries must be sought for in considerations which are at the same time more subtle and more solid than those mentioned above. Let us then first place him with respect to his contemporaries in the scientific world.

When Black was appointed in 1756 as Lecturer in Chemistry at Glasgow University he was 28 years of age. Stahl, originator of the theory of phlogiston, had been dead for 22 years, but his ideas were destined to tax the ingenuity of their expositors for another 40 years. Cavendish was 25 years old, Priestley 23, Lavoisier and Scheele were 13, and the most brilliant of his devotees, James Watt, was 20 ; but although none of these published any of their researches before 1766, Black had in 1754 written his classical thesis on Magnesia Alba for his Doctorate of Medicine.

Black commenced his studies in Chemistry at a time when this science had not been emancipated from the shackles of an Alchemical philosophy inherited from the Greeks. This was founded on the concept that the various kinds of matter were merely different forms of a single primordial substance which had four qualities, or which assumed as a kind of cloak the four properties of fire, air, earth, and water. The basic idea of this philosophy was that matter could not be perceived by any of the senses, but that it was the insensible nucleus around which collected certain properties recognisable by our sense perceptions. A material substance was thus somewhat analogous to a human being, who, apart from his material body, has spiritual qualities which though not directly perceived by the senses form his most important characteristics. Further, just as these spiritual qualities may be progressively refined and exalted so, in like manner, it is thought that a base metal was capable of " improvement " by chemical processes, so that the ultimate aim of these became the transmutation of base metals into the most noble element, gold. Although some glimmering of the modern idea of a property as characteristic of a chemical substance was shown occasionally during the latter period of the alchemists, it was not completely evident even in the time of Stahl. For example, phlogiston was not thought of consistently as a concrete thing but rather as an abstract and transferable property.

Shortly after Black's arrival in Glasgow as a student in 1746, a translation of Macquer, *Elemens de Chemie Theoretique*,[1] was published. As Macquer has been described by von Meyer[2] as one of the chief exponents of chemistry in France during the eighteenth century, and one who aided effectively in the spread of chemical knowledge by means of his textbooks, it is not unlikely that the book was read by Black in his studies. In assessing the state of chemical philosophy at that time, it is of interest to note how this book begins. On page 1 there is a paragraph to which the modern reader can take no exception on " The Object and chief End of Chymistry", followed by comments on the limits on analysis set by the production of substances which are incapable of further resolution. He goes on :

" To these substances we may in my opinion, give the title of Principles or Elements : at least they are really such with regard to us. Of this kind the principal are Earth, Water, Air, and Fire. For though there be reason to think that these are not the first components parts, or the most simple elements, of matter ; yet, as we know by experience that our senses cannot possibly discover the principles of which they are themselves composed, it seems more reasonable to fix upon them, and consider them as simple homogeneous bodies, and the principles of the rest, than to tire our minds with vain conjectures about the parts or elements of which they may consist ; seeing there is no criterion by which we can know whether we have hit upon the truth, or whether the notions we have formed are mere fancies. We shall therefore consider these four substances as the principles or elements of all the various compounds which nature presents to our enquiries : because of all those we know they are in fact the most simple ; and because all our decompositions, all our experiments on other bodies, plainly prove that they are as last resolvable into these primary parts."

It is in its contrast to writings of this kind that Black's thesis must be judged ; otherwise it might be described merely as an admirably written account of some twenty simple experiments, all links in a chain of evidence carefully chosen to determine decisively the problems he had set himself.

In reading *Magnesia Alba*,[3] the reader should bear in mind the state of knowledge of the times with regard to the following :

(i) That substances like pearl-ashes (K_2CO_3) and calcareous earth ($Ca\ CO_3$) were regarded as elementary substances.

(ii) That caustic alkali and quick-lime were regarded as compounds of these with the principle of fire or phlogiston.

(iii) That $MgCO_3$ had not been differentiated from $CaCO_3$, and that MgO was therefore unknown.

(iv) that the relationship between alkali and acid had not been clearly established.

(v) that the concept of different kinds of air (gases) had not yet been made. Any gases observed so far, such as those produced by the action of acids on iron and zinc or by distilling animal and vegetable matter, were regarded as atmospheric air modified in some manner.[4]

(vi) that no particular importance was attached to the property of weight, nor was it accepted as an essential property of matter. If some surprise is felt at this, it should be remembered how completely our present view of the material universe is dominated by the fundamental concepts of mass, length, and time of Newtonian mechanics, and that in Black's era the ideas of Newton had not had time to become the basis of all experimental science.

It may be of interest to note that as late as 1896, Ramsay, at a loss to explain the anomalous atomic weight of argon relative to that of potassium, speculates on the possibility of mass not being such an invariable property of matter as has been generally assumed.[4]

The contents of *Magnesia Alba* are so well known that only a brief tabulation in modern symbols of some of its experiments need be recorded here :

1. Pure magnesia is prepared from crude $MgSO_4$ and K_2CO_3, and the explanation given that it is the alkali in K_2CO_3 which separates the acid from $MgSO_4$ to leave $MgCO_3$, which is not soluble in water.

2. The reactions of H_2SO_4, HNO_3, HCl, and CH_3COOH with $MgCO_3$ are described, the first producing a soluble salt in every way similar to Epsom salt. This differentiates $MgCO_3$ from $CaCO_3$ because the latter with H_2SO_4 yields an insoluble salt.

3. $MgCO_3$ is distilled with NH_4Cl whereby some NH_4CO_3 is obtained, yet when this is added to a solution of $MgCl_2$ the $MgCO_3$ is restored. The relative affinities of NH_4CO_3 and $MgCO_3$ for HCl are thus contrasted under the different conditions of solution and of dry heating.

4. A resemblance between $MgCO_3$ and K_2CO_3 is demonstrated by the ability of both to render quicklime mild. This raises the question of whether or not $MgCO_3$ can be reduced to a quicklime by heating alone. MgO is thus discovered, and its reactions with acids studied. The surprising fact emerges that the salts produced are identical with those obtained by the action of acids on $MgCO_3$. No effervescence occurs, so Black characteristically concentrates his attack on the volatile part of $MgCO_3$.

5. Failing to condense the volatile part, he concludes that it is an air. He commences to work quantitatively. He carries out the following sequence of operations on a weighed amount of $MgCO_3$; Heating produces MgO, which is dissolved in H_2SO_4 to get $MgSO_4$, to which is added K_2CO_3, thus obtaining an amount of $MgCO_3$ practically equal to that with which he started. The revolutionary discovery is made that the acquired weight in the production of $MgCO_3$ from MgO must have been an air, and this

air must have come from the K_2CO_3, having been forced out of the latter by the acid in $MgSO_4$. " Air passes from alkali to earth at the same time that acid passes from the earth to the alkali."

6. The amount of H_2SO_4 required to neutralize a given weight of $MgCO_3$ is the same as that required to neutralize an equal weight of $MgCO_3$ previously converted into MgO. The acidic nature of CO_2 is deduced ; as is the essential difference between mild and caustic alkalis.

7. $Ca(OH)_2$ solution in shallow vessels exposed to the open air soon forms a crust of $CaCO_3$, but when contained in a loosely corked bottle does not do so. Hence $Ca(OH)_2$ is capable of combining with a particular species of air which is dispersed throughout the atmosphere.

In each of these seven experiments, Black's influence on the subsequent development of chemistry was profound. The bare outline of the work is given above, but the detailed description given in the thesis and the deductions he made from them have earned for him the following great achievements :

1. That he set a new standard of thought in correlating the properties of a substance with its quantitative chemical composition, and was among the first to raise the status of chemistry to a system of philosophy based on experiment as advocated by Boyle.

2. That he drew attention in a special manner towards the nature of gases, and so opened up the field of pneumatic chemistry for the subsequent work of Priestley, Scheele, Cavendish, and Lavoisier. Whereas his predecessors Boyle, van Helmont and Hales had considered gases to be ordinary air with various modifications, Black proved the distinct difference between carbonic acid and air, and their separability.

3. That he devoted great attention to the proportions by weight of the compounds which took part in reactions, and so paved the way for the definite knowledge of the true composition of important chemical compounds and the ultimate law of the constancy of chemical composition.

4. That he made no use of the theory of phlogiston, but alternatively realised the importance of the property of mass. The deductions that he made on the distinct character of fixed air may be contrasted with Priestley's description of it as a mode of union of phlogiston and " pure " air (dephlogisticated air) or with Cavendish's description in 1784 of inflammable air (H_2) as " water

united to phlogiston ". Indeed Black's work shook the phlogiston theory, and when oxygen was discovered by Priestley and by Scheele in 1774 the time was ripe for a new theory of combustion which finally displaced that of phlogiston ; and Black was a ready convert to Lavoisier's views.

5. That he laid the foundation of the quantitative study of the relations between acids, alkalis and salts.[5] His examination of the salts produced by adding the same acid to mild and caustic alkalis and to mild earth and quicklime advanced the study of salts as a class, by showing that the same salt may be formed by the interaction of an acid with two different compounds. Moreover, his use of the term base for substances which would not be classified together apart from their reactions with acids, contributed to the whole problem of the relations between acids, alkalis and salts and indicated the lines along which investigators of this problem must proceed.

6. Finally, Black's experiments on the reactions between $MgCO_3$ and NH_4Cl and between $MgCl_2$ and $(NH_4)_2CO_3$ give the first recorded instance of a reversible reaction ; but as a century elapsed before this subject was intensively studied, it can hardly be said that the study was stimulated by Black's work. Nevertheless, his line of approach to this and others of his experiments, notably his work on latent heat, give some support to the claim that may be made for him as the father of physical chemistry.

All this evidence of Black's influence on the science of chemistry is obtained from the one paper that he published on the subject. It might well be asked how it comes about that a single paper should have provided such an outstanding advance. We have seen several reasons which might be adduced in reply, but if one can be singled out as of special importance, it is that Black, although he does not specifically state the law of conservation of mass, yet based his work on an appreciation of its truth.

There remains to be noted three other directions in which Black's influence on Chemistry was profound, viz., his manner of lecturing, his way of inspiring his students, and his work on latent and specific heats. With the first of these, Professor Read has dealt in his commemoration lecture which is printed in this volume. It is clear that his lectures were of sufficient literary and philosophical merit as well as of sufficient experimental interest to attract large audiences counting amongst them many who were not attending for vocational reasons. Owing to the circumstance that Black did not publish anything during the long period 1766-99 when he was Professor of Medicine in the University of Edinburgh, it is difficult to assess accurately his influence on the progress of chemistry during this time. He apparently did some experiments, for it is recorded that he attempted in 1767 to inflate a balloon with hydrogen ; and he corresponded with his younger contemporaries, Lavoisier and others, who were carrying on the work that he had pioneered. It may be assumed that his philosophical insight had a continuous influence on his generation.

Of his ability to inspire his students, the names of only three of these need be mentioned. James Watt utilised Black's discovery of the latent heat of steam to design a steam engine that was destined to prove a fundamental factor in the whole field of industrial development. Rutherford, asked by Black to investigate the residual gas left after the combustion of carbonaceous bodies in air and the absorption of the resultant carbon dioxide, is credited with the discovery of nitrogen. Tennant, an Edinburgh student, was ultimately the discoverer of osmium and iridium.

Black's work on latent heat affords a striking illustration of his methods. As early as 1756, he had begun to meditate on the surprising slowness with which ice melts and with which water is dissipated on boiling. By noting that a solid at the temperature of its melting point can receive a large amount of heat which does not register on a thermometer, he draws a distinction between heat and temperature. He sets out to measure the amount of heat which is thus hidden or " latent ". Three methods are devised of great simplicity,[6] and two fundamental constants are thus obtained. The result of these researches were communicated to a literary society of Glasgow in 1762 as a sequel to a lecture given to the same society in 1760 when he originated the theory of specific heat, or thermal capacities of different substances. These theories were of course also expounded in his lectures to his students, many of whom wrote notes on them which have been preserved to this day.

And so we find Black's influence extending to another field of science. That his work was appreciated during his lifetime is evident by his unique reputation, not only in this country, but also throughout Europe ; and on his membership of scientific societies in St. Petersburg, Paris, and Edinburgh rests our assurance that his genius found scope to influence the minds of other men ; and this influence may well have been as great as, if not greater than that of any other scientist of his century.

NOTES AND REFERENCES

[1] M. Maquer, *Elemens de Chimie Theoretique*, trans. by A. Reid, London, 1758.

[2] von Meyer, *History of Chemistry*, trans. by McGowan, Macmillan & Co., London, 1891, p. 115.

[3] Joseph Black, *Experiments upon Magnesia Alba, Quick-lime, and other Alcaline Substances*,. Alembic Club Reprints, No. 1.

[4] Ramsay, *Gases of the Atmosphere*, Macmillan & Co., London, 1896. pp. 4, 237.

[5] Pattison Muir, *History of Chemical Theories and Laws*, Chapman and Hall, Ltd., London, 1907, p. 203.

[6] Cranston, " Bicentenary Address on Joseph Black ", *Proc. Roy. Phil. Soc. of Glasgow.*, 1929, vol. 57, p. 81.

THE INDUSTRIAL DEVELOPMENT OF SCOTLAND IN THE CULLEN-BLACK PERIOD

Alexander Fleck

THERE WERE no industrial considerations involved in the early history of our University, but as time has gone on, commercial and industrial matters have gained an appropriate and ever-growing place in its development as an influence in our social and cultural structure.

I propose to divide my subject into three sections :

First, some general observations and a review of the industrial scene in Scotland in the years before Cullen's appointment ; second, a description of Cullen and Black's contributions to some of the industrial problems, and last, a picture of the position of industry in Scotland while Cullen and Black passed from maturity into old age. The sketch will necessarily be selective and incomplete, and possibly over-simplified, but I hope I may be able to convey something of the progressive spirit which animated the technicians of the period.

An industrial system involving the lives and work of hundreds of thousands of individuals normally has roots that go down well into previous years, and if a change has to be made, such a change in any direction requires considerable effort. We see that to-day when we in this country are trying to go from an economy based on very liberal supplies of coal to an economy in which coal is not only expensive but also in very restricted supply. At the outset of my lecture, therefore, I should like to go back for a decade or two before Cullen and Black, so that we may understand better the industrial changes which took place when they were active on the Scottish stage.

The failure of the Darien scheme in 1698 left Scotland poorer in wealth and in spirit. The Union of 1707 had consequences far out-reaching the ideas and concepts of those important and far-sighted

people who promoted it. I am not concerned here with the
political consequences of that very necessary Act, but only with
some of the industrial consequences. There was general recognition that Scotland was not a rich country. Making a comparison
with England, Trevelyan states that Scotland contained approxi-
mately only one-fortieth of the wealth,[1] and arising out of the
relative positions of the two countries, I would recall to your mind
the history of the financial part of the Treaty of Union known
specifically as " The Equivalent ". The Scottish Commissioners
insisted that Scotland should have absolute equality to trade with
English Colonies, and the English Commisioners insisted that
there must be complete fiscal uniformity, including a share of the
then national debt. It was to ameliorate the hardship of this latter
part of the arrangements that it was agreed that England would
pay or credit to Scotland an equivalent amount of money as
compensation for assuming in the future a share of England's
debt. I quote from Trevelyan who says " By putting his hand into
his capacious pocket—a gesture to which he was even now
gradually accustoming himself—John Bull did something to wipe
out the abiding sense of a still unrequited wrong ".[2] The sum
considered by Trevelyan to be handsome was worked out in
detail to be £398,085 10s. 0d. I trust that the inclusion of the 10s.
will be taken to indicate a desire on both sides for accuracy rather
than that the Scottish Commisioners were of a nature that grasped
the minutest trifle. While a considerable portion of this money
was to be used for debt redemption, some of it was to be used for
well-intentioned purposes of industrial development. In due time
the result was the setting up of the Board of Trustees for Manufactures which existed and exercised influence from 1727 until it
was finally dissolved 100 years later.

From the industrial point of view, therefore, there are two
consequences of the Act of Union which had important bearing
on the period of Cullen and Black : the opening up of overseas
colonial trade to Scotland which had its immediate results in the
development of the tobacco trade through Glasgow, and in a
study, rather delayed in its start, of ways and means of promoting
industrial activities. The major outcome of this effort was the
great increase in the importance of the Scottish linen industry to
which I will revert.

Another event which deserves mention is the formation in

Edinburgh in 1723 of the Society of Improvers in the Knowledge of Agriculture.[3] This Society existed for a little over 20 years, when it became one of the important casualties of the 1745 Rebellion. In the course of its short life, it inaugurated a far-reaching agricultural revolution in which many famous people played their part such as the Earl of Haddington, Lord Loudon, the Duchess of Gordon, Sir James Grant of Monymusk, and the Earl of Stair.

I would like to emphasise especially that prior to the Cullen-Black period, these two organisations, the Trustees for Manu-factures and the Society for Improvers in the Knowledge of Agriculture, exercised their influence in these two parallel directions and made basic contributions to the evolution of the social structure that commenced in the middle of the eighteenth century. In discussing the industrial revolution, I am thinking not merely of a revolution which resulted in the use of mechanical power as contrasted with the unaided product of the physical effort of the individual : I include changes in agriculture as well as in mechanical technique because, as I hope to show, the state of mind which produces new advances in the chemical and mechani-cal field naturally has its direct reaction on our agricultural pro-gress. Two examples may be given—the U.S.A. is widely acknowledged as in the van of industrial progress, and we are all aware that their practice in agricultural machinery is very advanced. Another example is the U.K. to-day. We all acknow-ledge ourselves to be an advanced industrial community although we sometimes speak of agriculture as the Cinderella of our industries. When, however, we make comparisons with all European countries (only pre-1939 figures are available) we find that the annual output per active agricultural worker £120)[4] is greater in the U.K. than in any other country, and that the number of such workers per 100 acres of farmland is less than six in this country, a lower figure than any other European country. This illustrates the inevitable interconnection between mechanical industrial conditions and agriculture. As the former increases in efficiency, so also does the latter.

Throughout history, two of mankind's main considerations have been food and clothing ; the consequence of this is that when industrialisation commences, these needs bring into prominence the agricultural and textile industries. Scotland in the eighteenth century adhered to this generalisation. In the first part of the century Scotland was essentially a pastoral country with a small amount of coarse woollen and linen manufactures, the only departure from this generalisation being that quantities of coal were mined, mainly to be used for salt production. Flax was grown in small patches adjacent to the homestead and was spun into linen as a spare-time occupation by the housewife. It was on the growth of flax, and the development of the manufacture therefrom of linen, that the foundation of Scotland's industrial development was built at this time. Linen was the bridge by means of which Scotland moved from being mainly a food and clothing producing agricultural society (and a poor one at that) to a social order where manufactured goods held at least an equal share in the permanent structure of the community. The Trustees for Manufactures gave premiums for flax growing, they distributed seeds, they gave prizes for improved bleach fields, and they took steps to see that the linen produced was up to quality. In 1746 the British Linen Company (now the British Linen Bank) was founded, with the objective of encouraging all business connected with flax and linen, with a capital of £100,000 and the Duke of Argyle as chairman. Arrangements were also made for skilled linen weavers to be brought to Scotland from the north of France to teach the local inhabitants. Linen thread manufacture was established based on continental information.[5] Dr. Francis Home is credited with the discovery that the substitution of sour milk by dilute sulphuric acid in the " souring " operation of bleaching enabled the time required for this particular process to be cut by a matter of weeks.[6] This advance in bleaching technique (bleach-fields were first recorded in 1715) was the reason for the starting up of a sulphuric acid works at Prestonpans in 1749[7] undertaken by Dr. John Roebuck. This plant can be regarded as the first sulphuric works which was anything approaching in conception a modern sulphuric acid chamber plant. As indication of the development of the linen industry 2.18 million yards were marketed in 1728, and this was more than doubled in ten years. By the time Cullen and Black were fully established, it had multiplied five times, the figure for 1758 being 10.62 million yards. No other industry in Scotland could show such a record.

Some light can be thrown on the general conditions in Scotland at this time if we consider a few aspects of population. Edinburgh, starting in 1700 with 30,000, had doubled itself by 1763, Glasgow with 12,500 had grown to 28,300, and Paisley with 2,600 in 1700 had grown to 24,000 about 1770. This growth in population was not restricted to the larger towns, although their growth was very prominent. It is generally accepted by Parliamentary Reports that at the time of the Union the best estimate of the population of Scotland was 1.0 million compared with the figure of 6.1 millions for England and Wales, (i.e. in Great Britain 14.08% of the population was in Scotland). An unofficial census carried out by the Rev. Dr. Alexander Webster of Edinburgh in 1750 obtained the figure of 1.265 millions for Scotland and, at the same date, the figure for England and Wales was at 6.75 millions : the percentage for Scotland had thus gone up to 15.72. These figures are only estimates, but the fact does remain that the figure of 15.72% shows the highest population in Scotland relative to England at any time in our history. In 1801, the year of the first official census, the percentage dropped to 15.32 and it has gone on falling ever since—by 1821 it was down to 14.28%, by 1901 to just over 12%, and to-day it is something below 11%.[8] The main point is that the balance of evidence shows that the movement, general in the U.K., which resulted in a high and rapid increase in population following on a lower death rate with a continued high birth rate of the order of 32-34 per thousand, made a start in Scotland a decade or two before it started in England.

I would now sum up the industrial picture of Scotland at the time when Cullen was appointed teacher in Chemistry in Glasgow in 1747. It is a picture of a nation in a state of ferment and movement. There has, as yet, been no spectacular development such as was to come later in the ideas of James Watt, but there is very definite evidence that the whole people was becoming more alert and alive. This is not the place to discuss the whys and wherefores of the relative rapid growth in population, but the fact is there, and that in itself shows a vigorous community. Intellectually also, there are signs of an awakening and growth. William Carstares had returned to Scotland to inspire its academic life, Allan Ramsay, the elder, was writing, and Dr. William Robertson at Edinburgh had gained an international reputation as a historian. These were some of the forerunners who prepared the way for the giants of the latter half of the century such as Scott, Adam Smith, Burns, and Raeburn. It was to this very much alive and developing social structure that Glasgow University added its quota by deciding in 1747, that William Cullen should be made Lecturer in Chemistry.

The Contributions to Industry of William Cullen

Cullen's first contribution to industry was at the beginning of his second series of lectures when he announced the " plan of a course of Chemical lectures and experiments directed chiefly to the Arts and Manufactures to be given in the Laboratory of the College of Glasgow during the session 1748 ". We can but admire the quickness with which Cullen, the medical man, had assessed the opportunity and the need to give attention to developing the Arts and Manufactures. The rapidity of his action in this matter shows that he realised the new spirit which had commenced to come over the whole of the Scottish nation. He recognised also that chemistry is not very effective without a laboratory, and he obtained sanction from the University to spend £52 on this objective.[9] The cost turned out to be £136, and Cullen thus became, so far as I am aware, the first chemist to go on record as being guilty of an over-expenditure over the amount for which he had obtained sanction. This distinction alone should earn him a permanent place in the minds and thoughts of all industrial chemists.

That the spirit of his approach is quite sound is shown when he says that his object is " to supply students, in some measure, with the rudiments of such a useful and necessary piece of knowledge ; in our lectures, you will notice a great many terms that may seem affectedly pedantic. I am quite sensible of it ; but the first chemists were not only persons of a low taste, but they also affected to be mysterious and, therefore, introduced a number of uncouth terms which cannot now be easily got quit of, and it is quite necessary you should be acquainted with the meaning of them."[10]

At this time the important manufactures involving chemical operations were bleaching, which I have already mentioned, and salt manufacture. There is evidence that Cullen took an active interest in both of these, but his contributions do not seem to have been effective in causing improvements in practice.

The business of salt manufacture in these days was very intimately connected with the mining of coal, and Scotland produced considerable quantities of the latter, mainly for salt manufacture. Figures for Scottish coal production in the eighteenth century are

PLATE IX

Joseph Black, Lecturing.   (From the Kay cartoon, cf. p. 85)

vague, very largely because the exact magnitude of the units used is not now known, but Nef[11] gives his best estimate as 0.475 million tons *per annum* for the period 1681-90, and 1.6 million tons at the end of the eighteenth century. Cullen's interest in salt is displayed in correspondence between Black and Cullen dated 15th January 1754, from which it is clear that Cullen had been working on bittern, i.e. the mother liquor obtained after ordinary salt has been removed in the process of evaporation. There is also a letter from Lord Kames to Cullen of July 1752 where the former tells of discussions between the then Duke of Argyle and Kames on the subject of Cullen's project for purifying salt.[12] Cullen was urged to " communicate his secret " and to have faith in the Duke as a " trusty confidant ". Cullen's business methods do not seem to have been very energetic at this time because in the same letter Kames says " I find Lord Deskford has not yet got your lucubrations upon bleaching and upon ashes. If I do not get this summer some of your experiments about husbandry I will abandon you altogether as an utter bankrupt ". In the eighteenth century, Scottish salt did not have a high reputation for quality, and I can find no evidence that Cullen was able to improve it.

For his work on bleaching operations Cullen was awarded a present of three suits of table linen by the Trustees for Manufactures. His contributions on bleaching were concerned with the early steps of the operation. The first thing which had to be done was boiling the textile in an alkaline lye made from " ashes ". These " ashes " were mainly imported from abroad, and Francis Home suggests that the annual importations into Great Britain and Ireland were of the order of £300,000 per annum. Spanish " barilla " was the most important, but a very important commodity particularly used in bleaching was " Muscovy Ashes ". Cullen examined this and showed that part of the alkaline effect was due to lime, and this was acknowledged by Home.[13]

The other matter connected with bleaching on which Cullen worked was alternative sources of " ashes ". As I have stated, the cost of the importations was large and the Dutch were cornering supplies so, to quote Francis Home, " Both profit and necessity contribute to quicken our industry ". It is not surprising, therefore, that attempts were made to find an indigenous source. Cullen tried many kinds of plants, but failed to find any which adequately

replaced imported " ashes " and the limited quantity obtained
from the burning of kelp.

In his lectures Cullen devoted attention to the subject of heat,
and he made a contribution to the ultimate progress of industry by
directing thought to the subject. He gave information on the
variations in temperature that resulted from different chemical
reactions, and these and some observations on the melting of ice
in water were the subject of an essay read before the Literary
Society in the College of Glasgow. This essay has not been
preserved.

One observation he made, and by which he should be remembered, is the cooling effect produced by evaporating liquids. He
was unable to explain this phenomenon in terms of modern
concepts, but Black's attention was directed to the problem, and
writing in 1755 Black says " I have looked over your paper with
the highest pleasure and wish with all my heart that you would
prosecute this subject : it seems to be a copious and important
article in the history of heat ".[14] Cullen should, therefore, be
remembered for his part in directing Black's attention to the
subject of heat—probably a more important contribution to the
subject than his own observations on rapid evaporation.

His interests, however, were wider than academic science. He
had become friendly with Henry Home, later Lord Kames (not to
be confused with Dr. Francis Home), and they kept up a stream
of correspondence on agricultural matters. Cullen also managed
a farm at Parkhead, near Glasgow, and was thus a practising
agriculturist.

One possibility which was much considered in those days was
that of converting moss into the equivalent of farmyard manure.
Cullen had ideas on this subject and his friend, Lord Kames,
carried out trials. He writes " Do not forget your letter about
husbandry. Having been entertained with no theory now for a
long while, I am sinking into a mere practical farmer ".[15] The
important thing is that, arising out of his agricultural interest,
Cullen asked correct and pertinent questions, but the times were
not ripe, nor were the techniques then available adequate, for him
to get the right answers. This is shown in Cullen's questions
about the means by which plants are nourished through their
roots.[16] The questions are very sound ones, and it is worthy of
record that Cullen was anxious to apply the experimental methods

to these very proper questions. He earned for himself the reputation of being "a great master in the scientific branches of husbandry ". He died at his farm in Ormiston in 1790.

The Contributions to Industry of Joseph Black

You will recall that, born in 1728, he was student and researcher
in Edinburgh in the early 1750's and that he succeeded Cullen in
the teaching of chemistry at Glasgow in 1756. Before that date he
had made a big contribution to fundamental chemical knowledge
in his discovery and identification of fixed air or carbon dioxide. I
do not propose to elaborate on that discovery since its effect on
industrial development, while very important, was indirect.
Black's direct influence on industrial affairs was his discovery and
elucidation of the phenomena connected with heat. He made
three contributions of magnitude: an appreciation of the relationship between temperature and quantity of heat, specific heats
of different materials, and latent heats, first of water and then of
steam. He made these contributions mainly when he was in
Glasgow in the years 1762 to 1764. These properties of materials
are the most used and the most thought about of all the properties
of matter when we are concerned with large scale industrial
chemistry to-day. How to design a plant to take care of all the
quantities of heat, preferably by efficient utilisation or possibly by
adequate dispersion, is the constant pre-occupation of the industrial chemist of the present era and should have been much
more considered by the industrial chemist of the nineteenth century
than, in fact, it was. To Joseph Black, as one of the greatest of the
pioneer thinkers in these matters, we owe an immense debt of
gratitude. He thought clearly and correctly, his basic work being
carried out with a great degree of accuracy, and his ideas have
stood the test of time.

His work on heat, however, had as well a very immediate and
direct effect in that it inspired and directed the efforts of James
Watt and his work on the steam engine. That work is well known,
and there is no call for me to describe it to you. I will content
myself by saying that Black and Watt were friends and intimate
collaborators. Watt supplied Black with proofs and illustrations
in abundance of all the points on which the Professor required
information. " These were always recited in the class with the
most cordial acknowledgment of obligation to Mr. Watt." [17]

There is no doubt that Watt gained inspiration from the teachings of Black. In one of his lectures Black says " I have the
pleasure of thinking that the knowledge which we have acquired
... has contributed, in no inconsiderable degree, to the public
good by suggesting to my friend Mr. Watt ... his improvements
on this powerful engine." [18]

Robison, who edited Black's lectures and published them in
1803, writing in April of that year (it was, I may remind you, in
the uneasy interregnum between the Peace of Amiens of 1802 and
immediately prior to the renewed outbreak of war with Napoleonic
France in May 1803) links together Black's work as a teacher,
Watt's work on the improvement of the steam engine, " ... the
unparallelled state of prosperity of the British Empire resulting
from the skill, spirit and activity of its inhabitants ", and " the
imperious call now upon us for still greater exertion that we may
maintain ourselves in this, our envied pre-eminence ".[19] These
are words of weight and wisdom. They do justice to Black, but
written as they were at a difficult time in this nation's story, it is
worth while that we should remember them, facing as we do a
time when our capability for " maintaining ourselves in this, our
envied pre-eminence " is to-day widely questioned in different
nations throughout the world.

Black's removal to Edinburgh took place in 1766, accompanied
by many intrigues and suggestions too complicated for us to be
interested in or to consider here, except to say that they gave the
students of Edinburgh University an opportunity to air their views
—their ignorant views?—about Glasgow University. They did
so in these words : " But the prosecution of the science (chemistry)
may, with confidence, be expected from Dr. Black, a man whose
reputation as a chemist is justly celebrated throughout all Europe
and whose reputation at present supports the fame of an inferior
but rival University." [20]

After his installation at Edinburgh, Black took an interest in a
number of industrial matters, but his contributions were not of a
basic character. One of the things which interested almost all
chemists of the time, Black included, was the manufacture of
sodium carbonate. This problem was effectively solved by Le
Blanc in France in the early 1790's after he had commenced
experiments in 1784 and submitted his plans to the Duke of
Orleans in 1789. In 1781 the Le Blanc process was nearly fore-

stalled in this country by Dr. Brian Higgins, and then in 1782 Messrs. John Collison and Company of Southwark took out a patent which had the essentials of the Le Blanc process. Black received a sample of their product from Collison and says that he found it to be very strong and powerful.[21] It contained more alkali than the Alicant barilla in the proportion of 68 to 44 and more than the best kelp in the proportion of 68 to 10. This praiseworthy effort of Collison's never came to anything, and the firm itself has passed out of record—I can find no trace of it in the London records of 1801. Black continued his interest in sodium carbonate manufacture and participated financially in a Glasgow attempt based on the use of lead oxide in reaction with sodium chloride, but no material progress was made.

Black also played a small part in the introduction of the Turkey Red process into Glasgow in that the secret of its manufacture was communicated to him prior to the final conclusion of the arrangement between Papillon, the Frenchman who introduced the process, and George MacIntosh, who set up the works to carry it out. In other words, he was the mutually trusted honest broker who enabled the parties to be individually satisfied.

I have indicated what were some of Cullen and Black's contributions to industrial development. In this connection it would, I believe, be correct to appraise them as valuable members of a team rather than men who created for themselves an outstanding position in industrial matters. Both of them were trained as medical men, and like many others who had similar training, they switched over to chemistry. Their distinction was that they could see that chemistry was not only a valuable academic study, but that it could also play an important part in industrial progress, and therefore they are entitled to a permanent place in our records as pioneers in the application of scientific principles to industry. The full application of these principles is a task that is by no means complete to-day, but Cullen and Black made a commencement. The application of these basic ideas which they inaugurated remained much smaller in degree than it should have been until very recent years, but to-day we rejoice in its very wide acknowledgment and in its ever growing adoption.

Cullen lived to 1790, while Black passed away from the scene in 1799. In the time which is left at my disposal, I would like to devote some consideration to the Scottish industrial conditions which held while Cullen and Black passed from the prime of their power to old age.

Clearly the development of that period, which had the most lasting as well as most profound influence on industry, was the development of the steam engine initiated by James Watt who, as has already been explained, derived a great amount of inspiration from the teachings of Black. I do not propose to follow, even in outline, that development : for one thing, it is very widely known, and secondly the removal of James Watt to Birmingham and his partnership with Boulton quickly make the influence of the steam engine not a matter peculiar to, or even mainly a development of Scottish Industry. That story quickly becomes the development of British Industry. So far as Scotland is concerned, I will make this observation—that in going through the literature and documents of the period I have been struck by the rareness of references to the coal situation. I make this remark remembering that coal production for Scotland, even earlier than the eighteenth century, was an important matter. Thus, the Earl of Wemyss, speaking in 1658, said : " Coale is one of the greatest staple commodityes of the Scottish nation ".[22] I have not found any trace of Cullen mentioning it, and Black refers to coal only in very general terms and with no emphasis.

I would return to what I like to regard as the parallel developments in agricultural and manufacturing industries. The early part of the eighteenth century saw a start made towards an improved agricultural industry. About 1735, turnips and potatoes ceased to be very uncommon, and that period saw the introduction of clover and what are widely called " artificial " grasses—European grasses not indigenous to Scotland. These measures, and the arrangements made for English farmers and their labourers to be moved into Scotland from districts as far away as Dorset, definitely meant that an improvement was being initiated on the old inefficient system whereby oats were grown year after year on the land near the farm-house, while the far-away land was left in the form of uncared-for permanent pasture.

By the middle of the last half of the century, turnip growing in Scotland had become common, and a few years later wheat was introduced. An important document was issued in 1773 by Wight of the Commisioners for Forfeited Estates, who says that by then East Lothian led the way in the improvement of husbandry by the enclosure of land and the planting of new grasses. This period also saw systematic extension of sheep farming—1762 was the year of the first extended sheep farm in the Highlands, and 1782 saw an improved Border sheep introduced in the Western Highlands. Two far-reaching implement improvements were made—1763 was the year when Small of Berwickshire introduced his plough made of iron, which could be drawn by two horses, in place of the wooden affair requiring twelve oxen and two or three men. An even more basic change was the invention by Meikle of Dunbar of the first threshing machine, erected in Clackmannan in 1786.[23]

A more generalised tribute to the progress of Scottish agriculture comes from an English source. It is generally accepted to-day that the teachings and doctrines of Jethro Tull, who died in Buckinghamshire in 1740, are among the greatest advances in the technique of agriculture. His doctrine was the necessity and advantage of " cultivation " of the land, and the preparation of a good seed bed. Tull died with his gospel in general unaccepted, but Curtler in his " Short History of English Agriculture "[24] says that Scotland was the first to perceive the merits of the system.

The agricultural progress was such that in 1790 a writer could say " An observing man who was bred in Scotland is astonished when he sees in England the languor and indolence which almost everywhere prevails in regard to agriculture ".[25] After a few more years, instead of ploughmen coming from Dorset to teach the Scots farmer to work, East Lothian stewards and ploughmen were taken south. And so in Scotland at this time we have another example of the inter-relation between mechanical and agricultural industry. In the words of the writer of the period " The energy of its commercial industry is communicated by sympathy and example to its rural labours ".

No approach to the industrial development in the latter part of the eighteenth century, could omit a reference to the great progress that was made in the direction of ferrous metallurgy. The Carron Ironworks, founded in 1759, had as its founders Mr. Samuel Garbett, Dr. John Roebuck (the same who was active in the sulphuric acid industry in 1749), and Mr. William Cadell. The Carron Ironworks gained for itself a wide fame and was the forerunner of many iron producing works such as Wilsontown in Lanarkshire and the Clyde Iron Works.[26]

It is on the textile side, however, that I would stress the very interesting and far-reaching developments that took place. To improve quality, about 1769 the weavers began introducing cotton threads into linen textiles, and this prepared the way for a reputation for high quality work which was most useful when the time was ripe to go over to cotton fabrics. Thus, in Wadsworth and Mann's book on " The Cotton Trade and Industrial Lancashire " it is stated " In Scotland, however, especially in Glasgow, the linen industry had developed a prosperous cotton and linen section producing checks and cloths for printing which had obtained some importance by the seventies. Glasgow checks . . . were claimed by a contemporary historian to be ' superior to any from Manchester ' ".[27]

The next step in the development of the Scottish textile industry was facilitated by the effect of the American War of Independence on the Glasgow tobacco trade. The financial resources thus set free were deflected to establishing and developing a cotton industry centred in the Western Midland region. This was successful and the weaver attained very considerable power. The business was very profitable. For example, Robert Owen tells of raw cotton at 5s. per lb. being sold for £9 18s. 6d. when ready for the muslin weaver. From 1779 onwards a quick succession of cotton mills were brought into production, and towards the end of the century linen had dropped from being Scotland's most important textile industry, cotton having taken its place. In attaining considerable importance, the cotton weaver brought with him considerable economic problems, e.g. the four day working week—" Four days did the weaver work, for then four days was a week . . . "[28] I cannot follow the industry through its subsequent history of further growth and then decline. All I need say is that part of its greatness lay in the skill of its weavers : part of its weakness lay in the use of that skill for goods of fashion and fancy for which the demand was ephemeral—" The history of the industry was a succession of novelties. And this was the main difference between Lancashire and Scotland. The Scots made ' fanciful articles of show and taste ', the English made strong, plain and unchanging articles, plain cambrics, cotton for printing, fustians, etc." [29]

All this textile activity had direct repercussions on the chemical industry in that branch concerned with dyeing. The first activity of magnitude was the works erected by George MacIntosh, the father of Charles MacIntosh whose name is perpetuated in the garment of that name. A works was erected in Glasgow in 1780 for the manufacture of cudbear, a purple dye especially suitable for wool and silk. It was manufactured by the treatment of lichens of the genus *rocella* by ammonia solution. This activity was added to in 1785 by the far more important one of the manufacture of Turkey Red, carried out as a practical operation first of all in Glasgow by a Frenchman called Papillon. The manufacture of Turkey Red had been regarded as a desirable operation, particularly by the Manchester people, ever since the 1760's, and various efforts were made to introduce it, including special missions to the Near East. These obtained a quantity of information, but not enough for the development of a practical process, and so the matter remained until this Frenchman came along and interested George MacIntosh in it. Mr. P. F. Crosland, the present chairman of the United Turkey Red Co., Ltd., informs me that the decision to establish the Turkey Red business in Glasgow in preference to the Lancashire district was, in his opinion, an acknowledgment of the " enterprise, energy and foresight " of the Scottish cotton manufacturer Monteith and of MacIntosh who risked a good deal to establish the industry.

Reference must also be made to the progress that was made in the bleaching industry. I have already emphasised the interest of the Board of Trustees in this matter and how William Cullen endeavoured to find alternative sources of " ashes ", i.e. alkaline materials. No important change in the process was made until the French chemist Berthollet discovered the advantages of chlorine for this purpose in 1785. James Watt introduced this process into a Glasgow bleach field within one year, and a year later still, i.e. 1787, it was introduced into Aberdeen—another piece of evidence that the Scottish technicians of the period were quick to grasp the significance of chemical development. Scotland at the very end of the eighteenth century contributed a most important addition to bleaching technology in the discovery of " bleaching powder " by Charles Tennant in 1798. The great practical advantages of bleaching powder enabled it to maintain a place for itself as a bleaching agent down to our own generation.

I have tried to convey an outline of a textile industry full of movement and development, and I would bring a witness to support such a view in the person of John Galt. In " The Annals of the Parish " he says regarding 1788 " . . . still it was nevertheless a year of great activity. The minds of men were excited to new enterprises : a new genius, as it were, had descended upon the earth and there was an erect and outlooking spirit abroad that was not to be satisfied with the taciturn regularity of ancient affairs." Of 1789 he says " It was not remarkable for any extraordinary occurrences : but there was a hopefulness in the minds of men and a planning of new undertakings of which, whatever may be the upshot, the devising is ever rich in the cheerful anticipation of good ".

Summary, in Conclusion

First of all, during the century there is reason to suppose that the production of coal had been increased between three and four times. Secondly, a very good start had been made in the iron industry. At the end of the century the annual value of Scottish cast iron production was calculated at not far over £100,000 per year. Linen had made important and steady progress. Starting at just over 2 million yards per year it climbed rapidly, and then settled down at 20 million yards per annum and was valued at £900,000 per annum. Cotton came in, at first not very strongly, but in the last twenty years firmly established itself, so that by the end of the century its annual value was of the order of £2,000,000/£3,000,000. It is, of course, impossible to give figures for the value of the agricultural production. The Department of Agriculture only came into operation the best part of a hundred years later, so that there was no organisation to collect statistics on which agricultural totals can be estimated.

I would then suggest that we can claim for the industrialists of the time that their most outstanding characteristic was their very ready adaptability. I do not think we would be well advised to claim great industrial originality. James Watt, undoubtedly the most outstanding figure of his generation, was led to his far-reaching improvements, first of all by steps taken very tentatively by Cullen and then, far more specifically, by Black. The improved qualities of linen received material help from men skilled in Continental manufacture who were brought into this country. The development of agriculture which took place was built, in many instances, on basic practices and ideas imported from England, but the Scots of the time were quick to see the important implications of advances made both here and elsewhere and fearlessly moved on to industrial greatness founded on the intelligent and logical use of those advances.

I have described the country in the pre-Cullen period as being in a ferment—the mass was stirring, but there was no clear indications of how matters might develop. When Black died, lines of industrial development, valid for many years, were clearly indicated—agriculture, textiles, coal, iron and chemicals. With these and other industries arising from them, such as shipbuilding and mechanical engineering, Scotland moved on a widening and deepening stream of industrial stability and development throughout the nineteenth century. When the history of industrial Scotland for the twentieth century comes to be written, will the story still be the same? Will the set-backs and scarcities of the first half of the present century be seen to be but a temporary break in the upward curve? Will the diminishing availability of underground resources and our greater reliance on the yields of the surface of our land present us and our agriculture with problems beyond our solution? These are subjects which must present each one of us with many anxieties, but amid all the uncertainties, we do know this—that we have a great tradition of past achievements to inspire us to future efforts, and we have many examples like Cullen and Black who pioneered the way to industrial stability and who worthily played their part in the team which enabled us to make a great contribution to world progress.

If we emulate them and carry on our work in the future in their spirit and in their tradition, then not only can we rest content that
" . . . our greatness will not fail,
Through craven fears of being great "
but we can say more—that if we strive with unstinted labour, if we use fully the most advanced knowledge, and if we work with traditional courage, we can be confident that Scotland's problems will be resolved by the efforts of her people.

NOTES AND REFERENCES

[1] G. M. Trevelyan, *England under Queen Anne*, Longmans, Green & Co., London, 1932, Vol. II, " Ramillies and the Union with Scotland", p. 267.

[2] G. M. Trevelyan, *ibid.*, p. 268.

[3] J. Scott Watson and M. E. Hobbs, *Great Farmers*, Selwyn & Blount, London, 1937, pp. 223-6.

[4] P. Lamartine Yates and D. Warriner, *Food and Farming in Post-War Europe*, Oxford University Press, 1943, p. 39.

[5] H. Grey Graham, *Social Life of Scotland in the 18th Century*, A. & C. Black Ltd., London, 1937, p. 515.

[6] Francis Home, *Experiments with Bleach*, Kincaid & Donaldson, Edinburgh, 1756, p. 127.

[7] H. Hamilton, *The Industrial Revolution in Scotland*, Oxford University Press, 1932, p. 103.

[8] Population of Scotland compared with that of England and Wales.

Year	Scotland (Millions)	England and Wales (Millions)	Percentage of Total in Scotland
1707	1·0*	6·11	14·05
1750	1·265*	6·74	15·76
1801	1·608	8·89	15·30
1821	2·091	12·00	14·81
1901	4·472	32·53	12·10
1931	4·843	39·95	10·80

* Figures from Registrar General, Edinburgh.
Other figures from Whitaker's *Almanack*, 1945 p.608.

[9] John Thomson, *Life of Cullen*, Blackwood, Edinburgh, 1832, Vol. I, pp. 29 and 30.

[10] John Thomson, *ibid.*, p. 31.

[11] J. U. Nef, *The Rise of the British Coal Industry*, Routledge, London, 1932, Vol. I, p. 19.

[12] John Thomson, *ibid.*, p. 58.

[13] Francis Home, *ibid.*, p. 127.

[14] John Thomson, *ibid.*, p. 57.

[15] John Thomson, *ibid.*, p. 63.

[16] John Thomson, *ibid.*, p. 597.

[17] J. Robison, *Joseph Black, Lectures in Chemistry*, Edinburgh, 1803, Preface.

[18] J. Robison, *ibid.*

[19] J. Robison, Dedication to Reference (17).

[20] Address of the Students of Medicine to the Lord Provost, Magistrates and Town Council of the City of Edinburgh, 1766.

[21] Sir William Ramsay, *Life and Letters of Joseph Black*, M.D., Constable, London, 1918, p. 68.

[22] Earl of Wemyss, quoted by Nef in " The Rise of the British Coal Industry ", p. 4.

[23] H. Hamilton, *ibid.*, pp. 53 and 54.

[24] W. H. R. Curtler, *Short History of English Agriculture*, Clarendon Press, Oxford, 1909, p. 178.

[25] H. Grey Graham, *ibid.*, p. 213, quoting Anderson, " Agriculture in Aberdeenshire ", p. 151.

[26] H. Hamilton, *ibid.*, p. 161.

[27] A. P. Wadsworth and J. de Lacy Mann, *Cotton Trade in Industrial Lancashire*, 1600-1780, Manchester University Press, 1931, p. 171.

[28] William Thom of Inverary, *Rhymes and Recollections of a Hand Loom Weaver*, Paisley, 1845, p. 9.

[29] Hand Loom Weavers' Report, 1834.

JOHN ROBISON, M.A.

Born, 1739 : died, 30th January, 1805. Edcn : Grammar School and University of Glasgow (matriculated 1750, M.A., 1756, as John Robertson). LL.D., New Jersey, 1798, Glasgow, 1799. Lecturer in Chemistry, 1766-9. Inspector-general (Cronstadt, 1770-3). Professor of Natural Philosophy (Edinburgh, 1774-1805).

Sir Edmund Whittaker

THE SUCCESSOR of Dr. Black in the chemical lectureship was John Robison. Robison was the son of a prosperous Glasgow merchant, who had retired to his country estate of Boghill, in the parish of Baldernock ; where, in 1739, the subject of this memoir was born.

He was educated at the Grammar School of Glasgow, and in November 1750 entered the University, which was at that time distinguished for the lectures of Robert Simson in the chair of Mathematics and Adam Smith in that of Moral Philosophy. He took his degree in Arts in April 1756, and tried, but failed, to obtain appointment as an Assistant to Dr. Dick, the professor of Natural Philosophy. To this period of his life belongs his earliest recorded participation in scientific matters, which is thus described by James Watt in a note to the second volume of Robison's (posthumous) *System of Mechanical Philosophy*.[1]

" My attention was first directed in the year 1759 to the subject of steam-engines, by the late Dr. Robison himself, then a student in the University of Glasgow, and nearly of my own age. He at the time threw out an idea of applying the power of the steam-engine to the moving of wheel-carriages, and to other purposes, but the scheme was not matured, and was soon abandoned on his going abroad."

The " steam-engine " here referred to was of course the Newcomen engine, patented in 1705, in which the moving power was the pressure of the atmosphere, and steam was employed merely as the readiest method of producing a vacuum : the consumption of fuel was prodigious in proportion to the energy developed, and the machine was used chiefly to draw water from coal-pits where it could be fired with unsaleable small coal. Subsequently Robison kept closely in touch with Watt's own inventions, which were based on the substitution of steam for atmosphere as the power to force the piston down in the cylinder : and he acted as a witness in an important patent case relating to them.

In 1758, finding no congenial opening in Glasgow, he obtained a recommendation from professors Dick and Simson to persons of influence in London, and, by the good offices of Admiral Knowles, was engaged to go to sea as a midshipman in the fleet which sailed in February 1759 to co-operate with a military force in the reduction of Quebec. In the beginning of May the ascent of the St. Lawrence was made, and active operations were begun. The night before the decisive battle on the Plains of Abraham, Robison was on duty in the boat in which General Wolfe went to visit some of his posts : as they rowed, the General, with much feeling, recited Gray's *Elegy* to an officer who sat with him in the stern of the boat ; adding, as he concluded, that " he would prefer being the author of that poem to the glory of beating the French to-morrow ".

The following year his ship returned to England, and in 1761 he was sent to Jamaica in charge of Harrison's chronometer, in order to determine its reliability in the determination of longitudes. On his return he quitted the Navy and returned to Glasgow, where his friendship with Watt was renewed, and where he studied chemistry under Dr. Black, who not long before had made his great discovery of Latent Heat. The great advances made by his friends created an atmosphere of optimism and enthusiasm, in which his interests in pure and applied science were powerfully stimulated, and in 1766, when Black left Glasgow on his appointment as Professor of " Chemistry and Medicine " in Edinburgh University, Robison was chosen to succeed him.

Not long afterwards, however, his patron Admiral Knowles was recommended by the British Government to the Empress Catherine the Great of Russia as the most suitable adviser to effect a reformation in her navy, and was accordingly appointed President of the Russian Board of Admiralty : he engaged Robison as his private secretary, and they proceeded together to St. Petersburg in December 1770. Robison was nominated Inspector-General of the Imperial Corps of Marine Cadets at

Cronstadt, with the rank of Lieutenant-Colonel : his chief duty was to receive the reports of about 40 teachers and professors, regarding the studies of 400 young noblemen who were their pupils, and to class the latter according to his judgment of their merits. St. Petersburg was at this time the residence of the great Swiss mathematician Leonhard Euler, and of the German physicist F. U. T. Aepinus ; but Robison was unable to arrange to live near them, and Cronstadt in winter was deplorably melancholy : he was therefore induced without much difficulty in 1773 to accept (at some pecuniary sacrifice) the Professorship of Natural Philosophy at Edinburgh, which had become vacant by the death of James Russell, and to which he was recommended by the Principal of the University, William Robertson. The Russian Government granted him a pension of about £80 a year for life, but soon ceased to pay it.

He arrived in Edinburgh in September 1774, and continued to live there for the remaining thirty years of his life, paying only an annual visit to his native place, where he still possessed a part of his father's estate. In 1777 he married Rachel Wright, who bore him three sons and a daughter.

The choice of Robison as professor was justified particularly by his wide experience beyond ordinary academic life, and his acquaintance with eminent foreign mathematicians and natural philosophers. His course of lectures included Dynamics, Celestial Mechanics, Hydrodynamics, Optics, Electricity and Magnetism. According to a contemporary account, they " were given with great fluency and precision of language, and with the introduction of a good deal of mathematical demonstration. His views, always ingenious and comprehensive, were full of information, and never more interesting and instructive than when they touched on the history of science. His lectures, however, were often complained of, as difficult and hard to be followed, and this arose not from the depth of the mathematical demonstrations, but rather from the rapidity of his discourse, which was in general beyond the rate at which accurate reasoning can be easily followed. The singular facility of his own apprehension made him judge too favourably of the same power in others. To understand his lectures completely was, on account of the rapidity and the uniform flow of his discourse, not a very easy task, even for men tolerably familiar with the subject. On this account, his lectures were less popular

PLATE X

JOHN ROBISON

than might have been expected from such a combination of rare talents as the author of them possessed. This was assisted by the small number of experiments he introduced, and a view that he took of Natural Philosophy which left but a very subordinate place for them to occupy. An experiment, he would very truly observe, does not establish a general proposition, and never can do more than prove a particular fact. Hence, he inferred, or seemed to infer, that experiments are of no great use in establishing the principles of science.

At the time when Robison entered on the duties of his chair, there was in Edinburgh no society actively engaged in the promotion of original research. An association for the cultivation of literature and science had been founded in 1739, under the name of the Philosophical Society, and had published three volumes of Memoirs, entitled " Physical and Literary Essays " : but after the appearance of the last, in 1756, the movement had languished. The arrival of Robison gave it a new impetus : with the cordial co-operation of the Principal of the University, application was made for a Royal Charter, which was granted : and thus the Royal Society of Edinburgh came into being. Robison, one of the persons named in the Charter, was immediately appointed Secretary, and continued to discharge the duties of that office until, after many years, the state of his health compelled resignation.

The first volume of the *Trans. Roy. Soc. Edin.* contains his first published paper, " A Determination of the Orbit and Motion of the Georgium Sidus, directly from Observations ", read in March 1786.[2] This object was, of course, Uranus, which had been discovered by Herschel five years previously. The observational material available was scanty, and was in part contributed by himself : with a simple equatorial telescope he measured the differences of Right Ascension and Declination between the planet and known stars in its neighbourhood. His method of computing the orbit depended on a simple geometrical construction, and the elements which he derived do not suffer by comparison with the more accurate values determined subsequently.

His next publication was " On the Motion of Light, as affected by Refracting and Reflecting Substances, which are themselves in Motion ", read April 7, 1788.[3] Bradley's discovery of aberration, half a century earlier, had suggested many questions as to the

I

emission, reception, and transmission of light by moving bodies ; and Boscovich in 1785 had put forward some new speculations as to what would happen if the tube of a telescope were filled with water instead of air. " There is one deduction " said Robison " which Boscovich makes from his premises, extremely curious in itself, and having the most surprising consequences. It is this : If a telescope be constructed, having its tube filled with water, and be directed to a terrestial object properly situated, it will be found to deviate from that object by a certain determined quantity every day. It will follow from this, that a person shut up in a mine or dungeon may, without seeing the sun or heavens, discover the motion of the earth round the centre of the solar system, and also whether this centre be in motion, and the velocity and direction of this motion ". Robison criticised Boscovich's reasoning, and showed that the effects anticipated by him could not be expected : but the work was based on the corpuscular hypothesis (Young's vindication of the wave theory came many years afterwards), and it was not until 1818 that correct formulae for the velocity of light in a moving transparent body were obtained by Fresnel.

In December 1785 Robison was attacked by an illness, accompanied by violent spasms of pain, which remained with him for the rest of his life. Its nature was never understood : this however did not prevent him from engaging in a very laborious undertaking. The *Encyclopaedia Britannica* which had originated in Edinburgh, was now in preparation for a third edition, in which it was to be enlarged from three to eighteen volumes : and in 1793 Robison agreed to write several articles. His accession was an event of great importance in the history of the *Encyclopaedia*, for he was the first contributor who was professedly and really a man of science : and from that time it ceased to be a mere compilation. Between 1793 and 1801 he enriched it with treatises equivalent in the aggregate to a quarto volume of more than a thousand pages : many of them, such as *Projectiles, Pneumatics, Resistance of Fluids, Rivers, Seamanship, Telescope, Waterworks*, were closely connected with his interests in applied science : while of the articles in the *Supplement*, those on *Astronomy, Dynamics, Electricity, Magnetism*, and on *Boscovich*, contain notable contributions to theory, particularly that on Electricity : that is, Electrostatics, since he does not refer to the voltaic pile, which was discovered only towards the end of his life.

As is well known, two small globes charged with the same kind of electricity repel each other with a force inversely proportional to the square of the distance between their centres : this is commonly known as " Coulomb's Law ", though Coulomb, who published it in 1785, was not its first discoverer : it had been arrived at in 1767 by Priestley (who deduced it mathematically from the empirical fact that there is no electric force in the interior of a charged hollow conductor) and independently in 1769 by Robison by direct experiment.   Robison was an enthusiastic adherent of the doctrines of his friend Aepinus, whose *Testamen Theoriae Electricitatis et Magnetismi*, published at St. Petersburg in 1759, had definitely overthrown the theory of effluvia and replaced it by the conception of action at a distance : Robison's professional lectures on the subject in Edinburgh seem to have been devoted chiefly to showing how the theory of Aepinus accounted for all the electric phenomena then known.   After making considerable practical improvements in the design and construction of an electrometer, he employed the instrument to determine the mutual repulsion of two spheres similarly electrified (positively or negatively), and found that it varied as the inverse 2.06th power of their distance apart.   With balls having opposite electricities, he found the force to vary in defect from the inverse square, as the other result was in excess. " We therefore think " he said " that it may be concluded, that the action between two spheres is exactly in the inverse duplicate ratio of the distance of their centres ".

During the years when he was occupied chiefly with the *Encyclopaedia*, the attention of the world was focussed on the amazing developments of the French Revolution : he was not unaffected by the general alarm, and undertook to explain the causes of this extraordinary succession of events.   In 1797 he published a book entitled *Proofs of a Conspiracy against all the Religions and Governments of Europe*.   He asserts that this conspiracy originated in the lodges of the Freemasons, but that it first assumed a regular form among certain philosophic fanatics, known in Germany as *Illuminati* : that after the suppression of this society by governmental authority, the spirit was kept alive by what was called the German Union : that its principles gradually infected most of the philosophers of France and Germany, and lastly broke forth with full force in the French Revolution.   The history of *Illumination*, as it is called, forms the principal part of the work :

and the events related, and the characters described, are of so extraordinary a nature, that one can hardly accept the documents from which the narrative was composed as entitled to the confidence reposed in them. The book was, however, extremely popular, and carried the name of the author into places where his high attainments in science never gained admission for it : in the course of two years, it underwent no less than four editions.

Robison was a man of many accomplishments : he was a good linguist, he had great skill and taste in music, and he performed on several instruments. His powers of conversation were remarkable, and he wrote charming *vers de société*. In Cockburn's " Memorials of his time " there is a reference to his personal appearance in later life :

" John Robison made himself remarkable, like others of his class at that time, by humouring his own taste in the matter of dress. A pigtail so long and so thin that it curled far down his back, and a pair of huge blue worsted hose without soles, and covering the limbs from the heel to the top of the thigh, in which he both walked and lectured, seemed rather to improve his wise elephantine head and majestic person. A little hypochondria, induced by the frequent use of laudanum for the alleviation of pain, heightened the interest with which we gazed on a person who we knew combined such profound philosophy with such varied active life ".[4]

The illness from which he suffered rendered him occasionally unable to discharge his professional duties ; but there was no failing of his mind until at the end of January 1805 he was suddenly seized with a severe attack which terminated fatally in forty-eight hours.

NOTES AND REFERENCES

[1] John Robison, LL.D., *A System of Mechanical Philosophy*, Murray, Edinburgh, 1822, vol. II, p. 118.

[2] *Trans. Roy. Soc. Edin.*, 1788, *1*, 305.

[3] *Trans. Roy. Soc. Edin.*, 1790, 2, 83.

[4] Henry Cockburn, *Memorials of his Time*, Black, Edinburgh, 1856, p. 56.

A full list of biographical references will be found under " John Robison " in the *Dictionary of Natural Biography*.

JAMES WATT AND GLASGOW UNIVERSITY
Robert C. Howie

JAMES WATT made his first acquaintance with Glasgow University during his boyhood when visits to his mother's family in Glasgow provided a change from life in Greenock. During these visits he met his mother's kinsman, George Muirhead, later professor of Humanity, who introduced him to the University. He picked up some knowledge of chemistry and anatomy and later in life told his son that, had he been able to endure the sight of suffering, he might have become a surgeon. His regular association with the University began in June 1754. His father had suffered some business losses which made it desirable that James should learn some trade by which he could support himself. An aptitude for mathematics combined with unusual skill with tools of all sorts suggested instrument making and so, at the age of 18, he was sent to work with an optician in Glasgow where he lived with the Muirheads.

Professor Muirhead introduced him to, among others, the recently appointed professor of Anatomy and lecturer in Chemistry, Joseph Black, and to Robert Dick, professor of Natural Philosophy. Dick noted the young man's handling of astronomical instruments which had been acquired by the Natural Philosophy department and realised that he was not likely to learn much from the optician with whom he was working. He therefore suggested that Watt should go to London for further training and provided an introduction to James Short, an instrument maker in the Strand. In June, 1755, a year after his arrival in Glasgow, Watt set off for London. There he had difficulty in finding a master who could teach him much, as it was customary for an apprentice to be indentured for seven years, and he could only afford to stay one year. Eventually, however, Short was able to introduce him to John Morgan, one of the few instrument makers in the town, under whom he served an apprenticeship of one year. He learnt quickly, in spite of ill health and the activity of the press gangs which made it dangerous for him to venture out of doors, and at the end of the year felt himself competent to earn his living anywhere.

On his return to Glasgow, Watt found Professor Dick expecting the arrival of some astronomical instruments which had been bequeathed to the University by Alexander Macfarlane, a merchant, of Jamaica. When the instruments arrived, it was found that they had suffered on the voyage, and Dr. Dick was appointed by the University to ask Watt to repair them. For this purpose he was given the use of a small room in the college overlooking the quadrangle. The task occupied Watt for about six weeks. For it he received five pounds, possibly the first money he earned after his apprenticeship and, much more important, he began an intimate friendship with Professor Black which lasted throughout Black's life. Among the visitors to the workshop to see the Macfarlane instruments and the young man who worked on them was John Robison (at this time using his family name, Robertson, which, however, he changed soon afterwards to Robison) a young student who, later, in 1766, succeeded Black in the lectureship in Chemistry. Robison conceived an intense admiration for Black and a three-cornered friendship between Watt, Black and Robison resulted. It has been said that in this friendship Watt received and the other two gave. It is true that Watt's treatment of his friends, particularly Robison, was, at times, ungenerous, but there can be no doubt that he had a genuine affection for them. Throughout the earlier part of his life Watt was subject to frequent attacks of ill health and depression and this was probably the cause of his occasional bitterness.

After his work for the University was completed Watt returned to Greenock, possibly intending to set up in business there. He did not do so, but returned to Glasgow towards the end of 1757. Here he met with some opposition to his attempt to open a shop. It is not certain how far this opposition went, but in many of his biographies it is undoubtedly exaggerated. Watt was not a burgess of Glasgow nor was he a member of any of the trade corporations or guilds, and he would, therefore, be regarded as an interloper, but there is no record of any action against him in the Dean of Guild Court, which had jurisdiction in these matters. That the opposition was not very serious is shown by the fact that two years later he did set up a shop in the city. Whatever the facts may be regarding his persecution, his friends in the University came to his assistance. In addition to a room to be used for living accommodation (possibly the one he occupied during his earlier stay at the College) he was given the use of a room as a shop. This was situated on the ground floor of an old house forming part of the University buildings, opening on to High Street. He was also allowed to use the title of Mathematical Instrument Maker to the University. Watt lived in the College for six years, almost up to the time of his marriage in 1764 and retained the shop till he left Glasgow finally in 1773 after the death of his wife. During the first few years in which he occupied the shop there are occasional records of payments for repairs to apparatus belonging to the University, but the sales of apparatus outside the University were not profitable. In a letter to his father, written after he had been in business for nine months, he complains that " unless it be the Hadley's instruments (quadrants) there is little to be got by it ". His costs were higher than he had expected, due possibly to his inexperience.

Besides instrument making and repairing he undertook a wide range of work. This included the repair of musical instruments, though Watt was completely without any musical ability, and in 1761 he was invited to construct an organ for a mason's lodge in Glasgow. He first made a small one which he presented to Professor Black, and then a large one. Had he been given an entirely free hand it would have been an instrument such as no organist had ever played on before or since, for Watt, with his genius for mechanical invention, devised innumerable gauges and contrivances for measuring and controlling the draught in every part of the instrument. Watt later invented a machine for perspective drawing and in this case also he presented his first instrument to Professor Black.

After October 1759 Watt carried on his business in several shops in Glasgow, in partnership with John Craig, but he still retained his shop in the College.

Until his entry to the navy in 1759, John Robison was a frequent visitor to Watt's rooms and the two young men discussed many things. Robison later described Watt, at this period, as " a philosopher, as young as myself and always ready to instruct me ". Among the topics which they discussed were steam engines and " steam carriages ". Watt afterwards gave Robison the credit for introducing the subject. At that time the steam engine was used only for pumping water from mines and worked with steam at atmospheric pressure. Watt carried out some experiments with a model engine using high pressure steam, but abandoned them on account of the risk of explosion. These discussions and experiments were, however, to lead to the work on the steam engine on which his fame chiefly rests. The Natural Philosophy department possessed a model Newcomen steam engine. The model was not successful and had been sent to a London firm to be put in order. This they were apparently unable to do and Professor Anderson, successor to Professor Dick who helped Watt during his first stay in Glasgow, had been authorised to recover the model from London. In 1763 he asked Watt to work on it. Though Watt had discussed engines with Robison this was probably his first acquaintance with one, apart from his own models which involved only a boiler and a minute cylinder, and he had little practical knowledge of them.

The Newcomen or atmospheric engine was the only one in use at the time and was used, as stated above, for pumping water from mines. It consisted of a boiler which supplied steam at atmospheric pressure to a vertical cylinder. A piston in the cylinder was connected, usually by a rope or chain, to one end of a large wooden beam above the cylinder. The beam was pivoted in the middle and from the opposite end to the piston the connecting rods to the pump ran down the mine shaft. These rods were much heavier than the piston and when steam was admitted to the cylinder below the piston, the piston was pulled up by the weight of the rods. Steam was then cut off and a spray of water introduced to the cylinder. This condensed the steam, causing a partial vacuum and the pressure of the atmosphere acting on the upper side of the piston forced it down, so raising the pump rods. The cycle was then repeated. The College model was a scale model and the capacity of the boiler was much less in proportion to the surface of the cylinder than would be the case in a large engine, so that the loss of heat from the cylinder was proportionately more serious and the boiler was unable to supply enough steam to work the engine. Watt made a number of models in which various improvements were tried, such as the provision of fire tubes in the boiler to enable it to produce more steam, and he also carried out a long series of experiments. By measuring the volume of steam produced when a known weight of water is evaporated and also the weight of water used for each stroke of the engine, he was able to show that the steam consumed for each stroke amounted to about four times the volume of the cylinder. He realised that the waste of steam was due to the cooling of the cylinder by the water spray used to condense the steam. The cylinder had then to be heated again by the incoming steam, most of which was condensed and wasted in the process. Watt saw clearly that if this loss could be overcome, the efficiency of steam engines could be greatly increased, and he determined to construct an engine which would waste no steam. He found that, in condensing, steam gave out enough heat to raise five times its weight of water to boiling point, a result which he was unable to explain till Professor Black told him of his discovery of latent heat a few years before, in 1761. In all these experiments he was assisted by Black, both with advice and with money, and by Robison, now returned to Glasgow, who obtained books and papers for him.

Watt's account of his discovery, in May 1765, of the solution of his problem, has often been quoted, but it merits quoting again. He told the story long afterwards to a friend, " It was in the Green of Glasgow. I had gone to take a walk on a fine Sabbath after-noon . . . I was thinking upon the engine . . . and had gone as far as the Herd's House when the idea came into my mind that, as steam was an elastic body, it would rush into a vacuum, and if a communication was made between the cylinder and an exhausted vessel, it would rush into it, and might be there condensed without cooling the cylinder. I then saw that I must get rid of the con-densed steam and injection water if I used a jet as in Newcomen's engine . . . I had not walked further than the golf house when the whole thing was arranged in my mind." The next step was to make such an engine. This had to wait till the following day as Watt observed the Sabbath strictly, but on the Monday he con-structed the first steam engine with a separate condenser. Robi-son, coming to visit him, eager to talk of steam engines, found him with " a little tin cistern " on his knee and was told that the problem had been solved, but Watt refused to tell him how and pushed the model out of sight lest he should see. Robison generously ascribed this ingratitude to his having, a few days before, disclosed an invention of Watt's without permission, at which Watt had been annoyed.

The invention had now to be applied to a full size engine, and this proved both difficult and expensive. Watt was now married and his income was barely sufficient to maintain a home, but Professor Black continued his assistance and bore the whole cost of the early experiments. This assistance continued after Black's removal to Edinburgh in 1766. The story of the development of the steam engine in Watt's hands cannot be told here. By 1768 the work had progressed so far that trials were necessary on a larger scale than could be financed by Professor Black, and Watt entered into a partnership with John Roebuck to whom he had been introduced a few years before by Black. Roebuck had established the Carron Ironworks in 1760 and was opening coal mines at Bo'ness to supply coal for the ironworks. He was therefore interested in pumping machinery and had encouraged Watt to develop his engine, but had not, apparently, borne any share of the cost. Roebuck now took a two-third interest in the engine, in return for which he repaid Watt's debt to Professor Black, amounting to about £1,000, and undertook to pay the cost of a patent which was to be applied for. Watt, however, had still to support himself, which he now did by surveying and civil engineering, and had to work on the engine in his spare time. After Roebuck's failure in 1773, it was found that after the initial £1,000 he had made no further payment to Watt who had borne the cost of later experiments himself. The death of Watt's wife in the same year finally decided him to leave Glasgow and enter into a partnership with Matthew Boulton at Birmingham. He now gave up the shop in the College which he had occupied since 1757.

Watt's intimacy with Black and Robison continued throughout their lives. When Robison's works were being prepared for publication by Sir David Brewster after his death, Watt added some notes to Robison's account of the steam engine written for the *Encyclopedia Brittannica*. These notes are Watt's only published writings on the steam engine.

In 1805 Watt's advice was sought by the University regarding the heating of a building which was being erected to house the collection of anatomical specimens bequeathed to the University by William Hunter. The following year the University conferred upon Watt an honorary degree of Doctor of Laws and, in 1808, he replied by founding prizes in Natural Philosophy and Chemistry.

These prizes were converted, in 1895, into a James Watt Scholarship for work under the Professor of Civil Engineering. Watt would probably be remembered as a civil engineer if it were not for the overwhelming importance of his work on the steam engine. At the beginning of the century the University's new engineering laboratories were named in honour of James Watt. The laboratories were enlarged about 1920 (the centenary of Watt's death fell in 1919), and the following year saw established the Chairs of Electrical Engineering and Theory of Heat Engines, which serve as his memorial in the University which provided shelter, friendship and opportunity.

BIBLIOGRAPHY

The following books have been consulted in compiling this article. Most of the information in it is common to several of the books and it is not felt necessary to give authorities for statements, since all the books are readily available.

H. W. Dickinson, *James Watt*, Cambridge University Press, 1936.

H. W. Dickinson and Rhys Jenkins, *James Watt and the Steam Engine*, Clarendon Press, Oxford, 1927. A memorial volume prepared for the Watt Centenary Commemoration at Birmingham, 1919. Contains an extensive bibliography.

J. P. Muirhead, *The Origin and Progress of the Mechanical Inventions of James Watt*, 3 vols., John Murray, London, 1854.

J. P. Muirhead, *Life of James Watt*, John Murray, London, 1858. Largely reprinted from the above.

G. Williamson, *Memorials of the Lineage, Early Life, Education and Development of the Genius of James Watt*, Constable, Edinburgh, 1856.

S. Smiles, *Lives of Boulton and Watt*, John Murray, London, 1865.

J. Coutts, *History of the University of Glasgow*, Glasgow, 1909.

WILLIAM IRVINE, M.D.

Born, 1743 : died, 9th July, 1787. Edcn : Grammar School and University of Glasgow (matriculated 1756, M.D., 1766). Lecturer in Materia Medica (Glasgow, 1766-87). Lecturer in Chemistry, 1769-87.

Andrew Kent

WILLIAM IRVINE was the only son of Michael Irvine, a merchant in Glasgow. As a boy he attended the Grammar School of his native city, and at the age of thirteen he matriculated at its University. His class-mates, under Master James Moor, included one Bellamy Crawford from distant South Carolina : others who matriculated in the same year were James McGill, destined to found a Canadian University, Patrick Wilson, who became professor of Practical Astronomy at Glasgow, and James Jack, who was later to be the University's librarian. The usual sprinkling of presbyterian Irishmen included William Hazlitt, who had come from Tipperary and was to father the celebrated essayist.

There is no record of Irvine's graduation as Master of Arts. His educational experience as a physician included sojourns in London and in Paris. He graduated, as Doctor of Medicine, in 1766.

Despite his lengthy professional training, the young physician never devoted himself successfully to medical practice. Cleghorn attributes this to his lack of " sycophantic competence " and to the steadiness of a character which would not, or could not condescend to the " cringing servility of an Asiatic ".[1] Irvine had, in fact, some standing as an authority on the nervous system ; he was President of the Faculty of Physicians and Surgeons of Glasgow in 1775-77 and again in 1783-85 ;[2] but his main interest lay elsewhere, in Science rather than in Medicine.

Irvine had some talent for mathematics : he was a thoughtful student of botany : he had early attracted the notice of Joseph Black who recognised in him, as Robison puts it, " a young Student of Medicine of quick apprehension and sound under-

standing, and particularly disposed to study every thing mathematically, and who was greatly captivated with Chemical Science.
He engaged with great pleasure and zeal in all examinations
which seemed to interest the Professor." [3] In his year of graduation, Black left for Edinburgh. Irvine had been a favoured pupil
and research-colleague : he had already shown his capacity
with classes on materia medica and botany : it soon became
known that Black's successor in the chair of Medicine declined to
teach the chemistry class ; and Irvine had high hopes of the
lectureship. There seems to be little doubt that he was hurt and
disappointed by the preference of John Robison, and his blighted
expectations may not be unconnected with the " megrim " that
seriously affected his health for some time. [4]

When it was realised that Irvine proposed to leave Glasgow,
some members of the Senate moved to retain his services. His
friends revived Cullen's old project of a lectureship in materia
medica, for which as chemist and botanist, the young physician
was specially qualified. He was duly appointed to this position ;
and, three years later, he succeeded Robison in the coveted
lectureship in Chemistry, holding both lectureships thenceforward
till his death.

Irvine's reputation, so far as it has survived the assault of time,
is founded on his association with Black. Avenues of publication
from Glasgow, at this time, were difficult of access : Irvine, like
Black, relied on announcement to the local Literary Society and on
the appreciative memories of his students. It was only in 1805 that
his son achieved posthumous publication of some papers as prepared for this Society ; and these are almost the sole source of information on his father's range of scientific interests other than Heat. [5]

His botany covered the pioneering work of van Helmont,
Robert Boyle and Hales, more recent reports of the Swiss Bonnet's
surprisingly successful hydroponics and even early efforts to
improve plant growth by the use of electrified water. [6] One
chemical investigation led to original observations on the variable
colour of copper chloride preparations. These manifestly concerned the influence of light on cuprous chloride in acid suspensions
which is still a topic of chemical discussion. [7] More interesting
still was his application of these photo-chemical experiments to
support his view (1771) that light played some part in the trans-
formation of water and aerial nutriments into " the juices of

vegetables ". He suggested also, at this time, that plants might be the agents which restored the air vitiated " by contributing to inflammation and combustion ".[8] He always held himself as first to advance this theory ; and by 1778 he was confident that plants could separate from fixed air (carbon dioxide) " that part which it contains, upon which its difference from common air depends ".

His interest in water and fixed air were again combined in an investigation of petrifying springs at " Woodside, near Glasgow " and elsewhere. He announced, again in 1771, that their properties depended on the solubility of chalk in an aqueous solution of the gas, and supported his view by neat manipulations with alkaline hydroxides and carbonates.

In or about 1769, his association with glass manufacture led Irvine to an investigation of the colouring matter " manganese ". He appears to have reduced it with charcoal sufficiently to provide a substance soluble in the mineral acids. The colours of such solutions convinced him that he was dealing with " a metal of a particular kind ", and he obtained a characteristic white hydroxide. James Watt, who shared these researches, believed that they anticipated Bergman's later publications.[9]

About 1763 researches in Black's laboratory turned Irvine's attention to an old problem, the increase of weight resulting from the calcination of metals. He saw that this increase over-compensated the losses in effervescent gases, fumes and smoke ; and since a similar increase occurred when the dissolved metal was precipitated from acid by caustic alkali he soon abandoned the notion that absorption of " fixed air " was the cause. His outlook was further coloured by a study of Boyle's experiments, and by his own findings,[10] which Black confirmed, that silver or mercury with nitric acid could produce a solution of greater weight than the constituents—a further instance of the misleading " facts" which attended the early use of mineral acids.[11]

" All the chemists ", said Irvine, " agree that there is a principle common to inflammable and metallic bodies ". Black now suggested that this principle conferred *levity*.[12] Irvine, while admitting difficulties, could still assert, ten years later (1773) that this principle of levity " seems to be as well established by experiment, as experiment is capable of establishing any thing ".[13]

This Glasgow variety of phlogiston was strictly Stahlian, no more material and no more surprising than the repelling principle

N.B. Upon the thirteenth day of July last Dr. Black took away two capsals for Cucurbits & two separatories contained in the above list; he said they were part of some Glass Utensils left by him in the laboratory. Hath his receipt for them

College Glasgow May 11.th 1773

W Irvine

William Irvine. Handwriting and signature. (From a manuscript in possession of the department) Here, as on page 159, it is evident that apparatus was University property, and not, as often elsewhere at this time, the property of the incumbent.

in magnetism. It was neither heat nor flame : however conferred, it contributed inflammability and levity together. Gravity was inferentially, though not explicitly, a concomitant of incombusti-bility: matter could associate with either or both. It is not sur-prising that a theory of this nimble, treacherous type disarmed the steady scepticism of Irvine, especially as it emanated, with or with-out the stimulus of Juncker, from Joseph Black.

The author of " Magnesia Alba " had once assumed as self-evident the correlation of weight with the quantity of matter in his materials. The later professor taught the contrasted doctrine of levity to his class of 1765.[14] Irvine contemplated an *experimentia crucis* with a specially devised pendulum. Opinion on this subject had clearly not crystallised to certainty : what looks like incon-sistency to us may well, in the eighteenth century, have evidenced a wisely open mind. It transpires incidentally that Irvine had restored metallic properties to calces by repeated electric shocks, " many years " before 1773.[15] If this did not lead him to useful conclusions, it demonstrates the width and originality of his experimental enquiries.

None of his many interests were as consistently pursued as his enquiries on Heat. Anyone of his mathematical inclination was bound to be interested in Fahrenheit's reduction to standard numbers of this elusive phenomenon. Irvine assisted and extended Black's monumental researches : he offered a stubborn, friendly antagonism to his master's chief conclusions. His results and his opinions on this subject alone achieved a wide, if indirect circulation in his lifetime.

Black determined the Latent Heat imbibed by melting ice : Irvine, at his request, demonstrated the generality of this phenomenon by observations on melting spermaceti, bees-wax, tin and zinc ; and his " Latent Heats " were tabulated in various publications for almost a century thereafter.[16]

Black determined—by noting times of evaporation in an open apparatus—the Latent Heat of steam : Irvine made the first attempt to determine this in a calorimeter which condensed the evolving vapour. His first finding (430 v. 536 cals.) was later greatly improved by Watt (553 cals.).[17]

Black recognised the difference in Specific Heats of equal weights of mercury and water. Irvine measured the specific heat, relative to water, of sand, iron, glass and other substances : he then developed the technique of using such materials as standards where hot water was inconvenient, and so determined the specific heat of ice.[18]

Robison and others make it clear that Black's physical lassitude did not conduce to regular or prolonged experimentation. If his intuitions amounted to genius, he came early to rely for their full demonstration on the active assistance of such as Watt, Irvine and Robison ; and, in his lectures, he made generous, grateful acknowledgment.

Irvine, in particular, laboured long and effectively in support of his teacher's enquiries ; but following Black's departure for Edinburgh, this spagyric Man Friday showed a stubborn originality in the interpretation of their results. He found Black's theory of Latent Heat unwelcome for various reasons. It presumed a material view of Heat where the younger man was anxious to preserve an open mind : [19] it ascribed a duality of character to Heat, as ' free ' or ' combined ', which Irvine was anxious to avoid. Black agreed that the doctrine taught by his successor was " an ingenious thought ", but genially maintained his own opinion.[20]

Assuming with other early enquirers that specific heat was a

PLATE XI

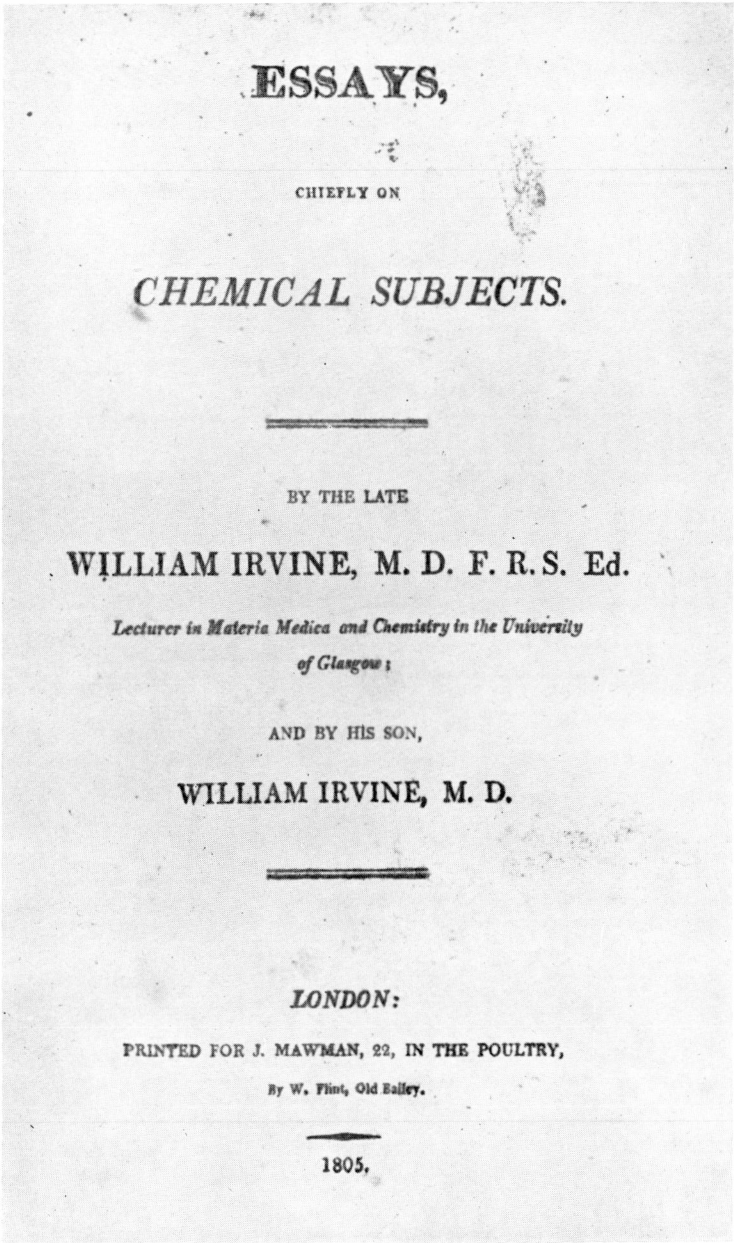

ESSAYS,

CHIEFLY ON

CHEMICAL SUBJECTS.

BY THE LATE

WILLIAM IRVINE, M. D. F. R. S. Ed.

*Lecturer in Materia Medica and Chemistry in the University
of Glasgow ;*

AND BY HIS SON,

WILLIAM IRVINE, M. D.

LONDON:

PRINTED FOR J. MAWMAN, 22, IN THE POULTRY,

By W. Flint, Old Bailey.

1805,

The fourth book reporting research work in the Chemistry Department at Glasgow (cf. p. 141). The third was Robison's well-known
edition of Black's *Lectures on the Elements of Chemistry* in 1803.
(Glasgow University Library)

PLATE XII

EXPERIMENTS AND OBSERVATIONS

ON

ANIMAL HEAT,

AND THE

INFLAMMATION

OF

COMBUSTIBLE BODIES;

BEING

An Attempt to Resolve these PHENOMENA into a
GENERAL LAW of NATURE.

———

By A. CRAWFORD, M.D. F.R.S. L. AND E.
AND MEMBER OF THE PHILOSOPHICAL SOCIETIES OF
DUBLIN AND PHILADELPHIA.

———

THE SECOND EDITION,
WITH VERY LARGE ADDITIONS.

———

LONDON:
PRINTED FOR J. JOHNSON, N° 72, ST. PAUL'S
CHURCH-YARD.

M.DCC.LXXXVIII.

The first edition (1779) of this work was the earliest book published
on research conducted largely in the Chemistry Department at
Glasgow (cf. p. 145). (Glasgow University Library)

constant and independent of temperature, Irvine considered it proportional to total heat-content. Latent heat was then the difference in heat-content between any two phases at the same temperature. This implied that the specific heat of a liquid phase was necessarily greater than that of the solid : Irvine had found this to be generally true.[21] It implied further, and mistakenly, that the specific heat of the gaseous phase must be greater still : Adair Crawford, in Irvine's laboratory, justified this by erroneous estimations of the specific heat of steam.[22] Irvine's theory was thus supported by available evidence. Although it did not " explain ", by combined heat, the difference between the solid, liquid and gaseous states of matter, it avoided some undesirable assumptions ; and this form of heat theory found many adherents.

Amontons had earlier deduced an Absolute Zero from considerations of gas-volume. Irvine now attempted this from considerations of specific heat. His calculations and the later attempts by Gadolin, Lavoisier, Dalton and others gave widely discordant results ; but the efforts provoked wide interest and James Watt is probably correct in attributing priority to Irvine.[23]

One enthusiastic adherent to Irvine's views on heat was Adair Crawford, an Ulster Scot (M.A., Glasgow, 1770 : M.D., Glasgow, 1780) who returned from London in 1776 to continue his studies under Irvine in preparation for his M.D. thesis.[24] Crawford applied Irvine's theory in explanation of " Animal Heat " ; and the two editions, 1779 and 1788, of his book on this subject achieved an international circulation. Although the author's resultant reputation was sufficient to daunt the young Dalton,[25] the book did not escape criticisms. These included one that he had been less than fair to Irvine. The second edition contains many amended observations and an exculpatory letter from the Glasgow lecturer. Yet dissatisfaction remained. " Dr. Crawford," wrote James Watt in 1801, " seems not to have been much disposed to do either Dr. Black or Dr. Irvine justice." [26]

However unwittingly, Crawford conveyed to his readers that some of Black's achievement and much of Irvine's theory were his own. Certainly when this theory was discussed or explained thereafter, it was attributed to Crawford or to others mentioned in his discussions. So Lavoisier deals only with Crawford : William Nicholson in his " Dictionary of Chemistry " gives him precedence over Irvine, and attributes formulae for Absolute Zero to Kirwan :

K

Leslie, of Edinburgh, sharing Irvine's views on the relationship of Latent and Specific Heats, attributes the exposition of Absolute Zero to Gadolin.[27]   Dalton, in discussing this topic, does not mention Irvine at all.

Robison's edition of Black's lectures in 1803, and the *Essays* of Irvine and Irvine in 1805 did something to restore the balance. Andrew Ure in 1820 writes of " Drs. Irvine, father and son, to both of whom the science of heat is deeply indebted " and asserts Irvine's priority in the calculation of Absolute Zero from Specific Heats. Donovan in 1832 gives a full and fair comparison of the views of Black and Irvine.   Turner comparing the two theories in 1827 considers Irvine's theory " less hypothetical than that of Dr. Black ".   Thomas Thomson in 1830 discusses " Irvine's explan-ation of liquidity " because of " the great importance attached to it, and the many ingenious theories founded upon it ".   Occasion-ally as with Mrs. Jane Marcet, Irvine's interpretation of Latent Heat is advanced without acknowledgment ; but the early nineteenth century treated him with more respect than his own.[28]

By this time, however, Irvine's views were largely of historical interest.   The enquiries of Dulong and Petit, for example, had undermined that constancy of specific heat (in any one phase) on which Irvine had particularly relied ; and Crawford's errors in measurement on gases had been corrected.   Unfortunately for Irvine's reputation, no belated recognition of priority could undo the effects of his being overlooked during that period of the eighteenth when his findings and opinions, transmitted by such as Magellan or Crawford, redounded to the credit of others.

Incidentally to their establishment of Black's priority, McKie and Heathcote demonstrate Irvine's valuable support, the degree of independence in his conclusions, and the misleading influence of Crawford.[29]   No full account of our knowledge of Heat can fairly overlook the early efforts of Irvine, the stimulating contrast of opinion between him and Joseph Black, or his clear conception of an Absolute Zero of temperature.

Irvine was also actively interested in applied chemistry.   Cleg-horn mentions the increase of local industries during the American war, and emphasises Irvine's assistance to those concerned with chemistry whom he instructed " with the utmost frankness and patience ".   " He solved their doubts : he corrected their errors ; he pointed out many improvements, in consequence of which they saved money." He had a close and particular association with glass manufacture.

These interests led eventually to a "most honourable and lucrative proposal", through Count de Luzuriaga, of an official appointment in Spain where the Glasgow chemist was to devote his attention to glass-making and metallurgy.[30] These negotiations were still proceeding when they were interrupted by Irvine's death, at the age of forty-four, in July 1787. A sudden illness proved unexpectedly fatal in a few days. He died in some distress of mind, occasioned by the thought of his young wife—sib to the "Anatomy Hamiltons"—and only son. His friends rallied round these unfortunates. His colleagues and the merchants of the city successfully solicited a State pension for his widow.[31] (His son achieved some distinction in medicine and in chemistry before he too died suddenly, in early middle-age, at Malta.[32])

The *Glasgow Mercury* of 11th July lamented the loss of " one of the first Chemists in Europe " : one of his academic colleagues expressed their common grief in verse.[33] It is evident that " Town and Gown " regretted sincerely this early demise of a respected and talented personality.

In some respects Irvine had not been a fortunate man. Shadowed, inevitably, by the giant figure of Joseph Black, frustrated for a time by the preference of John Robison, plagiarised by Adair Crawford, he never achieved in his life-time that status and reputation which he had worked so hard to deserve.

An expert and energetic practical worker, he was equally interested in advancing the new science and in its industrial application. Indeed as an ardent and original experimentalist, William Irvine ranks with any who have headed the department of Chemistry. His colleagues admired the integrity of his character and the ingenuity of his mind. " He thought for himself ", said Cleghorn, " he was not a mere operator—he struck out new lights, respecting not only the best mode of conducting chemical processes, but also respecting some of the sublimest doctrines of chemistry ".

NOTES AND REFERENCES

[1] Robert Cleghorn, *Medical Commentaries*, 1788, *12*, 459.

[2] A. Duncan, *Memorials of the Faculty of Physicians and Surgeons of Glasgow*, MacLehose and Sons, Glasgow, 1896, p. 261.

[3] Joseph Black, *Lectures on the Elements of Chemistry*, (ed. Robison) Longman and Rees, London, 1803, 1, xliv.

[4] Thomas Reid, *The Works of Thomas Reid, D.D.*, (ed. Hamilton) MacLachlan and Stewart, Edinburgh, 1863, pp. 46, 47.

[5] Irvine and Irvine, *Essays chiefly on Chemical Subjects*, Mawman, London, 1805.

[6] *Ibid.*, pp. 240, 263.

[7] *cf.* Gopal Singh, *J. Chem. Soc.*, 1922, *121*, 782.

[8] Irvine and Irvine, *Essays*, p. 432.

[9] *Ibid.*, pp. xxi, xxiii.

[10] *Ibid.*, pp. 413, 423.

[11] *cf.* A. Kent, *Proc. Phil. Soc.*, Glasgow, 1932, *60*, 109.

[12] Irvine and Irvine, *Essays*, p. 412.

[13] *Ibid.*, p. 415.

[14] Reid, *Works*, p. 41, *cf.* J. H. White, *The History of the Phlogiston Theory*, Arnold, London, 1932, p. 132.

[15] Irvine and Irvine, *Essays*, p. 421.

[16] *e.g.* Thomas Graham, *Elements of Chemistry*, Baillière, London, 1850, *1*, 44.

[17] Black, *Lectures on the Elements of Chemistry*, p. 171-3. Thomas Preston, *Theory of Heat*, Macmillan, London, 1904, p. 378.

[18] Irvine and Irvine, *Essays*, p. 87.

[19] *Ibid.*, p. 189.

[20] Black, *Lectures*, p. 194.

[21] Irvine and Irvine, *Essays*, p. 57.

[22] A. Crawford, *Experiments and Observations on Animal Heat*, 2nd ed., Johnson, London, 1788, p. 489.

[23] J. P. Muirhead, *Mechanical Inventions of James Watt*, Murray, London, 1854, *2*, p. 78.
   Writing in May, 1774, Watt says " My friend Dr. Irvine in winter discovered what is the lowest possible degree of heat, or the real beginning of the scale ". For Amontons see F. Cajori, *A History of Physics*, Macmillan, New York, 1899, p. 106.

[24] *cf.* D. N. B. This memoir does not indicate Crawford's early association with Glasgow.

[25] John Dalton, *A New System of Chemical Philosophy*, Bickerstaff, Manchester, 1808, *1*, 11, " overawed by the authority of Crawford ".

[26] Muirhead, *Mechanical Inventions of James Watt*, p. 275.

[27] John Leslie, *Dissertation Fourth*, Black, Edinburgh, n.d., p. 645.

[28] Andrew Ure, *A Dictionary of Chemistry*, 2nd ed., Tegg, London, 1824, pp. 271, 283.
   Michael Donovan, *A Treatise on Chemistry*, 3rd ed., Longman, Rees Orme, Brown and Green, London, 1832, p. 74.
   Edward Turner, *Elements of Chemistry*, Tait, Edinburgh, 1827, pp. 35, 42.

Thomas Thomson, *Heat and Electricity*, Baldwin and Cradock, London, 1830, pp. 81, 94.

Anon. (Mrs. Jane Marcet), *Conversations in Chemistry*, 8th ed., Longman, Hurst, Rees, Orme and Brown, London, 1822, p. 138.

[29] Douglas McKie and Niels H. de V. Heathcote, *The Discovery of Specific and Latent Heats*, Arnold, London, 1935.

[30] Cleghorn, *Medical Commentaries*, p. 461. It is interesting to notice that we were then at war with Spain.

[31] William Irvine, *Letters on Sicily*, Mawman, London, 1813, p. xxxix. The Public Record Office cannot trace this memorial. Dr. W. R. Cunningham writes, " At that particular date when Dundas was in power many of his official papers were looked upon as personal, and it is probable that the documents concerned never reached official custody ". See also W. R. Cunningham, *The Glasgow Herald*, 22nd March, 1930 for evidence of this memorial additional to that given by the editor of Dr. W. Irvine, Jr., and for Adam Smith's active support.

[32] *D. N. B.* W. Irvine, Jr. died in 1811 while on military service as a surgeon. Personal enquiries in Malta, and others very kindly undertaken by Chevalier Hannibal P. Scicluna failed to afford further information as to the circumstances of his death or the place of his internment. The fullest account is in the preface to his posthumous *Letters on Sicily*.

[33] *Scots Magazine*, 1787, 49, 553. Professors Richardson, Jardine, and Arthur were colleagues of Irvine at Glasgow.

ELEGIAC VERSES
Occasioned by the death of Dr. IRVINE, Lecturer in Chemistry
and Materia Medica in the University of Glasgow
by MR. RICHARDSON

O how precarious is the lot of man!
Our life, a vapour ; and our age, a span.
Gay in the sunshine of our opening years,
Th' extended scene a lovely aspect wears ;
With various tints glow our effulgent skies ;
And bowers of bliss on every side arise :
The green field blossoms : and the waving grove
Allures us with the tuneful voice of love.
Onward we journey, with high hope elate ;
But soon, too soon, lament our alter'd state.
Cold breezes blow : th' ascending vapour shrouds
Our youth's gay morning with a night of clouds :
The drizzly shower, th' impetuous storm descends—
Care, disappointment, and the loss of friends,
Th' unmerited reproach, th' undue return
For deeds of kindness, teach us soon—to mourn.

Timely ; O Jardine, to my wounded heart
The balm of thy serenity impart :
And teach me Arthur, while the tempests blow,
To stem, with fortitude, the tide of woe :
My friends, communicate the lenient cure :
Teach me to strive, to pardon, and endure.
    And yet, ah me! At this oppressive hour
Your hearts are troubled too : your spirits lower ;
The tear yet oozing in the redden'd eye,
The untimely vigil, and th' unbidden sigh,
Musings, and throbbings, when observ'd, supprest,
Prove the sad conflict of the troubled breast.
With you, I pour the tributary tear ;
With you, at Irvine's unexpected bier!
A beam of Science, parted soon, deplore!
Our fellow-labourer, alas, no more!
The partner of our social hours, with whom
We liv'd, the tenant of an early tomb!
Hasten, my friends, O haste and give relief
With the composure of becoming grief ;
Go! From the deeply, deeply smitten heart
Elicit tenderly the barbed dart :
Go to the chief in sorrow, who lament
Their staff now broken, and their bow unbent :
For sympathy with friendly counsel join'd,
May yield some solace to th' afflicted mind—
But how, with shaking knees, approach the door
Where Irvine liv'd?—Where Irvine lives no more!
How meet the sorrows that have cause to flow,
Or find excess in reasonable woe!
How soothe the pangs that rend a Widow's heart!
Or comfort to the Fatherless impart.—
Poor, little Boy! Affliction's early prey,
Grief hath soon clouded thy commencing day!
Who can thy loss, thy heavy loss, repair?
Who introduce thee to a world of care?
But yet I will not bid thy sorrow flow :
Soon wilt thou learn, too soon, thy load of woe ;
Amuse thee, Boy : or lose thyself in sleep :
'Tis thy poor Mother who must wake and weep.
    Spirits of Mercy! Unto whom 'tis given
To minister on earth the Peace of Heaven :
And soothe the suff'rings of a wayward doom :
Come, on the wings of Consolation come!
Breathe all your influence here, benign and mild.
To the lone Widow and her only Child.
Glasgow, August, 7th.

EARLY SCIENTIFIC LINKS BETWEEN SCOTLAND AND AMERICA

J. A. V. Butler

TWO HUNDRED years ago was a time like the present of new ideas, new institutions and of starting afresh. The old order was passing away and the world was feeling its way towards an incalculable future. Modern chemistry and medicine were emerging, chrysalis like, from the obscurity and superstition with which they were enveloped. The foundations of modern science were being laid.

The Leyden jar had been discovered in 1745 and Benjamin Franklin, visiting his mother in Boston in 1746, saw an apparatus which had been brought from Scotland by a Dr. Spence ; an electric tube which charged objects when rubbed. Franklin was fascinated by it and had a similar tube made.

" I never was before engaged in any study that so totally engrossed my attention and my time as this has done," he wrote. Out of these experiments, in 1747, came the concept of positive and negative electricity, the foundation of electrical science.

Two years later Franklin established the Academy and Charitable School in Philadelphia which later developed into the University of Pennsylvania. Among its early graduates were John Morgan and William Shippen, jr., who came to Europe to continue their studies and were greatly influenced by William Cullen. They both drew up plans for establishment of medical education in the north american colonies. Shippen returned first and started courses of lectures on anatomy and midwifery. Morgan arrived back three years later, after extensive travels in Europe and proposed that medical education be organised under the aegis of the already existing college. " Private schemes for propagating knowledge are unstable in their nature, and the cultivation of useful learning can only be effectively promoted under those who are patrons of science, and under the authority and direction of men incorporated for the improvement of literature."

He submitted his scheme to Thomas Penn, then proprietor of Pennsylvania, and on the recommendation of the latter the trustees of the college authorised him to found a medical school. Students were to be accepted only if they were well versed in latin, natural science and a modern language. The curriculum was to include anatomy, botany, chemistry, the nature and action of drugs, and clinical science. Shippen, his friend and rival, was appointed to the chair of anatomy and surgery. They soon had a staff of five-and they made Philadelphia the first centre of medical education in America, a position which it held for half a century. There is no space here to tell the later story of the rivalry of these two men, which had disastrous consequences in the revolutionary wars. It has been told in the fascinating stories of early medicine in America , *Doctors on Horseback*.[1]

Among their first pupils was Benjamin Rush, who later went to Europe where he studied under Black and Gregory and became a friend of Cullen, whose system he adopted. When he returned to Philadelphia in 1769, he was appointed professor of chemistry— the first appointment of this kind in America.

Let us now turn our attention from Philadelphia to the neighbouring University of Princeton, which has also been celebrating its bi-centenary during 1946-7. Founded as the College of New Jersey, it obtained its charter from George II on Oct. 22, 1746. As a presbyterian institution it was natural that it should draw heavily on Scotland for its staff. The most famous of its early Principals was the Rev. John Witherspoon, a native of Gifford, who was induced to leave the presbytery of Paisley in 1768 to direct the infant college. Though not a scientist he did much to encourage the disinterested study of science. A practical Scot, of the " Common Sense " school, he believed in observation and experimentation as the method for discovering the nature of the physical world, rather than the study of theological writings, and he spent considerable sums of money on scientific apparatus. His belief in liberty and the natural rights of man led him to support the independence movement and he became one of the most ardent of the revolutionists. " We are not only ripe (for independence) " he declared, " but rotting." He was one of the signatories of the Declaration of Independence.

In his recent bi-centennial address at Princeton, President Dodds describes Witherspoon's return to Princeton after the revolutionary war. The college had been occupied by troops after the Battle of Princeton and damaged ; the library had been scattered, the funds depleted. Standing in the shadow of the dilapidated college building, Witherspoon pointed out to the French general Chastellux, the sites on which new structures were to arise to accommodate expanded courses in philosophy, science, mathematics and the classics. His example may perhaps be an encouragement to those who at the present time are depressed by the spectacle of much of European civilisation in ruins.

Later Glasgow sent John Maclean to Princeton to be its first professor of chemistry. He was born in Glasgow in 1771, and his parents having died when he was young, he became the ward of George Macintosh, who brought him up with his own son Charles. In this household it was natural that his thoughts should be directed to chemistry. George Macintosh, the son of a Ross-shire farmer, had gone to Glasgow to work as a clerk in the Glasgow Tan Work Company, which among other activities made shoes for the colonies. In 1773 he set up a rival establishment and soon had five hundred men in employment. In 1777 he commenced the manufacture of cudbear, a modification of Orseille or Archella, usually obtained from the Lichen *rocella*. These dyes had been produced for centuries by peasants in the Highlands of Scotland from the Lichen *tartareus*.

It is said that one Gordon, a coppersmith in London, having been employed in repairing a boiler at a dyehouse in which Archella had been used, was impressed by the analogy, with the process of dyeing he had seen in his youth in the Highlands with *tartareus* or crottal. He communicated the idea to his nephew, Dr. Cuthbert Gordon, who obtained a patent for the process. These started a factory in Leith which was unsuccessful, and was removed to Glasgow with Mr. Macintosh as a partner.

The chief ingredient of cudbear after the lichen, was the ammonia with which the latter was macerated. George Macintosh and Company collected human urine for many years, in such quantity as to cost eight hundred pounds annually. About 1785 he and his son Charles, together with William Couper, set up a factory for the production of sal ammoniac from soot and vege-table and animal offal. This was continued until 1792, when it became unprofitable.

Entering the University at the age of 13, John Maclean was one of the group which, under Irvine founded a Chemical Society there in 1785 or 1786, one of the earliest in the world. In the memoir of John Maclean M.D., written by his son,[2] it is stated that " at the University he was, while yet a lad, a member of the Chemical Society, a club which appears to have met at the University, with the permission of the College authorities, if not under the over-sight of the Professors. The members submitted, for the con-sideration of the Society, papers and essays upon various matters connected with the object of their association, and some of these papers seem to have foreshadowed the eminence which the authors of them attained in after life, as proficients in the art of Chemistry."

Other members of this Society were William Couper, Charles Macintosh, Mr. Candlish, Dr. Tilloch, Dr. Crawford, Mr. John Wilson, Major Finlay, R.E., Mr. Cruikshank, Mr. Archer and Mr. Monroe.[3] The best known of these is of course, Charles Macintosh, later a pioneer of chemical industry and the inventor of the waterproof garment. The above list of names is mainly taken from a biography of him by his son,[4] which gives much information about science in and about Glasgow in this period. Of the remainder, Dr. A. Tilloch (1759-1825) was a printer, who invented stereotyping and a method of printing bank notes, and moving to London in 1787, he established the *Philosophical Magazine* in 1797. Adair Crawford (1748-95), returned from London to Scotland in 1776-7 and did experiments on heat in Glasgow and Edinburgh, where he was a friend of Irvine and Black. William Couper was a partner of Charles Macintosh in an ammonia factory and later became an eminent surgeon in Glasgow. Wilson and Finlay became partners of Macintosh in the Hurlet alum works, which were started near Paisley in 1796 for making alum from aluminium schist, in exhausted coal waste.

The attitude of these men was modern and practical. John Maclean is recorded as having read papers on respiration, on fermentation and on alkalis, while Macintosh read papers on alcohol, on alum, on crystallization, and on the application of blue colouring matter of vegetable bodies. The writer has looked through the surviving papers of John Maclean, which are now in Princeton University Library, but was unable to find any trace of those mentioned above ; although some later lectures, delivered in America, remain.

After leaving Glasgow at the age of 16, John Maclean studied with Dr. Black in Edinburgh and went on to London and Paris, where no doubt he encountered the best known scientists of the day, including Lavoisier and Berthollet. Returning to his native city, he practiced his profession for a year. He emigrated from Scotland in 1795, taking letters to Dr. Benjamin Rush, who suggested that he should settle in Princeton, where he was appointed professor of chemistry in the College of New Jersey— the first American professor of chemistry in a non-medical college. The reasons for his emigration are obscure. It is stated that he was in sympathy with the political sentiments of Americans, and he took with him a Scottish pebble inscribed with the motto " *ubi libertas, ibi patria.*" [5]

In 1797 his appointment was widened to include the subjects of mathematics and natural philosophy. He took his duties seriously and several courses of lectures have survived, which are well abreast of the knowledge of time. Soon after he arrived in Princeton, he engaged in a controversy with Dr. Priestley. The discoverer of oxygen had gone to live in America and, oddly enough, was one of the last surviving defenders of the phlogiston theory, which held that metals were compound substances containing phlogiston, which was driven off on heating. In 1796 Priestley published a pamphlet entitled " Considerations on the doctrine of phlogiston and the decomposition of water. One more appeal to the philosophical world to show that the doctrine of phlogiston is correct." Maclean, fresh from Lavoisier and Paris felt impelled to reply to this and in 1797 published " Two lectures on combustion, supplementary to a course of lectures on chemistry read at Nassau Hall. Containing an examination of Dr. Priestley's considerations of the doctrine of phlogiston and the decomposition of water." [6]

After 20 years in Princeton, Maclean went to the College of William and Mary in Williamsburgh, but he was taken ill and returned to Princeton to die. His son, John Maclean became the tenth president of Princeton.

These brief notes will illustrate the great debt of early American science to the Scottish pioneers. It may truly be said that Cullen was the father of American medicine and the grandfather of American chemistry.

NOTES AND REFERENCES

[1] James Thomas Flexner, *Doctors on Horseback, Pioneers of American Medicine*, New York, 1937.

[2] " A memoir of John Maclean, M.D., the first professor of chemistry in the College of New Jersey, by his son, John Maclean, the tenth president of the College." Printed for private circulation only at the " Press " office, Princeton, N.J., 1876.

[3] J. A. V. Butler, *J. Chemical Education*, 1941, 43.

[4] " Biographical Memoir of the late Charles Macintosh, F.R.S., of Campsee and Dunchattan," compiled by his son, George Macintosh, printed for private circulation by W. G. Blackie & Co., Villafield, Glasgow, 1847.

[5] Foster, *Science*, 1924, *60*, 306.

[6] Foster, *J. Chemical Education*, 1925, *2*, 743, see also *ibid*, 1929, *6*, 2104. Maclean's lectures were reprinted for the Princeton Commemoration in 1929.

THOMAS CHARLES HOPE, M.D.

*Born, 21st July, 1766 : died, 13th June, 1844. Edcn : High
School and University, Edinburgh (M.D., 1787). Lecturer in
Chemistry 1787-91. Assistant professor (1789-91) and
professor of Medicine (Glasgow, 1791-5) : assistant professor
(1795-9) and professor of Chemistry and Physic (Edinburgh,
1799-1844).*

James Kendall

THOUGH HIS fame is somewhat overshadowed by the superior
achievements of his predecessor Joseph Black, Thomas
Charles Hope, F.R.S., professor of Chemistry at the
University of Edinburgh from 1795 to 1844, ranks as a noteworthy contributor to the progress of science. He was the first
teacher in Great Britain to substitute the new doctrines of
Lavoisier for the phlogiston theory in his public lectures ; he
isolated and named the first known compound of strontium ; he
first established the exact point of the maximum density of water ;
and he recommended Humphry Davy to the notice of Count
Rumford as a suitable lecturer for the Royal Institution.

Hope's father was Regius professor of Botany in the University
of Edinburgh, and he himself entered as a student there at the
precocious age of 13. As was natural, he devoted much attention
to botany, and displayed such proficiency in this science that on
his father's death in 1786 he was put forward as a strong candidate
for the vacant chair. This was in accordance with the practice of
the times, since for a record period of 126 years the sister professorship of anatomy was occupied by Alexander Monro (three
successive generations, 1720-1846), but the young man of 20 was
forced to wait another year before he was selected to fill a responsible academic position, the lectureship in chemistry at the
University of Glasgow.

He was then, like his teacher in Edinburgh Joseph Black and all
his British colleagues, a strenuous supporter of the phlogiston
hypothesis of Stahl. His friend Sir James Hall, however, returned
to Scotland in the autumn of 1787 from Paris, where he had been

much in the society of Lavoisier, who exhibited to him several very important experiments not yet made known to the chemical world in general. Hall had many long discussions on the work of Lavoisier with Hope, and soon convinced him of the truth of the new ideas. That winter he taught them to his class, the first occasion on which the doctrines of Lavoisier were publicly promulgated in this country, and the following summer he himself spent in Paris, where the amiable manners and great abilities of Lavoisier made a strong and lasting impression upon him. As his biographer[8] remarks : " Few persons more sincerely deplored the sad fate of that accomplished man, from whom he had received the most flattering attentions."

In 1789, Hope obtained the appointment of assistant professor in medicine to his uncle Dr. Stevenson in the University of Glasgow, and on the death of his uncle in 1791 became the sole Professor of Practical Medicine. He then resigned the office of lecturer in chemistry, but continued his private researches in his favourite study, the first result of which was a masterly paper on a mineral from Strontian, communicated to the Royal Society of Edinburgh in 1793.

In this article[1] Hope proved, what had been previously only conjectured by Crawford and others, that this mineral contained a peculiar " earth ", differing decidedly in properties from barytes, with which it is associated. To this new earth Hope gave the name of *strontites*, from the village of Strontian, in Argyllshire, Scotland, at which it had been found. His original preparation (dated 1791) of what is now known as strontium hydroxide still stands in the museum of the department of chemistry at the University of Edinburgh : a clear saturated solution with a fine crop of crystals at the foot. Several other chemists have claimed the credit for the discovery of strontium (the metal itself it may be noted, was first isolated in 1808 by Humphry Davy), but critical examination of the literature justifies the statement of Traill : [8]

" The only chemist who has the slightest claim to the merit of an original detecter of Strontium earth, besides Dr. Hope, is M. Klaproth, who, in the *Chemische Annalen* for 1793-94, compared Strontianite with Witherite. Neither Klaproth nor Hope seems to have been aware of what the other had discovered, and both may therefore be considered as original discoverers, but the first full investigation of the subject is undoubtedly due to Dr. Hope."

This brilliant research, and the popularity of Hope's chemistry teaching at Glasgow, suggested to Joseph Black, then in declining health, the idea of securing his promising pupil as his assistant and successor in the chair of chemistry at Edinburgh, and in Edinburgh, and in November 1795 the patrons chose Hope in that capacity. In the following session, Black found it necessary at last to relinquish his long-famous lectures and introduced Hope to his class in the following terms :

" After having, for between thirty and forty years, believed and taught the chemical doctrines of Stahl, I have become a convert to the new views of chemical action ; I subscribe to almost all M. Lavoisier's doctrines and scruple not to teach them. But they will be fully explained to you by my colleague and friend Dr. Hope, who has had the advantage of having them from the mouth of their ingenious author."

Thomas Charles Hope. Handwriting and signature. (From a manuscript in possession of the department)

On Black's death in December 1799 Hope became the sole professor of Chemistry at Edinburgh University.

That position he held for forty-five years. The variety and excellence of his illustrations, and his dexterity in chemical manipulations, made him the most popular teacher of the science that had ever appeared in Great Britain.

" Not only was his lecture-room crowded with medical students from every part of the British dominions, but numerous foreigners resorted to Edinburgh and became his pupils. The large class-room was filled to overflowing, and he who was not there before the commencement of the lecture had no chance of a seat."

That this quotation[8] is no exaggeration is shown by the fact that the average attendance at Hope's lectures increased from 225 at the time of his appointment to 575 in 1827 ; the total number of tickets issued for his chemical course during his tenure of office was no fewer than 16,800. In 1838, on the completion of his fiftieth year as a professor of chemistry, he was invited by a numerous body of his former pupils to a public dinner, at which he stated that he had never been, either as a student or as a teacher, detained from the duties of his class, except for *six days by indisposition*.

Such scrupulous attention to academic responsibilities inevitably restricted Hope's output of research to a minimum during the period of his prime. He reconciled himself with some regret to this limitation, and among his private papers there was found after his death the following interesting statement :

" Those who devote themselves to the science of chemistry may be divided into two classes. 1st, Those whose labours are employed in original researches, to extend our knowledge of facts and principles. 2dly, Those whose business it is to collect the knowledge of all that has been discovered or is going forward, to digest and arrange that knowledge into lectures, to contrive appropriate and illustrative experiments, and devise suitable apparatus for the purpose of communicating a knowledge of chemistry to the rising generation, or others who may desire to obtain it. From my professional situation I consider myself, *as Dr. Black had done before me*, as belonging to the second class of chemists. I consider my vocation to be the teaching of science."

Some time, nevertheless, he did manage to set aside for research. In 1804 he presented an important memoir to the Royal Society of Edinburgh on the contraction of water by heat at low temperatures.[2] As long ago as 1667, the singular fact had been noted by the Florentine academicians that water expands as it cools towards its freezing-point, and Croune had shown this phenomenon to the Royal Society of London in a Gresham Lecture in 1683. Several subsequent investigators had endeavoured to determine the exact temperature at which water attains its

PLATE XIII

Early class-tickets in Chemistry. The signature on the 1850 specimen
is that of Thomas Thomson's nephew (cf. p. 178).

PLATE XIV

ELEMENS

D E

CHYMIE-THEORIQUE.

Par M. MACQUER, *de l'Académie Royale des Sciences, Censeur Royal, Docteur-Régent de la Faculté de Médecine en l'Université de Paris, & ancien Professeur de Pharmacie.*

NOUVELLE EDITION.

A PARIS,

Chés JEAN-THOMAS HERISSANT, rue S. Jacques, à S. Paul & à S. Hilaire.

M. DCC. LIII.

Avec Approbation & Privilége du Roi.

Macquer's widely-read text-books were still, at this date, based on the theory of Four Elements, and contained an influential re-statement of phlogiston theory (cf. pp. 67, 100). (Ferguson Collection, Glasgow University Library) maximum density, but could not derive consistent results. All their experiments were made in tubes with large bulbs at one extremity, like huge thermometers.

It was contended by Hooke, after the delivery of Croune's lecture, that the expansion observed was only apparent, not real ; arising from the sudden contraction of the material of the bulb on the application of cold. This opinion was still held more than a hundred years later by many eminent chemists, including Dalton, who carried out a series of inconclusive experiments on the phenomenon and finally drew Hope's attention to it in a private letter. Hope settled the question for ever by experiments in which a change in the capacity of the containing vessels could have no influence on the results.

He took a cylindrical glass vessel, 8½ in. deep and 4½ in. wide, which was filled with water at the freezing-point, 32° F. Two delicate thermometers were suspended in the vessel, the bulb of one being half an inch below the top of the liquid and that of the other as far from the bottom. The apparatus was placed in a room at a temperature of 60°, and the progressive changes in the temperature of the water were carefully noted on both thermometers. From 32° to 38°, the lower thermometer was invariably higher than the upper ; a proof that throughout this interval the water was becoming more dense as the temperature rose. On reversing the experiment by placing water at 53° in an environment cooled to 32°, Hope found that while the temperature of the water was falling to 40°, the water at the bottom was always the colder, but that in cooling from 40° to the freezing-point, the thermometer at the bottom remained higher than that near the surface.

The temperature of the maximum density of water was thus established as lying between 38° and 40°; Hope's final value, after he had varied his technique in different ways, was 39.1°. This is in good accordance with the modern figure of 39.2 F°. (3.98° C.).

Dalton admitted the accuracy of Hope's observations, but a long note attached to the main paper failed to convince Count Rumford that Hope had also demonstrated conclusively the fallacy of his theory that liquids were absolute non-conductors of heat. It is rather strange that Rumford should have hesitated to acknowledge Hope's scientific acumen, since he was directly indebted to him for the discovery of Humphry Davy. Passing

L

through Bristol in 1799, Hope visited Dr. Thomas Beddoes, who had been his fellow-student at Edinburgh and was, indeed, one of the original members of the Chemical Society of the University of Edinburgh in 1785.[6] In Beddoes' laboratory at the Pneumatic Institution, he found the twenty-year-old Davy immersed in his experiments on nitrous oxide, and was deeply struck by his originality and inventive genius. Soon afterwards, Hope was consulted regarding a " lecturer of talent " required by Rumford for the Royal Institution ; he strongly recommended Davy to the notice of the Count and, in 1801, Davy received the appointment. Never in the history of chemistry was a recommendation more richly justified by subsequent results.

Hope also evidently made an impression on Davy. Unable to realise his own cherished ambition to obtain an Edinburgh degree, Davy sent his younger brother (and future biographer) John to be trained as a chemist in Hope's laboratory. It was there that John carried out a series of decisive demonstrations upon the elementary nature of chlorine to refute the criticisms of Murray on Humphry's work.

In 1826, at the ripe age of 60, Hope emulated Davy's social triumphs at the Royal Institution by instituting " a short course of chemical lectures for Ladies and Gentlemen ". His vast lecture-room was packed with a most brilliant audience ; and he gave the proceeds—a sum of £800—to the Senatus Academicus to establish a prize " to the author of the best essay on a given chemical subject, illustrated by experiment ". This fund has since been augmented, and five Hope Prize Scholarships are now awarded annually to deserving Edinburgh students of chemistry.

Hope never married. His department was his wife, his pupils were his family. His very chair serves as a support to his present successor while he writes this article ; it is not perhaps as inspiring as that of Joseph Black, which stands opposite it, but it is certainly more comfortable. His portrait by Raeburn had an interesting history. When George IV visited Edinburgh in 1822, the patriotic fervour of the Scots induced such a run upon representations of his royal figure that engravings of this picture, with the sash of the Order of the Garter across the chest as the sole alteration, were utilised to fill the local deficiency. These " false Hopes," according to information received some years ago from Sir James Walker, are now very scarce and command a high

PLATE XV

THOMAS CHARLES HOPE

price.   History does not disclose who was the more flattered by the incident—Hope or George IV!

Long after the latter's reign was ended, however, his scientific double continued his chemical activities.   Hope delivered his last series of lectures in 1843.   In the spring of the same year, at the age of 77, he blossomed out anew as a research worker in three communications to the Royal Society of Edinburgh, of which body he was then a vice-president.   Two of these[3] [4] dealt with the constitution of the colouring matters in the leaves and flowers of plants, the third[5] discussed the temperature phenomena of the famous freezing cavern at Orenburg.   With the coming of autumn, Hope's health deteriorated ; he passed away on 13th June, 1844.   His friend Dalton died only a few weeks later.

One human touch, for which I am indebted to my teacher and colleague Dr. J. E. Mackenzie,[7] may be added to conclude this memoir.   During one of Hope's lectures, an unruly student threw a handful of peas at the professor and some struck him in the face. He started to reprimand the offender in dignified language, but suddenly lapsed into broad Scots as follows : " Such conduct is unbecoming of a gentleman and moreover—it's daumed sair! "

NOTES AND REFERENCES

[1] Hope, T. S., " An Account of a Mineral from Strontian and of a peculiar species of Earth which it contains," Trans. Roy. Soc. Edin., 1798, 4, 3.

[2] Idem., " On the Contraction of Water by Heat, at Low Temperatures," Trans. Roy. Soc. Edin., 1805, 5, 379.

[3] Idem., " Observations and Experiments on the Coloured and Colourable Matters in the Leaves and Flowers of Plants," Proc. Roy. Soc. Edin., 1845, 1, 126.

[4] Idem., " Observations on the Flowers of the Camellia Japonica, etc.," Proc. Roy. Soc. Edin., 1845, 1, 419.

[5] Idem., " An Attempt to explain the Phenomena of the Freezing Cavern at Orenburg," Proc. Roy. Soc. Edin., 1845, 1, 429.

[6] Kendall, James, "Some Eighteenth-century Chemical Societies," Endeavour, 1942, 1, 106.

[7] Mackenzie, J. E., " The Chair of Chemistry in the University of Edinburgh in the XVIIIth and XIXth Centuries," J. Chem. Educ., 1935, 12, 503.

[8] Traill, T. S., " Memoir of Dr. Thomas Charles Hope, late Professor of Chemistry in the University of Edinburgh," Trans. Roy. Soc. Edin., 1848, 16, 419.

ROBERT CLEGHORN, M.D.

Born, 1755 (?) : died, 18th June, 1821. Edcn. : University of Edinburgh (M.D., 1783). Lecturer in Materia Medica (Glasgow, 1788-91). Lecturer in Chemistry, 1791-1817.

George Thomson

IN 1791 the surname Cleghorn had a prominence in university circles disproportionate to the frequency of its occurrence elsewhere : in St. Andrews, Hugh Cleghorn, soon to embark on that romantic design which secured the annexation of Ceylon, had been since 1773 a somewhat casual occupant of the Chair of Civil and Natural History ; [1] in Trinity College, Dublin, James Cleghorn had, in 1790, succeeded his distinguished uncle George Cleghorn as professor of Anatomy ; in Glasgow, Robert Cleghorn had just been appointed to the lectureship in Chemistry. Yet these three Universities appear to have been served by distinct branches of the Cleghorn family and identification of any person referred to as Professor or Dr. Cleghorn in writings of the period is not always easy.

Our Dr. Cleghorn had exchanged the lectureship in Materia Medica for that in Chemistry. From 1769 until 1788 the two lectureships had been held in common (by Dr. William Irvine till his death in 1787 and for the next session by Dr. Thomas Charles Hope) but in June, 1788 the lectureships resumed their independence : the faculty reappointed Hope to the lectureship in Chemistry with a salary of £50 and appointed Dr. Robert Cleghorn lecturer in Materia Medica with a salary of £25.[2] In 1791 Hope succeeded his uncle, Alexander Stevenson, as professor of Medicine and the faculty transferred Cleghorn to the vacant lectureship in Chemistry. Nepotism so governed these matters that one wonders how Cleghorn ever obtained a University appointment.

His origins and early life are obscure. When he died in June, 1821, he was said to be aged 66[3] which would put the date of his birth between July, 1754, and June, 1755. The first indisputable fact about him is that in 1783 he took the degree of M.D. at Edinburgh, presenting a thesis *De Somno* in which he describes himself as " Scotus ". At this time he would be about 28 years of age, somewhat older than was customary for a man proceeding to his first degree. Yet there is no evidence that he prosecuted studies elsewhere ; the British Museum Catalogue in the entry concerning his thesis inaccurately describes him as " A.B. Trinity College, Dublin ".[4] The thesis bears a fulsome dedication to George Cleghorn, M.D., the famous professor of Anatomy in Trinity College, Dublin, but not in terms which hint at a family relationship. A relationship, indeed, appears improbable.[5]

By December, 1785, Robert Cleghorn had come to Glasgow ;[6] in 1786 he became a Fellow of the Faculty of Physicians and Surgeons in Glasgow and soon established for himself a reputation as a physician ; from 1788 to 1791 he was President of the Faculty and in 1792 he became Librarian.[7] In the same year he was re-elected Secretary of the Glasgow Humane Society of which David Dale, the philanthropist and industrialist, founder of New Lanark, was President.[8] About the same time Cleghorn began his long association with the Glasgow Royal Infirmary : he was one of the original managers and one of its first physicians.[9] He was made a Burgess of Stirling in 1789, of Aberdeen in 1794, of Hamilton in 1807. These public and professional honours are indicative of an established reputation and from his extensive practice—it could hardly have been from the salary attached to his University appointment—he acquired a modicum of wealth which enabled him to purchase in 1801 a portion of the estate of Shawfield (near Rutherglen)[10] on which he built Shawfield House and laid out a park, a shrubbery and a garden. Thereafter, like the majority of college professors and successful city merchants, he had his town house and his country retreat. When the Glasgow Royal Asylum for Lunatics was projected Cleghorn actively interested himself in the scheme and, from its foundation in 1814 until 1819, acted as its senior physician and also as a director ; there is general agreement that he was in a large measure responsible for the enlightened attitude to its inmates which characterised the conduct of this institution.

Robert Cleghorn, then, was a man prominent in his profession as a physician and a kenspeckle figure in Glasgow ; he had been mentioned as one of the characters of the town in John Gibson

Lockhart's ballad " The Death of Captain Paton ".[11] And yet after his death on 18th June, 1821, not a single Glasgow newspaper, not a single medical journal published more than a bare statement that his death had occurred ; the Annual Reports of the Royal Asylum which had made no reference to his retiral are equally silent about his death.   There is no obvious explanation of this unanimous reticence ; neither personal unpopularity nor political heterodoxy appears sufficient reason but reason there must have been and it would be interesting to know what it was.

The Chemistry class was at that time regarded as a medical class and advertised as such in the Glasgow press ; [12] a German visitor wrote,[13] " The University of Glasgow contains no complete Medical Faculty.   Medical science is taught by only two professors, Dr. Freer and Dr. Jaffray.   The one lectures on the Theory of Medicine, the other on Anatomy and Botany. Besides the proper professors they reckon in this University another sort of teachers who are known under the name of lecturers.   They have no share in the faculty business but deliver their praelections like the proper professors.   The Medical lecturers are Dr. Millar and Dr. Cleghorn.   The first lectures on Materia Medica, the latter on Chemistry."

Cleghorn did not himself carry out any significant original investigations in Chemistry nor did he conduct a practical class ; in fact in his time the Chemistry Laboratory, which had been established by Cullen in 1747, ceased to exist as such.[14]   Cleghorn's manuscript note books (vide infra) show that he had a lively interest in the work of others but the demands made on his time by an extensive medical practice and by the positions he occupied on both public and professional bodies must have left him little time to indulge any inclination he may have had for research. The class began on 1st November and ended in May.[13]   His lectures were given (as had been those of his predecessor, Dr. Irvine) at 7 p.m., probably to enable members of the public to attend, and one can picture the difficulties of conducting an evening lecture class in the winter months in a low-roofed classroom of the Old College by the light of a few guttering candles. Unfortunately we have no record of what he taught but we can infer with a considerable degree of confidence that he taught the newer ideas of Lavoisier, for while Cleghorn was lecturer in Materia Medica his colleague Thomas Charles Hope, in

Chemistry, had been teaching Lavoisier's ideas and in 1790 Robert Kerr had produced his translation of Lavoisier's *Elemens de Chemie* avowedly for the University classes in Edinburgh. It would be in keeping with what we can learn of the character of Cleghorn that he should be abreast of contemporary developments in the philosophy of his subject ; moreover, had Cleghorn, when he succeeded Hope, reverted to teaching pre-Lavoisierian chemistry his own successor, Thomas Thomson,[15] would of a surety have had some caustic comment to make.

As to his popularity as a lecturer we may quote Thomas Thomson, himself a fiery enthusiast for practical chemistry with a guid conceit of himself and, as so often happens, little sense of humour to redeem it. " My own class," says Thomson,[15] " is much more expensive than any other in the College. Chemistry may, indeed, be taught at a very small expense and in this way the teacher may be popular and the audience delighted. This was the system followed by my predecessor who at a very trifling expense delivered a course of lectures that charmed his hearers. My object being to teach the science and to raise up a race of practical chemists my expenses are necessarily much enhanced."

But at least one of Cleghorn's hearers was inspired as well as charmed by his lectures. It was at that time the custom for the Irish Presbyterian Church to require its theological students to attend a course of medical lectures in order that they should acquire some knowledge of the cure of the body as well as of the soul and in the 1790's one such student, Josias Christopher Gamble, attended Cleghorn's class in Chemistry. The lecturer and the subject so fascinated Gamble that he spent his long vacations experimenting in chemistry particularly in trying to prepare chlorine solutions for bleaching the handwoven linen of his native Enniskillen. After a few years in the ministry of the Irish Presbyterian Church he resigned his charge to become a chemical manufacturer first in Ireland and later in England where, in company with James Muspratt, he became one of the founders of the alkali industry in St. Helens, Lancashire.[16]

In 1817, Cleghorn resigned the lectureship in Chemistry[17] after a tenure of office extending over the long period of 26 years.

Robert Cleghorn was commonly taken to be the physician pilloried as Dr. Wormwood in *Northern Sketches*,[18] now a rare book, in the following vitriolic passages. " ... Dr. Wormwood's

abilities and knowledge have deservedly acquired him a large
share of professional reputation. Intimately acquainted with the
various relations of the human constitution and possessed of
strong powers of judgment and discrimination, no man perhaps is
better able to sift the prognosis of a case and, of course, to apply its
remedy . . . Wormwood presents none of that affability which
every physician ought to possess in order to inspire confidence ;
none of that tenderness necessary to alleviate shame or to countenance delicacy. Stern and sarcastic in his manners . . . his face
appears to have made a perpetual divorce from smiles. He treats
his patients rather as subjects for ridicule, than relief ; indulges in
impertinent and superfluous interrogatories ; and is not always
observant of that fidelity which ought to distinguish so confidential
a character as a physician.

" Fully sensible of his skill he is not less careful that it shall have
its price. The worthy Doctor cannot perhaps charge his con-
science with the iniquity of one single gratuitous act ; unless
where he had the view of gaining more by his generosity than he
could by his extortion . . .

" The love of money produces many singular changes and
contortions on this worthy Doctor. He is not content with
pursuing it by professional means . . . He farms, builds, exports :
he dabbles in everything by which he can make money and in the
way of making a bargain may defy rivalship . . .

" With all these blemishes in his character Wormwood is a man
who has drunk deeply from the streams of literature ; whose fame
for varied and extensive knowledge, for ingenious and able
disquisition, is spread far and wide."

This pseudonymous author accuses Cleghorn—if Wormwood
be Cleghorn—of hardness and avarice while admitting his ability
and extensive knowledge. Against the charge of avarice may be
set the facts that he contributed generously to the building funds
of both the Glasgow Royal Infirmary[19] and the Royal Asylum
and that an Annual General Meeting of the Asylum expressed its
thanks " for his liberality in declining, on account of the situation
of the funds, to receive his salary as a physician for the past two
years." [20] Whether or not Cleghorn was lacking in affability
towards his patients we cannot tell. He was, however, so unpopu-
lar among his fellow practitioners that he was one of the few not
admitted to membership of the Medical Club.[21] On the other

hand, Joseph Frank, the German visitor mentioned earlier, was received by Cleghorn with an affability which he found in pleasant contrast to the dryness of his reception by Professor Cumin to whom he had brought a letter of introduction. This affability was all the more creditable since Frank was mercilessly outspoken in his criticism of the Glasgow Royal Infirmary.[13]

Although Robert Cleghorn was primarily a physician he had a variety of other interests : he was admitted a Correspondent Member of the Royal Society of Antiquaries in Scotland in August, 1783 ; in June, 1788, he was elected a Fellow of the Royal Society of Edinburgh ; he is said to have started at Langside Cottage a Botanic Garden for the use of his students ; [22] he was interested in lightning conductors (" thunder rods ") and was severely criticised for the inefficiency of one which he designed for the jail (now the Justiciary Buildings) at the foot of the Saltmarket ; [23] he was a member of the Literary Society which met in the College,[24] a Society in which " all the talents of Glasgow were brought to a focus," a Society to which William Cullen, Joseph Black, William Irvine, Adam Smith and Robert and Andrew Foulis at various times discoursed. One would like to believe that Robert Cleghorn was the Dr. Cleghorn to whom Thomas Reid the philosopher undertook to submit James Gregory's paper on " The Theory of the Moods of Verbs ".[25]

The extraordinary range of his interests is plainly evident in three manuscript volumes in the Library of the Faculty of Physicians and Surgeons in Glasgow, two volumes entitled *Adversaria* and one of his Case Books. The first volume of *Adversaria* (begun in Edinburgh in 1782) opens with 43 pages in Latin of a " Synopsis Medicinae " [26] which may be student notes. There follows a long discussion on animal heat and a description of experiments on the effects of " heterogeneous " liquids introduced into the blood stream of animals. Later a number of curious observations occur which may or may not be quotations (" burning the helix of the ear cures the toothache ") and there are frequent references to the views and observations of John Hunter (referred to as J. H^r, Johnny or simply John) ; p. 218 has at the end of a paragraph "End of John Hunter ". The second volume contains considerable discussion of various foods, drugs, etc., and after p. 139 which is dated " Glasgow December, 2nd, 1785 " appears to become a sort of case book recording especially the detailed

results of post mortem examinations but on p. 233 is an account of
" Mr. Headerick's proposals for improving the manufacture of
salt " and on p. 241 an extract from a letter dated 20th February,
1792, from a Dr. Crawford to a Mr. McLain in which Crawford
criticises Irvine's views on the absolute zero.

The Case Book[27] might almost be better described as a common-
place book in which Cleghorn noted an account of anything that
interested him.   Interspersed among notes of cases and of post
mortem examinations are recorded an account of the Solway Moss
disaster of 16th November, 1771, an account of gold in Ireland
(by the Countess of Moira), an extract from a letter dated 16th
November, 1795 from Professor Pictet of Geneva,[28] a series of
extracts from Tennant's *Tours*, an account of Dr. Adair's
failures with " Dr. McLean's process for procuring alkalis ", an
account of Tennant's experiments on burning diamonds (evidently
an abstract of Tennant's paper in the *Philosophical Transactions*[29]), notes from *Memoires de L'Academie, 1747*, on
" inflammation of various oils by nitrous acid ", an account of
relics from an eruption of Vesuvius, notes on gunpowder, on the
temperatures of springs and deep wells in Ireland, on China and
the Chinese, a most entertaining recipe for a Gout Cordial " from
Lord Dundas's family receipts ".[30]

From the intimate details of cases recorded in this Case Book it
is easy to understand how he came to be accused of indulgence in
" impertinent and superfluous interrogatories " but on occasion
he produces with a minimum of words delightful sketches of his
patients : Miss Lang—" a little feeble lively body " ; [31] William
Hutcheson—" a little strong-built man of an iron colour, a harsh
voice, very energetick, a Cameronian " ; Helen McLenachan—
" a ruddy hale Irish Anabaptist " ; Miss Limon—" a poor
emaciated, coughing, breathless, ill-coloured West Indian ".

Apart from these manuscript volumes there is little that can
with certainty be attributed to Cleghorn's pen. Duncan[7] says :
" Cleghorn was a considerable contributor to the periodical
medical press and his biographical notices of some of his contemporaries were especially sympathetic and neat," but an extensive search has revealed not a single contribution by *Robert*
Cleghorn on medical topics and only one signed biographical
notice,[32] that of William Hamilton, Professor of Anatomy and
Botany in the University of Glasgow 1781-1790. The editor of

Letters from Sicily, however, attributes to Cleghorn the very fine notice of William Irvine which appeared in *Medical Commentaries*.[33] G. Graham Thomson[34] quotes from Cleghorn's journal (presumably manuscript) of an extensive tour he made through Scotland in 1794. It is particularly unfortunate that efforts to trace this diary have so far been unsuccessful for the variety of interests and shrewdness of observation shown in the Case Book suggest that the account of this tour might well prove an important contribution to the history of the social life of Scotland at that time. A letter dated 22nd April, 1796 from Cleghorn to Professor John McLean of Princeton University[35] points to the writer's association with chemical manufacturers in Glasgow, notably McIntosh. It also gives the information that after Hope resigned the chair of Medicine in Glasgow, to become assistant and successor to Joseph Black in Edinburgh, Cleghorn taught the class for a session until, in 1796, Robert Freer was appointed to the chair. Cleghorn alleges that he was passed over on account of his political views—" because I am a Democrate ".

He had the distinction of being the subject of three portraits by Raeburn.[36]

In 1787 Cleghorn married Margaret Johnston, the widowed eldest daughter of Andrew Thomson of Faskine (partner of Robert Carrick in Glasgow's famous Ship Bank). She died in 1791. The only child of the marriage, Helen, born in 1790, died in 1853 at Shawfield predeceased by her husband, Major Walker in 1844 : they had no family.[37] Robert Cleghorn, his wife and daughter were all interred in the Old College burial ground attached to Blackfriars Church which, with the Old College itself, was removed to make room for College Goods Station. It appears probable that their remains were re-interred in the Necropolis in 1876.[38]

Robert Cleghorn was a physician rather than a chemist, a physician of widely recognised ability with a catholicity of interest in the true University tradition, a physician whose advanced opinions imbued the Glasgow Royal Asylum with a humanitarian attitude towards its patients unusual in similar institutions of the period. But although he was respected for his professional ability, his shrewd worldliness caused mistrust of his motives, brought accusations of mercenariness and denied him popular affection.

NOTES AND REFERENCES

[1] William Neil (editor), *The Cleghorn Papers*, A. & C. Black, Ltd., London, 1927.

[2] James Coutts, *History of the University of Glasgow*, MacLehose, Glasgow, 1909, pp. 495-496, *Glasgow Mercury*, 18th June, 1788.

[3] D. J. F. S. Gordon, *Glasghu Facies*, John Tweed, Glasgow, 1872, vol. I, p. 335.

[4] No Robert Cleghorn is to be found in Burtchaell and Sadleir's *Alumni Dublinensis* (1935) and the Assistant Keeper of the Printed Books now admits (private communication, 1st January, 1947) that the ascription cannot be justified.

[5] George Cleghorn (1716-1789) was born at the farm of Granton in the parish of Cramond near Edinburgh, the youngest of five children. His only brother, John, died in 1774, leaving his widow and nine children of whom three were boys, William, James and Thomas. George Cleghorn had no children of his own and assumed responsibility for the education of these three nephews who all became members of the medical profession : James succeeded his uncle as Professor of Anatomy in Trinity College, Dublin and William for the two years immediately preceding his own untimely death in 1783 had been his uncle's assistant. *c.f. Dictionary of National Biography* under George Cleghorn : also T. P. C. Kirkpatrick, *History of the Medical School in Trinity College, Dublin*, Hannah and Neale, Dublin, 1912, p. 126 *et seq.*

[6] p. 139 of the second volume of his manuscript *Adversaria* is headed " Glasgow, December, 2nd, 1785 ".

[7] Alexander Duncan, *Memorials of the Faculty of Physicians and Surgeons in Glasgow*, MacLehose, Glasgow, 1896, p. 263.

[8] *Glasgow Courier*, 14th February, 1792.

[9] M. S. Buchanan, *History of the Glasgow Royal Infirmary*, James Lumsden and Son, Glasgow, 1832, p. 26.

[10] Lanark Sasines, 4071.

[11]
" And in spite of all that Cleghorn
And Corkindale could do,
It was plain from twenty symptoms
That death was in his view.
So the Captain made his test'ment
And submitted to his foe :
And we laid him by the Ramshorn Kirk,
'Tis the way we all must go.
Oh! we ne'er shall see the like of Captain Paton no mo! "

[12] e.g. *Glasgow Courier*, 11th October, 1791. " On Tuesday the 1st of November, 1791 the following MEDICAL CLASSES will be opened in the College

The Materia Medica   by Dr. Millar at 11 a.m.
The Theory and Practice of Physic by Dr. Hope at 12 noon.
The Anatomy   by Dr. Jeffray at 2 p.m.
The Chemistry   by Dr. Cleghorn at 7 p.m."

[13] Joseph Frank, *Reise nach Paris, London, etc.*, Vienna, 1804, p. 281 *et seq.*

[14] Thomas Thomson in *Evidence taken by the Commisioners in the Universities of Scotland* 1826/1830, vol. II, p. 203.

[15] Thomas Thomson, *loc. cit.*, p. 205.

[16] J. Fenwick Allen, *Some Founders of the Chemical Industry*, Sherrat and Hughes, London and Manchester, 1906, p. 39 *et seq.*

[17] Thomas Thomson, *loc. cit.*, p. 206.

[18] Leonard Smith (pseudonym), *Northern Sketches or Characters of G******* (i.e. Glasgow), J. Dick, London (1810?), pp. 9, *et seq.* In the Glasgow University Library copy the name Cleghorn is written in above Wormwood.

[19] *Glasgow Courier*, 27th March, 1792.

[20] Annual Report of the Glasgow Royal Asylum for 1818.

[21] Strang, *Glasgow and its Clubs*, R. Griffith & Co., London and Glasgow, 1856, p. 301, f.n.

[22] *Glasgow Herald*, 27th August, 1888.

[23] *Glasgow Mechanics Magazine*, vol. II, p. 398 : vol. III, p. 29.

[24] Richard Duncan, *Literary History of Glasgow*, Maitland Club, 1831, p. 134.

[25] *vide* letter dated 26th August 1787 from Reid to Dr. James Gregory printed in *Collected Works of Thomas Reid, D.D.*, Maclachlan, Stewart and Co., Edinburgh, 1846, p. 70.

[26] " Synopsis Medicinae, paucula de anatomia, de physiologia, de morbisque partium corporis praecipuarium, a capite ordiens, amplectens. Die 9° ante Kal. Junii 1782 ".

[27] This Case Book, in which the last entry is dated 8th July, 1818, is inscribed " One of several sent to my father from the library of Dr. Cleghorn as a present for attending him on his death bed. Eben. Watson, 30th April, 1882." It would be interesting to know if any others of this set of Case Books still exist.

[28] William Irvine Jr., (*Essays chiefly on chemical subjects*, Mawman, London, 1805, p. 38) ascribes to Cleghorn views on the phenomena of heat (caloric) very similar to those of Pictet.

[29] *Phil. Trans.*, 1797, vol. LXXXVII, p. 123.

[30] Take 2 gallons or 9 bottles of Brandy, 1 gallon Malaga or good Mountain, 4oz. of Senna picked clean, 10 oz. best Turkey Rhubarb, bruised, 4 oz. Juniper berries bruised, 4 oz. Guiac shavings, 4 lbs. Raisins of the Sun picked and stoned, 2 oz. Lesser Cardamon seeds bruised, 1 oz. Fennel seeds bruised, 1 oz. Coriander seeds bruised,

2 oz. Stick liquorice bruised, 1/2 oz. Saffron bruised, 1/2 oz. Cochineal bruised.

Put in a large stone bottle near a fire shaking the bottle often, let it stand 10 or 12 days then strain it off : then add to the materials 1 gallon more brandy and 3 bottles of Wine which must stand by the fire for a month. Shake it once a day then strain it and mixing both together bottle the whole.

[31] Body *Anglice* person.

[32] *Edin. Phil. Trans.*, 1798, vol. IV, appendix p. 35.

[33] William Irvine, *Letters from Sicily* (ed. J. Dunlop?), Mawman, London, 1813, p. xxxvi, f.n. : *Medical Commentaries*, 1787, 2nd series, vol. II, p. 455.

[34] G. Graham Thomson, *Transactions Old Glasgow Club*, 1908, vol. I, p. 239.

[35] Dr. J. A. V. Butler very kindly provided the following transcript of this letter.

Glasgow, April, 22nd 1796.

Dear Sir,

I received yours which gave me much information for which I thank you. In return I send you a letter of mere business. Of late I have often asked Mr. McIntosh about your process and I had the mortification to find that nothing had been done since you left Britain, and that nothing seemed likely to be done. Meantime, I knew the process had taken air and I had some reason to think that steps were taking on a large scale for executing it. Accordingly, I mentioned it to a Friend confidentially and he immediately agreed to give a hundred guineas for it, provided you would empower him to take out a patent.

I stated this to Mr. Glassford who replied that he had given up all thoughts of the process : and, together with the papers which are now in my possession, he pledges his honour that no use should be made of your communications. Upon this declaration I communicated the process to Dr. McKiltrick (?) Adair, who is come to this neighbourhood as Manager for chemical works belonging to Lord Dundas of Dundonald, with whom he is in some kind of partnership. I now have his letter obliging him to give me for your behoof one hundred guineas as soon as you shall send me a power of attorney enabling him to take out a patent in proper form and I request your answer by the very first ship.

If you think this sum too small there is no obligation on your part to confirm what I have done. I will restore your papers to McIntosh and take Dr. Adair's promise (he is a man of honour) that he shall not use what I have told him to your prejudice. In my opinion, however, this is the only chance you can possibly have of asking anything by your process, and if you do not close with Dr. Adair, I believe it will never yield you one shilling in Britain. Should you be of the same opinion I shall expect, by the first ship, a power of

Plate XVI

ROBERT CLEGHORN

attorney together with any information respecting the process which may now occur to you. Dr. Adair wishes to have your opinion respecting the most proper plan for large works, and especially for the evaporating vessels, on which, I think, you suggested some improvements ; for the furnace and for the bellows. In short, any details that occur to you will be most acceptable, and the Dr. talks of rewarding you still more liberally from the profits of the works, should it succeed. On this, however, I lay no stress : because projectors are always poor and must naturally be so since one successful scheme generates a thousand, of which some must fail, and the failure of one eats up the profit of many.

I have no leisure to send you news. The war still rages, tho' the government is nearly bankrupt. As to the issue of the present plans no person can form the smallest guess and few people care to make the attempt. Evil comes too soon, and good is always welcome.

As to this spot, you have now probably heard that Dr. Hope is gone to Edinburgh, the Assistant and Successor of Dr. Black. I have taught his class this season by appointment of the Faculty, but Dr. Freer of Edinburgh has now got the class because I am a Democrate. The manoevres against me would have surprised you or any honest man even while you breathed this servile air, but now they would appear to you utter . . .

(Here a portion of the letter is destroyed)

remember me most kindly to the Millars or to any of my other acquaintances who have had the wisdom and good Fortune to cross the Atlantic. *Fortunate mimi (u) sua si bona norint*—With great esteem and regard I am

My dear Sir,
Robt. Cleghorn.

[36] Catalogues of portraits by Raeburn list only two portraits of Cleghorn but in 1919 there were three in existence. One, which had been presented to the Glasgow Royal Asylum by Archibald Smith of Jordanhill, hung at Gartnavel till 1918 when it was deposited in the Glasgow Art Galleries at Kelvingrove. A second portrait, evidently painted from the same sitting, was exhibited at the Glasgow International Exhibition in 1901 and in 1919 was sold as one of the items in the Brechin Collection which also contained a third Raeburn portrait of Cleghorn. The second portrait mentioned is probably now in the United States ; photographs of it are in the Witt Library, London. The third portrait has not been traced after the 1919 sale.

[37] *Glasgow Courier*, 20th September 1853 ; G. Graham Thomson, *An Old Glasgow Family of Thomson*, Glasgow, 1903.

[38] David Murray, *Memories of the Old College of Glasgow*, Jackson, Wylie & Co., Glasgow, 1927, pp. 413-414.

THOMAS THOMSON, M.D.

Born, 12th April, 1773 : died, 2nd July, 1852. Edcn. : Universities of St. Andrews and Edinburgh (M.D., 1799). Lecturer in Chemistry, 1817-18. Regius professor of Chemistry (Glasgow, 1818-52).

J. R. Partington

THOMAS THOMSON, first Regius Professor of Chemistry in the University of Glasgow, was born [1-5] on 12th April, 1773, at Crieff in Perthshire, the seventh child and youngest son of John Thomson and Elizabeth Ewan. After education in the parish school of Crieff he went in 1786 to the burgh school of Stirling, where he received a good classical education, and in 1788, having won an open bursary, he entered the University of St. Andrews. Moving in 1791 to Edinburgh with the intention of studying medicine, he attended in 1795-6 the lectures on Chemistry of the celebrated Joseph Black (of which he left three volumes of notes),[3] and he graduated M.D. in 1799 with a dissertation *De Aere Atmospherico*. Thomson was a good linguist, mathematician (he composed a manuscript treatise on the differential and integral calculus for the use of his family), mineralogist, and geologist ; his mineral collection was lodged by his nephew, R. D. Thomson, in the Museum of St. Thomas's Hospital, London.[3] He studied theology and contemplated entering the Church, but gave up this project about 1798.

In 1796, aged 23, he succeeded his elder brother James as Editor of the *Supplement* to the *Encyclopædia Britannica*, to which he contributed articles on " Chemistry ",[6] " Mineralogy ",[7] and " Vegetable and Animal Substances and Dyeing ".[8] From about 1800 until 1811 he lectured[9] on Chemistry at Edinburgh, prepared his famous treatise, *A System of Chemistry*, carried out research work, and, at least as early as 1807, opened a laboratory for practical instruction in Chemistry (a class-list being extant) ; this must have been the earliest laboratory of its kind in Great Britain.[1] Among his pupils was W. Henry of Manchester, who worked on the analysis of coal gas. Thomson became F.R.S. in 1811. At the end of the session 1810-11 he moved to London. In 1816 he married Miss Agnes Colquhoun, daughter of a Stirling distiller ; they lived rent-free at 1, Queen's Square, Westminster, the town house of Jeremy Bentham. Mrs. Thomson died in 1834. Their son, Thomas Thomson, of the Bengal Army, was a distinguished botanist, and the daughter married her cousin, Dr. R. D. Thomson. Thomas Thomson founded the *Annals of Philosophy*[10] in 1813. This contained original articles (including the two papers by Prout,[48] in 1815-16, on integral atomic weights), translations of foreign memoirs (including many by Berzelius), notes on current affairs and reports of meetings of learned societies, and annual reports on the progress of science. In the autumn of 1812 he paid a visit to Sweden, of which he wrote an interesting account,[11] including detailed information on the history, politics, topography, geology, botany, zoology, mineralogy, mining, industries, and commerce of the country, with tables of statistics. He visited the University of Uppsala and saw Bergman's house and laboratory. Afzelius, the Professor of Chemistry, being infirm, Thomson was shown round by the Lecturer, Ekeberg, who was then deaf and nearly blind. The lecture room was small but good, and practical instruction was given to the students. The collection of models said to have been made for Bergman was quite small, and had been presented by von Swab. The laboratory was small but well fitted. Thomson visited the copper mine at Fahlun (worked since 1347) and saw Assessor J. Gottlieb Gahn, who, although then aged 68, was well up in the latest advances in science, and had a fine set of platinum apparatus. Gahn showed him a collection of Scheele's letters and notes (published[12] in 1892). Although Thomson made enquiries at Köping and other places about Scheele, who died in 1786, he found no traces of him, and no portrait of him then existed.

In October, 1817, Thomson was appointed Lecturer in Chemistry in the University of Glasgow on the recommendation of Sir Joseph Banks.[1][13] The Lectureship, in the Faculty of Medicine, was first held by William Cullen, appointed in 1747, who was followed in 1756 by Joseph Black. At the instance of the Duke of Montrose, a Regius Professorship of Chemistry was instituted by George III, and the first incumbent, Thomas Thomson, took up the appointment on 17th March, 1818, with an annual salary of £50.   Thomson's devotion to pure research in the first ten years of his professorship is noteworthy in view of the salary and the opportunities he had of doing more remunerative work.   He had no laboratory until the summer of 1818 ; [14] it was a damp ground-floor room.   The chemistry lectures were daily except Sunday, and " even practical experimenting is not neglected ".[15]   His statements[16] that for some years before 1825 he " had been engaged in teaching practical chemistry ", and that a manuscript manual of quantitative analysis was available to students in his laboratory, show that he gave practical instruction in Glasgow as well as, earlier, in Edinburgh.[17]   There is no information available that Cullen's and Black's laboratories in Glasgow were ever open to students.[18]

The new buildings for the Chemistry Department, erected in Shuttle Street at a short distance from the University, and opened in 1831, included a laboratory.   When London University was founded in 1827, Thomson was invited to occupy the Chair of Chemistry, but declined, and Edward Turner was appointed.[1][19]

Thomson entered fully into the scientific life of his time ; he knew personally or corresponded with, most of the eminent scientists of the day, and his part in the foundation of the Wernerian Society of Edinburgh, and the Geological Society of London, is emphasised by Professor Robert Jameson.[20]

From 1841, Thomson was assisted in his teaching work by his nephew Robert Dundas Thomson (1810-1864),[21] with whom he collaborated in issuing a short-lived journal.[22]   Thomas Thomson continued to give the lectures on Inorganic Chemistry until 1846, when R. D. Thomson assumed all the duties of the Chair.   Thomas Thomson died on 2nd July,[23] 1852, at Kilmun, Argyleshire, and was succeeded as Regius Professor by Thomas Anderson.

Sir Robert Christison says[24] Thomson " was a very little, well-made man, with small, sharp, handsome features, a calm, contemplative eye, and smooth untroubled brow ".   Although warm-hearted and good-natured, he was reserved, and often adopted a rather cynical pose, but he was no intriguer, and was a man of very open, fearless, and independent character, not hesitating to express his convictions.

There is a good bust of Thomson by Steel, and a fine portrait of him by Graham Gilbert (reproduced here) in the rooms of the Glasgow Philosophical Society.

Researches

Although he carried out a large amount of experimental work, Thomson did not make any imposing discoveries. He analysed a great number of minerals, but these did not happen to contain new elements. In one or two cases he was on the track of important discoveries, but he failed to follow up the clues which were before him, and others reached the prize.

A list of his published papers[4] [25] contains 201 items, all but two without another author, although he probably had the assistance of his students in his later researches. He was a good analyst, and if not satisfied would repeat his experiments many times until he was convinced that he had obtained the correct result.[26] His first paper[27] was on " Experiments to determine whether or not Fluids be Conductors of Caloric ", showing that, contrary to the results of Count Rumford, liquids are conductors of heat. He discovered sulphur chloride[28] (" sulphuretted muriatic acid "), but failed to determine its composition correctly : if he had followed up his analyses he could have anticipated Davy in disclosing the elementary nature of chlorine, which view Thomson was one of the first to accept.[29] The determination of the density of a solid by flotation in a liquid was, apparently, first described by him.[30] Among many organic materials he investigated ulmin, a rare black excretion from the elm and other trees.[31] He introduced [32] the names *protoxide, deutoxide, tritoxide, and peroxide*, and later[33] used Greek and Latin prefixes for the numbers of atoms of radical and oxygen, respectively.

In an important paper[34] " On Oxalic Acid ", Thomson gave the first example of the law of multiple proportions by showing that, in the normal and acid oxalates of potassium and strontium, one salt, for the same amount of acid, " contains just double the proportion of base contained in the second," and he drew attention to the bearing of the result on Dalton's Atomic Theory. In this paper he uses chemical symbols in a *quantitative* sense.[35] The atoms of oxygen, carbon, and hydrogen, are denoted by w, c, and h, and the formulae of carbon dioxide, methane, carbon monoxide, water, oxalic acid, and sugar by $2w + c$, $c + h$, $w + c$, $w + h$, $4w + 3c + 2h$, and $5w + 3c + 4h$. In 1818 he used[36] the symbols o, h, c, *ch*, *p*, etc., for the atoms of oxygen, hydrogen, carbon, chlorine, phosphorus, etc.

In an investigation of the action of hydrogen sulphide on sulphur dioxide in presence of water, he suspected the presence, in the precipitate of sulphur, of a new oxyacid of sulphur which he called *hydrosulphurous acid*.[37] This was afterwards recognised, as pentathionic acid, by Wackenroder in 1845, who was unaware of Thomson's work, which, if he had followed it up, would have given him the credit of the discovery. In Thomson's paper[38] " On some Compounds of Chromium " he describes the discovery (" about a year and a half ago ") of chromyl chloride (" chloro-chromic acid "), which he thought was a compound of " 1 atom chromic acid " and " 1 atom chlorine ", of chromium chromate, some new chromates and dichromates, and some double and complex compounds of chromium. Some compounds he de-described were mixtures, and some (" carbonate of chromium " and " disulphuretted oxide of chromium ") non-existent. He described many new salts, without claim to discovery, in his *System of Chemistry*. He analysed a large number of minerals, and described some new species, such as *allanite* and *sodalite* ; the mineral *thomsonite*, a species of zeolite, was named after him.

Thomson and the Atomic Theory

In 1804 Thomson travelled from Glasgow to Greenock, and thence by sea to Liverpool. From there he went to Manchester, where he visited his former pupil, Dr. William Henry. On 26th August he met Dalton, with whom he spent two or three days, and from him received an account of the Atomic Theory. In his *History of Chemistry*[39] Thomson states that Dalton told him that the Atomic Theory was invented as an explanation of the multiple proportions of carbon and hydrogen in marsh gas and ethylene, with the analyses of which Dalton was then engaged. Dalton probably did give this account, which is nevertheless incorrect.[40] Thomson later[41] said that Dalton was led to the theory as a result of his analyses of two oxides of nitrogen, which is nearer the truth.

As a result of Dalton's conversation, Thomson in 1807 pub-lished[42] the first account of Dalton's Atomic Theory and Dalton's symbols. This is fuller than[2, 3] the account given in 1808 by Dalton[43] himself. Thomson was the first to accept Dalton's

PLATE XVII

THOMAS THOMSON

theory, and for the rest of his life he was devoted to it. Even Henry, who was fully conversant with Dalton's views, spoke[44] of the theory in rather guarded terms in 1810. Thomson followed with a series of papers[45] " On the Daltonian Theory of Definite Proportions in Chemical Combination ", in which he surveys, tabulates, recalculates, and criticises all the available experimental material (including that of Berzelius). His own work on the oxalates had given an experimental background, and he was very near the theory before Dalton. In his *Encyclopædia* article[46] Thomson had explained the neutralisation of sulphuric acid by potash by supposing that " the integrant particle " of sulphuric acid is a tetrahedron and " the particles of potass are of such a form, that one of them can attach itself to each of the sides of the acid particle : in that case, an integrant particle of sulphate of potass would be composed of five particles, one of acid and four of alkali . . . and . . . the acid would then be saturated, or . . . incapable of receiving any more alkaline particles in combination with it ". He did not follow up this idea. Thomson was greatly attracted by the hypothesis of William Prout (whose accuracy and skill were greatly admired by his contemporaries[47]), put forward anonymously in two papers[48] in Thomson's *Annals of Philosophy* in 1815-16, to the effect that atomic weights are whole multiples of that of hydrogen. Thomson took oxygen = 1 as his standard, but since he took O = 8 when H = 1, the same whole number ratio would follow. He thought[49] all other atomic weights were whole multiples of *twice* the atomic weight of hydrogen, i.e. of 2 × 0.125 = 0.25. For ten years, Thomson made a large number of experiments with the object of testing Prout's hypothesis, publishing[26] the results in 1825. The experimental methods involved the determination of weight ratios, the determination of the weights of salts giving complete precipitation reactions in solution, and (in the case of organic compounds) combustion analyses by heating with copper oxide in a copper tube, as " originally suggested by Gay-Lussac ".[50]

He repeatedly refers in terms of praise to the results of Berzelius, who had been engaged for many years in the exact determination of atomic weights, paying tribute to " the sagacity and skill of this most indefatigable chemist ",[51] but he does not hesitate to suggest that results in agreement with Prout's hypothesis were to be preferred. This, not unnaturally, displeased

Berzelius, who, in his *Annual Report*,[52] says of Thomson's book : " This work belongs to those few productions from which science will derive no advantage whatever. Much of the experimental part, even of the fundamental experiments, appears to have been made at the writing desk ; and the greatest civility which his contemporaries can show its author, is to forget that it was ever published ". This passage was republished in the *Philosophical Magazine*,[53] the Editor, Richard Taylor, in a note, defending Thomson's integrity and saying that : " we are satisfied that Dr. Thomson himself is more deceived than any one. It is possible that, misled by a favourable hypothesis, he may, like many before him, have been too eager in seizing parts favourable to his views, and too tardy in perceiving those that are unfavourable ". Thomson[54] repudiated the charge of fraud (and no one who studies the records of his life and character can possibly entertain it), but says he would continue to speak of Berzelius " with that respect for his talents and industry which I feel ". Berzelius's words were no hasty outburst : [55] they are unworthy of him, and foreign to his general character. The cause can be unfolded by a study of the relevant documents, particularly of the correspondence of Thomson and Berzelius : [56] it is psychological, and of the same character as that which later led to the estrangement of Berzelius and Liebig.[57] There is no doubt that Thomson's work is based on innumerable experiments : in the Preface he says the book " contains the result of many thousand experiments . . . repeated so often, and varied in so many ways, that I repose the most perfect confidence in their accuracy ".

Many experiments were performed or repeated by his pupils, and the results still existed in a series of note-books.[1] [54] Crum[2] concluded that the figures given " are not to be understood as the actual results of any one experiment, or even as the mean of several experiments, but rather as results which might fairly be deduced from them ; and . . . the experiments he related were undertaken, and described, more as instructions to his pupils than as contributions to the science ". The agreement with Prout's hypothesis " was not only complete, but if taken literally, was altogether marvellous ". It may be of interest to compare some of the values found by Thomson[58] and Berzelius[59] (in both cases brought to the modern integral ratio of equivalent to atomic weight) with the present values.

	H	O	Cl	C	N	S
Thomson (1825)	1	16	36	12	14	32
Berzelius(1826)	1·000	16·026	35·470	12·250	14·186	32·239
Modern (H=1)	1·000	15·88	35·18	11·91	13·90	31·81

	Fe	Ag	Hg
Thomson(1825)	56	110	200
Berzelius(1826)	56·361	108·305	202·863
Modern(H=1)	55·4	107·04	199

Determinations of the densities of gases,[60] made in Thomson's laboratory by Harvey, were claimed to be accurate to 1 part in 1000 (the fully loaded balance was sensible to 0·001 grain). He " corrected " the values (found with reference to air = 1) on the assumption that air is a definite compound N_4O, and also with reference to Prout's hypothesis. Although the relative density of oxygen was found in three experiments to be 1·1117, he took the theoretical value 1·1111, and for nitrogen instead of the observed value of 0·9728 he took 0·9722. The observed and adopted (on the basis of Prout's hypothesis) values were as follows, the adopted values being in brackets. The two values were the same for hydrogen and chlorine (Cl = 36) :

Air	1·0000	CO	0·9698(0·9722̇)
O_2	1·1117(1·1111̇)	C_2H_4	0·9709(0·9722̇)
N_2	0·9728(0·9722)	CH_4	0·5576(0·5555̇)
H_2	0·06940	C_2N_2	1·80395(1·8055)
N_2O	1·5269(1·5277)	$COCl_2$	3·4604(3·4722̇)
NO	1·04096(1·04166)	SO_2	2·2216̇(2·2222̇)
NH_3	0·5931(0·59027)	H_2S	1·17906̇(1·1805̇)
HCl	1·2844(1·2847)	PH_3	0·90325(0·90277̇)
CO_2	1·52673̇(1·5277̇)	HI	4·37566̇(4·375̇)

The great discrepancies found with euchlorine, which he supposed (on the basis of Davy's analyses) was an oxide Cl_2O, could, if followed up, have led Thomson to the discovery that the gas is a mixture in varying proportions of chlorine dioxide and chlorine.

Writings

On the basis of his *Encyclopædia* articles,[6 7 8] Thomson, while lecturer in Edinburgh, composed his famous text-book, *A System of Chemistry*.[61] The first edition appeared in 1802 and in the Preface (altered in each edition) he remarks that, in England, the composition of text-books was regarded " as a piece of drudgery, below the dignity of a philosopher " ; on the Continent, especially in France, the leaders of the science produced comprehensive works, but in them they appropriated too much as national possessions : " not satisfied with a part [they] have laid claim to the whole ". The only previous comparable work was the large treatise by Fourcroy,[62] which was inferior to Thomson's in content and style ; it lacked an adequate use of important and numerous English sources. An unfavourable but in part just review[63] of his book (perhaps by Dr. Andrew Duncan junr.) was answered by Thomson in a pamphlet.[64] An elementary work in one volume[65] was published in 1810. The *System* was finally split into separate works on Inorganic Chemistry,[66] Organic Chemistry,[67] Mineralogy,[68] and Heat and Electricity.[69] Thomson[70] says he had to teach the last subjects, but " it would be better if a new chair were instituted in each of our Universities, and that it should be the province of him who fills it to explain the principles of *heat, light, electricity, and magnetism* ", as is the case in France, where " this important branch of science is distinguished by the name of *physique* ". The style in all Thomson's books is clear, concise, and positive; the material is well-arranged, and the numerical data are tabulated—the last feature being characteristic. The text in succeeding editions showed a decreasing tendency to build the subject round a scaffolding of hypotheses. The arrangement of the *System*, which Thomson says[71] was " disapproved by every reviewer and copied by every subsequent author ", is first into imponderable bodies and ponderable bodies, the latter being divided into simple supporters of combustion and simple combustibles, the combustibles being acidifiable or alkalifiable ; then follow compounds of various classes, theoretical sections on affinity and states of aggregation, and accounts of meteorology, minerals, and vegetable and animal chemistry. The treatment is mostly historical, a method never in favour with authors who are anxious to emphasise their own contributions, but one which Thomson says lends interest, and assists the memory of the student.

Other works by Thomson are a contribution to an encyclopaedia[72] and to a treatise on brewing.[73] His *History of the Royal Society*[74] gives an account of the history of each science as nearly as possible from its origin, and a summary of the contents of the Royal Society papers arranged under subjects, with biographical accounts of the authors ; the work is, therefore, much more comprehensive than its title indicates. After his *System of Chemistry*, Thomson's best known work is his *History of Chemistry*.[39] Cullen had lectured on this subject.[75] The only previous comprehensive book was a chaotic work by Gmelin.[76] Thomson's book is written in a very interesting style ; it gives a large amount of valuable information, largely based on original sources, at least in the later parts,[77] and is still of value. A curious error in the work[78] is the attribution of the discovery of the law of equivalents to Wenzel instead of to Richter, a mistake which had been pointed out to Thomson by Professor Brunner in a letter[79] in 1826. Wollaston[80] in 1814 had also emphasised that Wenzel's results are incompatible with the law.

Thomson was a most successful author, taking great pains to acquire and systematise his material, and the popularity of his books was well deserved. They undoubtedly exercised a very good influence on the progress of Chemistry in Great Britain. His *System of Chemistry* could have been continued after his death, but it gave way to Gmelin's *Handbuch der Chemie*, first published in two volumes in 1817-19 ; a later edition of this was translated into English in 19 volumes in 1847-72, and the work is still current in a new German edition.

NOTES AND REFERENCES

[1] R. D. Thomson, *Edin. New Phil. J.*, 1852-3, *54*, 86.

[2] W. Crum, *Proc. Phil. Soc. Glas.*, 1855, *3*, 250.

[3] Anon., *Glasgow Med. J.*, 1857, *5*, 69, 121 (with portrait).

[4] J. C. Poggendorff, *Biographisch-Literarisches Handwörterbuch*, Barth, Leipzig, 1863, vol. II, cols. 644, 1097-1100.

[5] A. Harden, *Dictionary of National Biography*, Smith, Elder, London, 1898, vol. LVI, p. 271.

[6] *Supplement to the Encyclopædia Britannica*, Edinburgh, 1801, I, i, pp. 210f (this part appeared before 10th December 1800).

[7] *Ibid.*, 1801, II, i, pp. 193f (this part is said to have appeared in 1798).

[8] *Ibid.*, 1801, II, ii, pp. 529f.

[9] There is a small volume of MS. notes of Thomson's lectures in the Library of the Chemical Society, London.

10 *Annals of Philosophy*, vols. I-XVI, London, 1813-20, continued by Richard Phillips, vols. XVII-XXVIII, 1821-26 ; then merged into the *Philosophical Magazine*.

11 T. Thomson, *Travels in Sweden in the Autumn of* 1812, Baldwin, London, 1813.

12 A. E. Nordenskiöld, *Scheele, Nachgelassene Briefe und Aufzeichnungen*, Norstedt and Sons, Stockholm, 1892.

13 T. Thomson, *Annals of Philosophy*, 1819, *13*, i.

14 T. Thomson, *Annals of Philosophy*, 1822, *19* ; 261; ref. [26], vol. I, pp. 25, 315.

15 T. Thomson, *Annals of Philosophy*, 1822, *19*, 243.

16 T. Thomson, *Phil. Mag.*, 1829, *5*, 217.

17 E. von Meyer's statement in *A History of Chemistry*, Macmillan, London, 1906, pp. 203, 648, that " the first chemical laboratory for general instruction in any country " was " that of Thomas Thomson in Glasgow in 1817 ", is thus incorrect.

18 J. Coutts, *A History of the University of Glasgow from its Foundation in 1451 to 1909*, MacLehose, Glasgow, 1909, pp. 533-5, who points out that Cullen and Black had research laboratories in Edinburgh. These were also used for lecture preparations. See also J. C. Speakman, *Chem. and Ind.*, 1947, 219.

19 H. Terrey, *Annals of Science*, 1937, *2*, 137.

20 [R. Jameson], footnote in *Edin. New Phil. J.*, 1852-3, *54*, 98.

21 W. W. Webb, Ref.[5], vol. LVI. p. 268.

22 *Records of General Science*, edited by R. D. Thomson, with the assistance of T. Thomson, 4 vols., London, 1835-6.

23 J. Coutts, ref. [18], p. 535, says 29th June, 1852.

24 *The Life of Sir R. Christison, Bart.*, edited by his Sons, Blackwood, Edinburgh and London, 1885, vol. I, p. 366 ; the anonymous biographer in ref. [3] says Thomson's eyes were " fine, black and expressive ".

25 *Catalogue of Scientific Papers compiled by the Royal Society of London*, Clay, London, 1871, vol. V, pp. 970-76.

26 See e.g., *An Attempt to Establish the First Principles of Chemistry by Experiment*, 2 vols., Baldwin, Cradock, and Joy, London, 1825, vol. I, p. 432. H. C. Bolton, *A Select Bibliography of Chemistry*, Smithsonian Institution, Washington, 1893, p. 871, lists a French translation : *Principes de la Chimie établis par les Expériences : ou Essai sur les Proportions Définies dans la Composition des Corps. Traduction de l'Anglais publiée avec l'Assentiment de l'Auteur*, 2 vols., Paris, 1825.

27 T. Thomson, *Nicholson's J.*, 1801, *4*, 529.

28 T. Thomson, *Nicholson's J.*, 1803, *6*, 92 (104).

29 T. Thomson, *Annals of Philosophy*, 1814, *4*, 11.

30 Ref. 61 (b), 1804, vol. I, p. 353 [not in the first edition of 1802]; as pointed out by E. Cohen, *Chem. Weekbl.*, 1933, *30*, 191, and again by H. Irving, *Sci. Progress*, 1937, *31*, 654, this preceded the use of the method by Davy, *Phil. Trans.*, 1808, *98*, 21, mentioned by Ostwald, *Z. phys. Chem.*, 1893, *12*, 94; it is usually attributed to Dufour, *Compt. rend.*, 1860, *50*, 1039; 1862, *54*, 1079.

31 T. Thomson, *Annals of Philosophy*, 1813, *1*, 23; 1813, *2*, 11.

32 T. Thomson, *Nicholson's J.*, 1804, *8*, 280.

33 Ref. 26, vol. I, Preface.

34 T. Thomson, *Phil. Trans.*, 1808, *98*, I, 63 (read 14th January); *Phil. Mag.*, 1808, *31*, 102, 244; 1808, *32*, 39 (in full).

35 For his earlier qualitative symbols, see ref. 7 and ref. 61 (a), vol. III, p. 431; J. R. Partington, *J. Soc. Chem. Ind.*, 1936, *55*, 759.

36 T. Thomson, *Annals of Philosophy*, 1818, *12*, 338, 436.

37 T. Thomson, *Annals of Philosophy*, 1818, *12*, 441; Berzelius in letters of 1846-7 gave Thomson credit for this work: *Briefwechsel zwischen J. Berzelius und F. Wöhler*, edit. O. Wallach, Engelmann, Leipzig, 1901, vol. II, pp. 637, 664.

38 T. Thomson, *Phil. Trans.*, 1827, *117*, II, 159.

39 T. Thomson, *The History of Chemistry*, 2 vols., Colburn and Bentley, London, 1830-31 (Gleig's *National Library*, Nos. 3 and 10), 2nd edit., n.d., in one volume, Colburn and Bentley, London, vol. II, pp. 289-292.

40 H. E. Roscoe and A. Harden, *A New View of the Origin of Dalton's Atomic Theory*, Macmillan, London, 1896; A. N. Meldrum, *Mem. Manchester Lit. and Phil. Soc.*, 1910, *55*, Nos. 3-6. For a summary, see J. R. Partington, *A Short History of Chemistry*, Macmillan, London, 1937, p. 170.

41 T. Thomson, *Proc. Phil. Soc. Glasgow*, 1850, *3*, 135.

42 Ref. 61 (c), vol. III, p. 425, and later pages.

43 J. Dalton, *A New System of Chemical Philosophy*, Russell, Manchester, 1808, vol. I, part i, pp. 211-216, and plate 4.

44 W. Henry, *The Elements of Experimental Chemistry*, 6th edit., Johnson, London, 1810, vol. I, pp. 81-2; vol. II, pp. 475-8 (probably containing material supplied by Dalton): " This doctrine, it must be confessed, cannot at present be regarded in any other light than that of an hypothesis ... which has been developed with great ingenuity and patience of investigation, and which is supported by many striking and daily increasing analogies " (p. 82); " The instances in which it agrees with these results [of analysis] are already very numerous; and none have hitherto been shown to be directly contradictory to it " (pp. 475-8). The longer account in the seventh edition, Baldwin and Cradock, London, 1815, vol. I, pp. 27-38, is more favourable. See ref. 65.

[45] T. Thomson, *Annals of Philosophy*, 1813, *2*, 32, 109, 167, 293 ; 1814, *3*, 134, 375 ; 1814, *4*, 11, 83 ; 1818, *12*, 338, 436.

[46] Ref. *6*, p. 343.

[47] See, e.g., C. Daubeny, *Edin. New Phil. J.*, 1852, *53*, 98.

[48] Anon. [W. Prout], *Annals of Philosophy*, 1815, *6*, 321 ; 1816, *7*, 111 ; for authorship, see W. Prout, *Phil. Trans.*, 1827, *117*, II, 355 ; Thomson, *Annals of Philosophy*, 1820, *16*, 327.

[49] Ref. [26], vol. II, p. 457 ; cf. *Annals of Philosophy*, 1820, 16, 1(16), 321.

[50] T. Thomson, *Annals of Philosophy*, 1820, *16*, 1(4) ; ref. [26], vol. II, pp. 107, 117, 123.

[51] Ref. [26], vol. I, p. 149.

[52] J. Berzelius, *Jahres-Bericht*, trans. F. Wöhler, 1827, *6*, 77, 179-81.

[53] Anon., *Phil. Mag.*, 1828, *4*, 450.

[54] T. Thomson, *Phil. Mag.*, 1829, *5*, 217.

[55] See his letters to Wöhler, 1825-29, in ref. [37], vol. I, pp. 78, 127, 253, 271.

[56] J. Berzelius, *Bref*, publ. for the Svenska Vetenskaps. Akademien by Amqvist and Weksells, Uppsala, 1920, vol. III, pt. i, especially pp. 17, 24, 26, 56, 58, see also Berzelius, *Nouveau Système de Minéralogie* ... ", Paris, 1819, preface, for an attack on Thomson.

[57] *Berzelius und Liebig. Ihre Briefe von* 1831-1845, edit. by J. Carrière, Lehmann, Munich and Leipzig, 1893.

[58] Ref. [26], vol. II, pp. 457f., 479f.

[59] J. J. Berzelius, *Traité de Chimie*, transl. by Esslinger, Didot, Paris, 1831, vol. V, Table at end.

[60] T. Thomson, *Annals of Philosophy*, 1820, *15*, 232 ; 1820, *16*, 161, 241 ; for method, see T. Thomson, *Mem. Wernerian Soc.*, 1811, *1*, 504.

[61] T. Thomson, *A System of Chemistry*; (*a*) first edition, Bell, Bradfute, and Balfour, 4 vols., Edinburgh, 1802 ; (*b*) second edition, Bell and Bradfute, Edinburgh, 4 vols., 1804 ; (*c*) third edition, Bell, Bradfute, and Balfour, Edinburgh, 5 vols., 1807 (interesting as containing the first account of Dalton's Atomic Theory) ; (*d*) fourth edition, Bell and Bradfute, Edinburgh, 5 vols., 1810 ; (*e*) fifth edition, Baldwin, Cradock, and Joy, London, 4 vols., 1817 ; (*f*) sixth edition, Baldwin, Cradock, and Joy, London, 4 vols., 1820 ; (*g*) seventh edition, *A System of Chemistry of Inorganic Bodies. Seventh Edition*, Baldwin and Cradock, London, 2 vols., 1831. I have seen all these editions. (*h*) French translation (of the fifth edition) by J(ea)n (René Denis) Riffault (des Hêtres), *Système de Chimie* ... *Précédé D'une Introduction de M. C. L. Berthollet*, 9 vols., Bernard, Paris, 1809, interesting for Berthollet's comments ; another French edition of 4 vols., 1818 and Supplement, 1822 (translated from the fifth English edition) mentioned in refs. [3] and [4], which I have not seen, contained original communications on Light by A. Fresnel. (*i*) German translation *System der Chimie in vier Bänden. Nach der zweiten Ausgabe* [1804]

aus dem englischen übersetzt von Friederich Wolff, Berlin, 4 vols., 1805, and a fifth volume in two parts : *Zusätze und Erweiterung der Wissenschaft seit 1805*, Berlin, 1811. I know this only from the notice in Bolton, ref. [26], p. 871, who also lists two American editions : (*k*) *A New System of Chemistry, including Mineralogy and Vegetable, Animal and Dyeing Substances, comprehending the latest Discoveries and Improvements of the Science*, Philadelphia, 1803 (4to, 364pp.) ; and another (*l*) with Notes by Thomas Cooper, from the fifth London Edition, Philadelphia, 4 vols., 1818.

[62] A. F. [de] Fourcroy, *Système des Connaissances Chimiques, et de leurs Applications aux Phénomènes de la Nature et de l'Art*, Baudouin, Paris, 11 vols., An IX [1801]; translated by W. Nicholson, *A General System of Chemical Knowledge, and its Applications to the Phenomena of Nature and Art*, London, 11 vols., 1804. This work is diffuse, out of date for its time, and confined largely to French work.

[63] *The Edinburgh Review*, 1804, *4*, 120-151 (review of the second edition). Another long unfavourable review (by Brande?) in *Quart. J. Sci. Lit. and the Arts*, 1821, *11*, 119-171, was answered by Thomson, *Annals of Philosophy*, 1822, *19*, 240.

[64] *Remarks on the Edinburgh Review of Thomson's System of Chemistry* : *by the Author of that Work*, Edinburgh, 1804.

[65] T. Thomson, *The Elements of Chemistry*, Blackwood, Edinburgh, 1810 : it contains no reference to the Atomic Theory, compositions being given in percentages.

[66] See ref. [61](*g*).

[67] T. Thomson, *Chemistry of Organic Bodies. Vegetables*, Baillière, London, 1838 ; *Chemistry of Animal Bodies*, A. and C. Black, Edinburgh, 1843.

[68] T. Thomson, *Outlines of Mineralogy, Geology, and Mineral Analysis*, Baldwin and Cradock, London, 2 vols., 1836.

[69] T. Thomson, *An Outline of the Sciences of Heat and Electricity*, Baldwin and Cradock, London, and Blackwood, Edinburgh, 1830 ; second edition, Baillière, London, 1840, Poggendorff, ref. [4], gives " Edinburgh 1829, London, 1830 ", but I have not found an edition of 1829.

[70] Ref. [69], 1840, preface.

[71] *Annals of Philosophy*, 1813, *1*, 373.

[72] D. K. Sandford, *The Popular Encyclopædia*, 7 vols., Glasgow, 1841 : *Progress of Science*, by T. Thomson.

[73] T. Thomson, *Brewing and Distillation. With Practical Instruction for Brewing Porter and Ales according to the English and Scottish Method, by W. Stewart*, Edinburgh, A. and C. Black, 1849 (from his *Encyclopædia* article).

[74] T. Thomson, *History of the Royal Society, from its Institution to the end of the Eighteenth Century*, Baldwin, London, 1812. This was intended

as a supplement to the *Abridgement of the Philosophical Transactions*, 18 vols., London, 1809.

[75] A MS. of these lectures was in the possession of the late Professor J. Miller Thomson.

[76] J. F. Gmelin, *Geschichte der Chemie*, Rosenbusch, Göttingen, 3 vols., 1797-9.

[77] The parts on Paracelsus and van Helmont are, as W. Whewell, *History of the Inductive Sciences*, third edition, Parker, London, 1857, vol. III, p. 97, noted, literal translations from K. Sprengel, *Histoire de la Médicine*, trans. by A. J. L. Jourdain and E. F. M. Bosquillon, 9 vols., Paris, 1815-32, vol. III, p. 284, vol. IV, p. 22. Mention of the source is omitted by Thomson.

[78] Ref. [39], vol. II, pp. 279-82 : the numerical examples given are not from Wenzel's book, *Lehre von der Verwandschaft der Körper*, Dresden, 1777, see also ref. [26], vol. I, p. 1f.

[79] Ref. [3], p. 140 : letter (in English) of 1 November, 1826, saying he had read Wenzel's book and " could not find in it any hint belonging to the theory of atoms . . . in some examples of mutual decomposition he gives at the end of his work, he calculates the required proportions and finds always that one of the bodies is in excess or in less ". See J. R. Partington, *Textbook of Inorganic Chemistry*, Macmillan, London, 1921, p. 117.

[80] W. H. Wollaston, *Phil. Trans.*, 1814, *104*, 1 (read 4th November, 1813) ; *Ann. Chim.*, 1814, *90*, 138 ; where he says, " I have not been desirous of warping my numbers according to an atomic theory ", and attributes Gay-Lussac's law of volumes to W. Higgins, who " in his conception of union by ultimate particles clearly preceded Mr. Dalton in his atomic views of chemical combination ". Wollaston's equivalents, recalculated to $O = 16$ and as atomic weights, include : $H = 1 \cdot 056$, $C = 12 \cdot 064$, $S = 32 \cdot 00$, $P = 27 \cdot 84$, $N = 14 \cdot 032$, $Cl = 35 \cdot 28$.

SOME OBSERVATIONS AND AN ANECDOTE

T. S. Patterson

IN RESPONSE to the welcome invitation to be represented in this publication, I can, unfortunately, do no more than contribute two small notes, one about Black the other about Thomson, on topics unlikely to be dealt with elsewhere in the book.

Perhaps, however, as an opening, the general observation may be permitted that in the early days of the Lectureship in Glasgow, it was possible for the Lecturer to take *all* Chemistry for his oyster ; his lectures were intended to represent, and probably did represent, the whole subject, whereas at the present time the Ordinary Class of 100 lectures can merely touch its fringe. In those days this must have lent a feeling of completeness and homogeneity to the course, so that the Scots lad could rise from his feast feeling that he really had " done Chemistry ". On the other hand the Lecturer, having finished the Winter's work, including the examinations, had accomplished his statutory duties for that year, and then had some six months before him in which to recast his lectures, to do experimental work in which he was interested, or, perhaps, to devote more attention than he otherwise could to his medical practice.

The student, for his part, depended mostly for his knowledge of the subject on his memory of the professor's lectures and upon the notes he had taken in the class. Comparatively few books existed which would be suitable for the lectures of some other professor ; there was, perhaps, too little general system about the subject. There were, nevertheless, a few good books ; one which has always struck me as particularly so being Peter Shaw's translation and amplification of Boerhaave's Chemistry, a book which, it is interesting to recall, Black warmly recommended. From the various copies of student lecture-notes which have been preserved, it is possible to trace the very gradual growth which took place in the views of the time.

Towards the end of Black's career, however, these changes were greatly accelerated, and it must have become much more difficult to keep pace with the subject. In Black's day eminent people mostly wrote books only towards the close of their lives so that the matter contained therein was the result of long experience. Cullen was engaged upon his Materia Medica at 78, Black died before his book was finished ; but from the latter, when it did come, we obtain some very interesting information about Black's views, especially regarding his attitude to Lavoisier's new System.

Black had, in very marked degree, one characteristic too much lacking at the present time ; he was a firm believer in strict inductive method, and it is very much to be desired that what he had to say then should be taken to heart now. Although not antagonistic to the new views of Lavoisier, he still did not like Lavoisier's way of forwarding them. He may very possibly have felt, like many others of the time, that the good fairy Phlogiston who, after all, had lent a most useful hand in the development of Chemistry for many years and had evoked so many valuable facts, ought not to be bundled out in the unceremonious fashion that Lavoisier and his colleagues proposed ; it was ungentlemanly, not to say indecent ; we ought rather to reverence old friends. Perhaps he was indeed almost hypercritical in this, for it can hardly be asserted that Lavoisier was greatly to blame in his methods, although he may have been somewhat impatient, since it took him a surprisingly long time to get anyone to believe in his views. But Black insisted upon developing Lavoisier's theory even more carefully than Lavoisier himself, for he held that Chemistry was not then a science,[1] and that everything having pretentions to a complete system [2] should be avoided. Chemistry should be analytical ; and a principle, or general law, should only be arrived at, at the very end of an induction ; certainly not at the beginning.

One ought not, he said, to start off from a first principle, merely a sagacious observation of a universal fact, not itself the direct physical result of an induction which may perhaps be suitable for the comprehension of adepts, but which is quite unsuitable for instructing a novice. He therefore proposes, in his lectures, to lead gradually up to this principle ; and, in order to get at the proofs on which its validity must rest, it is necessary to start from very complex substances and considerations ; and the conclusions to be inferred are such as beginners cannot possibly draw, although it may be easy enough for a Lavoisier, a Cavendish, a Berthollet, to grasp them. But even such men as these are not suitable judges in this matter ; the thing must make its appeal to the common man ; does the force of the proof seem incontrovertible to him?[3] Direct proofs of the fundamental propositions, however, are scanty, and this is a fault in any system intended for the instruction of the ignorant. The new views were too anxious to leave no blank, no open link, in their structure ; they wished to leave nothing unexplained, and this sort of thing nourishes an itch for theory and is the worst of philosophical habits for beginners.

Black admitted almost all Lavoisier's doctrines,but preferred to teach them so as to give a better impression of their validity. He will develop them piecemeal, so that they will be arrived at easily and with confidence in their truth. This will distribute the reformation over the whole course and in especial will bring students acquainted with the work of men like Newton, Stahl, Margraaf, Cramer, Scheele, Bergmann, geniuses certainly not below the common level ; whereas one " who learns Chemistry by Lavoisier's scheme may remain ignorant of all that was done by former chemists, and unable to read their excellent writings." [4]

The foregoing is a summary of Black's own pronouncement on this subject. He believed in putting the horse of fact before the cart of theory, and one can easily imagine how little he would have approved of modern methods of teaching, which are almost entirely based on just the opposite idea, in spite of having to deal with much more difficult material. Modern books are nearly all written on the " cart before the horse " principle ; they assume to begin with, what they wish to establish in the end, and it would require both courage and enterprise to invert their structure. But the effort would be well worth while.

If the above should seem an exaggerated statement, it may be mentioned that a few years ago a master at one of the English schools published an account of his method of teaching chemistry in his classes. He starts off, he says, by giving a full account of the theory of the subject—that is, the abstractions the final inductions, inferences that it is the whole business of science to establish—and then proceeds to *hang the facts on to it*. He thus accomplishes the very opposite of Black's ideal, and presents his

N

pupils with some sagacious—very sagacious—observations, hope-
lessly unsuitable, in fact incomprehensible, for novices. Surely
the " cart before the horse " method could be carried no further
than that.

The start is usually made, nowadays, from the electronic
theory of matter, and it is most unfortunate that these modern
views, dealing with what Black would rightly have called very
complex substances and considerations, can be crudely expressed
in a speciously simple and misleading language without even any
particularly hard words in it, in something this way : Matter is
mainly made up of electrons. The electron is merely a bit of
electricity ; rather a small bit—about the eighteen hundred and
fiftieth part of the mass of a hydrogen atom, a statement which is
supposed immediately to set its smallness clearly before the youthful mind, and indeed the youthful mind may easily be of opinion
that it has grasped it. But for all its smallness it still has mass and
weight and even a diameter. When one seeks it, however, it isn't
there, for flicking its little tail it becomes, suddenly, a mere
wriggle in the ether. Then there are other rather similar—except
that they are entirely different—things called protons and neutrons
and nuclei ; these last, said to have a diameter of one ten thou-
sandth of that of the atom, must be composed of matter—or
something else—having about one billion times the density of any
average gross material ; that being, perhaps, the most solemn
thought of all. Then, from these components, and electrons, and
other things which are constantly being added or withdrawn in
accordance with current research ; and, by various partnerships
and dances, from the simple waltz to the eightsome reel, all the
other elements are made up in a way which depends for its
simplicity merely on pedagogic authority, so that even the most
childish lips can lisp in electronics.[5]

Direct proofs of these fundamental principles are not merely
scanty, they may be said to be non-existent, and to be discoverable
only by enormously complicated methods, taxing the ablest
brains. In fact it is likely that even of those who talk the language
of electronics not more than one in ten thousand can form any
real comprehension of the profound significance of these ideas ; at
least that is the opinion of one of the less qualified of the other nine
thousand, nine hundred and ninety nine. These principles
certainly cannot make any incontrovertible appeal to the common

man, since they are far too difficult and he is quite unqualified to judge. Whether they can or do take any shine out of the morning face of the average schoolboy is more doubtful ; that genial individual soon learns to take this kind of news in his stride, having been brought up in his infancy on the miracles of Hans Andersen and the Grimms. He has a memory and a care-free outlook as well as a resilient personality which enable him to treat these stupendous pieces of information as the merest platitudes ; and he may proceed cheerfully to draw, as his next day's task, a pathetic little picture of a planetary system which, by a supreme effort of faith is supposed to explain—save the mark!— the constitution and behaviour of one or other of the various atoms. All this probably involves, however, the ruination of any gift of imagination with which he may be endowed—a very sore loss indeed.

There is little doubt that Black would think that the course in modern chemistry should commence with the most obvious and simple experimental facts of the subject and, ultimately, in four or five years perhaps, lead up to the later development in the way of electronics ; in fact a course in chemistry ought to be : " The History of Chemistry from its Early Beginnings to its most Recent Developments ", which would render the subject homogeneous once more. Such a course might not be easy to plan or to accomplish—it is always necessary to compromise—but I believe it could be done. Some cleansing of the Augean Stables of Chemical History would be desirable in anticipation, but that need not be difficult once the Alchemical nonsense, as dear to modern writers as to those of the Middle Ages and the Sixteenth and Seventeenth Centuries, was cleared out. The naked facts are simple enough, it is the mass of verbiage with which they are entangled—the Black Crows and White Eagles, the Philosophic Egg, the Green Lion, the Bird of Hermes, the numerous purely imaginary alchemists, such as Pope John XXII, Raymond Lully, Nicolas Flamel, etc., and the many deliberate lies invented by Dorn, by Thölde, by Michael Maier, by Arnauld and others—that makes the going so difficult. Otherwise it would be comparatively simple.

A final word, closely connected with what has been said, may be added in regard to the many books that are written on : " Chemistry from the Point of View of the Periodic Law." This again is the complete antithesis of Black's message. The Periodic System, is nowadays and for the most part, Electronics writ large, but with a considerable infusion of other remarkable facts and assumptions. To discuss the properties of the elements by deducing them from the Periodic System is merely to read out of the system what has just been read into it. Instead of being taken as axiomatic, the System ought to be developed as an induction It ought to be remembered that the System, great as may be its power, is not necessarily a permanency. In another hundred years, perhaps even in less time, it may no longer be there. But the facts will be there ; facts remain whilst theories pass away, and the Periodic System is a theory. " A Course in Chemistry leading up to the Periodic System and the Electronic Theory of Matter " : ought to be the aim of the teacher. Again it comes merely to : " Chemistry from the Historical Point of View ". Let us hope that, ultimately, this view will prevail, so that Joseph Black may henceforth rest more easily in his grave than he probably has done during the last hundred and fifty years.

*   *   *   *

The second matter that may be worth relating here is an amusing story told me, a number of years ago, by John Millar Thomson, at one time Professor of Chemistry in King's College, London. He was the son of Allen Thomson[6] who was in turn, the son of John Thomson[7] and the great grandson, on his mother's side of John Millar,[8] an ancestry of which Millar Thomson was rather proud. Thomas Thomson and Millar Thomson, however, were not related. The latter was born[9] in the Old College about three years before Thomas Thomson's death, so that he would often have opportunity, later on, of hearing reminiscences and much of the gossip of the Old University.

According to this tale, Thomas Thomson, at the time when steamboats began to ply on the Clyde, happened to take a trip down the river with his wife, and, being interested in other branches of science besides chemistry, he took with him also a pail attached to a rope, with which he intended to fetch up small marine animals from the river as he went along. But the art of pulling a pailful of water into a steamer under way—although, doubtless, the speed was not what it is now—is not altogether an easy one, and Thomson was perhaps not skilful at it. If the pail is allowed to drag too far behind the operator it is practically impossible to withdraw it, and either the pail and the operator must part company, or the operator go with the pail.

Thomson got involved in this predicament, and being of a very stubborn disposition, he refused to leave go, the consequence being that he had to go himself. He was recovered from the river in an extremely wet, and highly indignant condition. His wife, who had naturally been very anxious, fell on his neck and embraced him fondly when he regained the deck, but Thomson, failing to take this in the proper spirit, testily exclaimed : " Tut, tut, my dear, this is neither time nor place for demonstrations of conjugal felicity! "

There is no particular reason why this story should not be true ; J. M. Thomson seemed to believe in it, and it might even yet receive corroboration. If it is true it is perhaps worth preserving, and if it is not, no great harm is likely to have been done by its mention.

NOTES AND REFERENCES

[1] Will it ever be one, and what will that mean?

[2] Which neither chemistry nor any similar subject is ever likely to be.

[3] Presumably Black means here : Does the *prima facie* evidence seem sound and convincing to the ordinary layman ?

[4] Black's *Lectures on the Elements of Chemistry*, Edinburgh, 1803, I, p. 549.

[5] It is satisfactory to observe that this very difficult if easily pronounced subject has not, so far, invaded the Chemistry paper of the Scottish Universities Entrance Board, or the University of Glasgow Bursary Examination.

[6] *b*. 1809—*d*. 1881 ; Prof. Anat. Glas. 1848-1877.

[7] *b*. 1765—*d*. 1846 ; Prof. Milit. Surg. 1806, and Path. 1832-1841, Edin.

[8] *b*. 1735—*d*. 1801 ; 1761-1801, Prof. Law. Glas.

[9] *b*. 7 Mar. 1849—*d*. 22 Mar. 1933.

THE CHEMICAL LABORATORY AT GLASGOW SIXTY YEARS AGO

Robert Broom

I WENT TO the Chemical Laboratory at the University in the summer of 1883 to be a sort of junior assistant. The idea seemed to be that I was to pick up what chemical training I could get and in return give any general assistance required. I was there for three years. In the summer session I gave general assistance in the practical classes for Medical Students, and the last year I was there I did all the chemical analyses that came to the department. My position was not very well defined. I got no salary. I was too proud to ask for any ; and Professor Ferguson never thought of paying me any. But I managed however, to pick up a pretty good knowledge of chemistry.

Professor Ferguson took very little interest in the dozen or so students who were supposed to be studying chemistry for a science degree or for a general training in Chemistry. He visited the laboratory perhaps about once a week and had a general look at what one or two students were doing. No one took him seriously as a chemist. He never did any chemical research and never published—at least after he became a professor—any chemical papers. Of course we all knew he was deeply interested in the early history of Chemistry, and in Paracelsus, and others of the Middle Ages, and we knew he was a great collector of Incunabula.

Ferguson's two official assistants were John Hutcheson and J. J. Dobbie. Hutcheson was a good general analytical chemist, but not interested in chemical research, and so far as I know never published anything of importance. Every one liked him, and he did most of the general teaching in the laboratory.

J. J. Dobbie was a man of some ambition ; and had published the analyses of some rare minerals. He was also interested in organic chemistry. For a time I was practically his assistant ; but in 1884 or -5 he became Professor of Chemistry in Bangor, and ultimately became Government Chemist in London. He became F.R.S. and was knighted.

Perhaps about 1884, G. G. Henderson came to the department, and succeeded Dobbie as the main tutorial assistant.

It was probably also in 1884 that two other junior assistants also became attached to the laboratory, J. Holms Pollok and Joshua Buchanan. Pollok came of a distinguished family, two of his uncles being members of Parliament. His father had been a silk manufacturer in Govan. Pollok was a genius ; and he and I spent many hours discussing the constitution of matter and other similar abstruse problems. I wrote my first scientific paper " On the Volume of Mixed Liquids " in 1885, and this was communicated to the Royal Society of Edinburgh by Dr. J. T. Bottomley. Shortly after, Pollok also had a paper on a similar question. He also made many experiments on liquids in an endeavour to find some clue to their nature.

About this time Pollok's brother was in South Africa, and as the Goldfields at Barberton were opening up, and a little later those of Johannesburg his father had also gone out to South Africa. Then the question arose how to extract gold satisfactorily from the Banket Reefs. Mr. Pollok, senior, sent the problem to his son in Glasgow ; and within a short time our Pollok had got a satisfactory solution—a Chlorination process. With the assistance of his uncles he floated a company with a capital of £200,000. The 5s. shares boomed to over £2, and had J. H. Pollok been interested in merely making money he might have become a very wealthy man. Buchanan became his assistant and visits were paid to South Africa, South America and I believe Australia, in connection with the company.

Unfortunately it was found in Johannesburg that the Cyanide process was even better than the Chlorination, and gradually Pollok's company was superseded. Ultimately he had some teaching post in Dublin. He died comparatively young. Till the end he was as excitedly enthusiastic as ever. I had a letter from him not long before his death telling me he believed he had discovered two new elements.

Two others in the laboratory were almost as interesting as the scientists. There was an old woman who had been a cleaner in the department since 1846, and who had many interesting recollections of Professors Thomson and Anderson. And we had Old John—John Gray.

Old John was the bottle washer, and Ferguson's factotum. He was a character. Usually when we had any differences of opinion in the laboratory we would call in John for his views, and he was always ready to give his conclusions. Once we were discussing the relative advantages of the Decimal and Duodecimal system of Coinage. When John was asked for his opinion he replied, " Weel, ye see its like this. A pound's even money ; but a dollar's four and twopence—and ye can never get awa' frae that. "

John had been in the department since 1867, and been Anderson's factotum before he was Ferguson's. Once in the old High Street days Anderson had wanted some glass-blowing done for some apparatus. He met the expert workman, but wanted to go to the place to see it being made. The man tried to explain where his workshop was, by reference to the various public houses that had to be passed. Anderson who was a very rabid teetotaler was shocked at being thought to be acquainted with all the public houses.

In 1913, I had been invited to give the Croonian Lecture at the Royal Society in London, and was at the Conversazione of that year. Dobbie was there, and also Ramsay. I had never met Ramsay, so I asked Dobbie for an introduction. At once Ramsay began talking of the old laboratory and of course John was regarded as the leading personage ; and he told us two good stories.

Once Ramsay had said to John, " Hoo's your son getting on now, John?" " Oh, Mr. Ramsay he's daein' real weel." " Ay, what's he daein? " " Oh he's in the Post Office, and he's getting 18s. a week." " Eh, John ye'll hae to watch him. If he's getting 18s. a week he'll be spending a guid deal on the lassies." " Na, na, Mr. Ramsay, he no ane of that kind. He never spends naething on the lassies, besides he gie's his wages a' tae his mither." " Whit, do ye gie him naething? " " Na, na, his mither gie's him twopence a week for his pocket, but he's tae tell his mither whit he does wi' it."

John always went up to the Beadle's house every morning exactly at 9 o'clock for the Professor's letters, and was always seen setting his watch by Sir William Thomson's electric clock. Someone said to him, " Whit way are ye winding up your watch every morning, John?" " Weel, ye see it's like this. I've got the kitchen clock to gang by when I get hame. So I only row my watch up half, and don't ye see by only rowing it up half it'll last twice as lang."

Though I have only once been in the old lab. since 1889, I believe it is much changed. I saw Henderson when he was at the Technical College, and I had a few letters from him after his wife died, and he had retired to the West Highlands.

I deserted Chemistry for Medicine in 1886, and have since deserted Medicine for Palaeontology and Comparative Anatomy ; but I can never forget the years 1883 to 1886. The ghosts of Thomson and Anderson still lingered in the laboratory, and the fact that only shortly before this time Ramsay had worked here, made us feel that we were in contact with some of the great men of the nineteenth century ; and though only my first paper was a physico-chemical one I feel I am still one of the old family. And the facts that I have recently been elected an honorary Fellow of the Royal Society of Edinburgh, have been awarded that society's Neill Prize, and have been further honoured by an LL.D. from Glasgow University, make me feel I am still regarded as a Scot though I left Scotland more than fifty years ago.

GLASGOW CHEMISTRY IN THE TWENTIETH CENTURY

A. R. Todd

I SHOULD LIKE to express my deep appreciation of the honour done me by inviting me to participate in the celebration of the bi-centenary of the foundation of a Lectureship in Chemistry, the forerunner of the present Regius chair of Chemistry, in the University of Glasgow. The opportunity thus afforded me, I have accepted with perhaps more than ordinary pleasure, firstly because I am myself a product of Glasgow University, and secondly because I have the honour to occupy what I believe to be the oldest chair of Chemistry in Britain, being the twelfth in an unbroken line of occupants since its foundation at the University of Cambridge in 1702.

I must essay the delineation of Glasgow's position in the twentieth century and seek an assessment of the future outlook. This task may seem at first sight easier than attempting to appraise the position during the early days of the Glasgow Lectureship, but contemporary history is one of the most difficult of studies. Only with the lapse of time can events be seen in their true perspective ; in dealing with events which form part of the experience of those now living it is all too easy to exaggerate the importance of certain happenings which seize upon the public imagination and to ignore others, the significance of which only becomes later apparent. My views, based necessarily on personal opinions and reflections, may differ from those, possibly more significant, which are held by others.

What then was the position at the opening of the twentieth century? On the national scale Britain had undergone a continuous increase in prosperity and imperial expansion in the latter part of the nineteenth century, and now in the closing years of Queen Victoria's reign, stood apparently on the threshold of a boundless era of power and prosperity. The study of chemistry in Glasgow seemed to be in tune with the national prosperity and the outlook was similarly bright. It is perhaps desirable for us first to look at what had been happening in the chemical sphere both in Glasgow and elsewhere if we wish to appreciate the situation, for much had happened since the foundation of the Lectureship which we now commemorate.

As regards the University, it is, I think, fair to say that from its inception chemistry, as a subject of study, underwent normal, if slow, development. The subject grew in importance, the original Lectureship became in due course the Regius chair of Chemistry, founded by George III in 1817, whose first occupant was Thomas Thomson, and by the end of the nineteenth century organic and inorganic chemistry and metallurgy were all represented in the activities of the Chemistry Department, although the new branch of physical chemistry was not as yet recognised by a staff appointment. Other developments of great significance had however taken place in Glasgow. In 1796 Anderson's University (later Anderson's College, popularly known as " the Andersonian ") was founded under the will of John Anderson, professor of Natural Philosophy in the University of Glasgow, and friend of James Watt. This institution founded for " the good of mankind and the improvement of science " was destined to play an important role in the development of chemistry in Glasgow. Its first professor of Chemistry and Natural Philosophy, Dr. Garnett, was succeeded in 1799 by George Birkbeck, who " in the belief that men should be taught the principles of the arts they practise "— an admirable definition of technical education—ran a special class for the public on Mechanical and Chemical Philosophy. This fact I mention for two reasons. Firstly, this class led, after the departure of Birkbeck to London, to the foundation of the Mechanics Institution in 1823 (its title was subsequently changed to the College of Science and Arts) ; Birkbeck, incidentally, founded in London a year later a similar Mechanics Institution which has developed into the modern Birkbeck College, a constituent of the University of London. Secondly, although the population of Glasgow at the time was only about 70,000, it is recorded that Birkbeck's class attracted no fewer than 700 students and had to be held in the Trades Hall ; this phenomenal attendance is one more example of the traditional Scottish urge to educational improvement, which has played so large a part in our country's history. Anderson's University and the Mechanics Institution, which had, so to speak, broken from each other in 1823, functioned as separate bodies for 63 years until in 1886 they merged again forming the Glasgow and West of Scotland Technical College, the immediate forerunner of the present Royal Technical College.

It is in the history of the Andersonian that one finds the most striking Glasgow chemical figures in the nineteenth century. Thomas Graham, appointed professor of Chemistry there in 1830, remained in office for seven years, during which time much of his classical work on the diffusion of gases was carried out, and for the first time systematic laboratory instruction in chemistry was given in Anderson's University. Graham's name is firmly inscribed as one of the immortals in chemistry, and here we need only note that James Young, founder of the Scottish shale oil industry, was one of his students in Glasgow. It was the same James Young, who, being convinced of the need for training in applied chemistry, founded in 1870 the chair of Technical Chemistry in the Andersonian, a chair which was occupied during the first few years of its existence by Dr. (afterwards Sir) William Henry Perkin, famous as the discoverer of the coal tar dyes. It is perhaps rather a chastening thought that the synthetic dyestuff industry, which owed its origin to Perkin, might, had the necessary encouragement been given, have been developed here in Scotland rather than in Germany. In the same year as Perkin, too, there was appointed to the Andersonian chair of Chemistry Dr. (later Sir) T. E. Thorpe, who was succeeded by William Dittmar in 1874. Dittmar, also a famous chemist and excellent teacher, occupied the chair until his death in 1892 and was followed by George Gerald Henderson. At the end of the nineteenth century we find Henderson as professor of Chemistry and E. J. Mills as professor of Technical Chemistry in the Glasgow and West of Scotland Technical College.

It should be noted that the second half of the nineteenth century was an epoch of major discoveries and developments in chemistry, discoveries and developments which became the solid foundation of the science as we know it to-day. Inorganic chemistry—the chemistry of the inanimate world in its original definition—was systematised and given a great impetus by Mendeléeff in 1869 when he propounded the periodic classification of the elements. Structural ideas in organic chemistry really date from the conceptions of Couper (a Kirkintilloch man) and Kekulé

(1865) regarding benzene. In the years that followed there was a rapid succession of discoveries of great moment to the science. On the organic side the old radical theories were replaced by modern structural concepts, and from the postulate of the tetrahedral carbon atom by Van't Hoff and Le Bel arose the edifice of stereochemistry. New elements were recognised, among which the inert gases discovered in 1894 by Rayleigh and Ramsay—who had been student and teacher at Glasgow University—were of particular theoretical interest, whilst in the years that followed Crookes' demonstration that the cathode rays were made up of negatively charged particles (1879) a new ferment was at work which profoundly altered ideas of atomic structure ; the phenomenon of radioactivity was first described by Becquerel in 1896. Parallel with all these a new branch of chemistry—now known as physical chemistry—was beginning to emerge as a result of brilliant contributions, among the most significant of which were the work of Arrhenius, of Ostwald, whose Dilution Law was published in 1888, and of Willard Gibbs, whose work on the Phase Rule appeared between 1874 and 1878. At the end of the century then, the chemist was equipped as never before to venture forth into new fields, and the future was bright and beckoning.

Our picture would, however, be incomplete if we confined our attention to developments in the great teaching institutions. Chemical industry and a variety of other industries, whose progress is interwoven with chemistry, were also an important feature in the West of Scotland by the end of the nineteenth century. The chemical industrial position was reviewed in some detail in an extremely interesting pamphlet written by the late Professor Henderson on the occasion of the British Association meeting at Glasgow in 1901, and in reading it one is struck by the change in emphasis which occurred as the chemical industries moved forward from the mists of empiricism to the scientific precision of their modern equivalents. Considerable changes in Scotland's chemical industries were, of course, to be expected during the second half of the century on economic grounds. Whereas earlier there would, I think, be an understandable tendency for such an area as the West of Scotland to develop nearly all forms of basic chemical manufacture, the vast increase in ease of transport and the tendency of industry to operate in ever larger units inevitably led to the concentration of some industries in localities particularly suited to their pursuit, either through proximity of raw materials, or for some other economic reason, and to the nation-wide distribution of the products from one or two centres. A striking example of this is found in the alkali industry. The manufacture of soda ash (by the Leblanc process), and caustic soda from salt, grew to be a large and important industry in Scotland during the first half of the nineteenth century, and then suffered an almost total eclipse, so that it had virtually disappeared by the end of the century. Whilst there were doubtless a variety of factors responsible for this, I would suggest that the major ones were the welding of most of the alkali industry of Britain into one company and the obvious advantages of locating the production of alkalies close to the natural salt deposits of Cheshire, where the industry remains largely concentrated to-day. On the other hand, sulphuric acid production which was developed as a corollary to the alkali industry remained a large factor in the Glasgow area at the end of the nineteenth century. Britain is not self-supporting in the raw materials for sulphuric acid manufacture, so that proximity to raw material is less vital and, the transport of acid being rather costly, there was every incentive to the production of this important chemical in quantity sufficient to meet the needs of a large number of local industries. It is worth noting however that the latter part of the century saw the virtual disappearance of the alkali industry and the rapid dwindling of others such as refined sugar, alum, iodine and ferrocyanide production. Among those which sprang into prominence at the same time, we may note the manufacture of cyanide and compressed gases in Glasgow itself. Close by, at Ardeer, rapid strides were being made by the young Scottish explosives industry, destined to become a major factor in British chemical industry. Started in 1873 by Alfred Nobel with 47 workers, the Ardeer factory expanded rapidly and employed 1,300 by the end of the century. Mention too must be made of the great development of the shale oil industry in Scotland during this period, an industry which owed so much to James Young. In addition to these, there flourished in the Glasgow area a very wide range of chemical industries, many of them in the hands of small companies, which supplied almost every type of commercially important chemical product from vegetable dyes to dichromates.

Such then was the general picture, and it is I think worth while to consider now the strength and weakness of it, particularly on the academic side, so that we may appreciate the significance of subsequent events. Glasgow, with no less than three chairs of Chemistry, had apparently all that was needed to take advantages offered as a result of what might almost be described as the scientific revolution wrought, as I have indicated, in the previous quarter of a century. In order to do so, however, vigour in leadership was necessary as well as wisdom and foresight. It is, in my view, indisputable that Glasgow had been slow in developing some branches of chemistry. In the University the growing and already large subject of organic chemistry had been somewhat neglected, and indeed it was only in 1898 that a lectureship had been established in this branch with W. R. Lang as its first occupant. This deficiency had been realised earlier by a young man, George Gerald Henderson, who in the late eighties, while a demonstrator in inorganic chemistry, was spending his vacations working in Leipzig with Wislicenus, one of the great German masters of organic chemistry, and propagating the new faith in Glasgow. Henderson, as we have seen, succeeded Dittmar at the Technical College in 1892 and was destined not only to develop organic chemistry there but to become the dominating figure of the new century in Glasgow chemistry. The new physical chemistry, too, had not yet found a recognised place in the University. Again, there were physical weaknesses in the rather cramped and uncomfortable quarters in which chemistry was housed, particularly in the Technical College.

The weaknesses above mentioned were quickly remedied. On the side of the University, organic chemistry was rapidly expanded and became a major activity under Thomas Stewart Patterson, who in 1904 followed Matthew Parker as Lecturer. In the years that followed a great flow of research on stereochemical topics, particularly in relation to optical activity, issued from the laboratories at Gilmorehill. In 1904, too, a Lectureship in Physical Chemistry was founded with Frederick Soddy as its first occupant. Soddy, who remained in Glasgow until his departure to Aberdeen in 1914, gave the new lectureship a flying start, and during his tenure he carried out an extensive series of important researches now enshrined among the notable achievements in physical chemistry. The tradition set up by Soddy was carried on first by

Alfred W. Stewart (later professor of Chemistry at Belfast) and then by Robert Wright, the succeeding lecturer.

Metallurgy, too, for which a Lectureship had been established in 1898, also progressed notably under the successive guidance of W. C. Anderson (1898), C. E. Fawcitt (1905) and C. H. Desch (1909). During all this period the University Department was directed by the Regius Professor, John Ferguson, who held the chair during the long period from 1874 to 1915. Ferguson, although born in Alloa received his education in Glasgow, first at the High School and later at the University, where he had a brilliant career as an undergraduate in the Faculty of Arts. It was only later that he turned to science, first interesting himself in physics as an assistant to William Thomson (later Lord Kelvin), and subsequently turning to chemistry. He finally became assistant to Anderson, the then Regius Professor, and because of the latter's ill-health was largely responsible for arranging the removal of chemistry to Gilmorehill when the University moved from the old College site in the city. In due course he succeeded Anderson as Regius Professor. I mention these facts now, for they help to make the work of Ferguson more readily understood. He was primarily a scholar of broad interests and he devoted himself throughout most of his tenure of the Chair to the study of the history and philosophy of chemistry and largely eschewed experimental research. This was in some ways a pity, since the period during which Ferguson occupied the Glasgow Chair was, as we have seen, one in which the experimental side of the subject was making revolutionary progress. Nevertheless, it must be conceded that Ferguson's scholarly papers on the early history of chemistry were notable contributions and his monumental *Bibliotheca Chemica*—originally planned as a catalogue of the historical library of James Young—is in fact an encyclopaedia of the history of chemistry from earliest times. His magnificent collection of alchemical literature came partly to the University of Glasgow, which as a result now has a widely famed collection of early works on chemistry. Ferguson's work, if not of the type usually associated with a professor of chemistry, will long be remembered, and it is of interest to note that his insistence on the importance of the historical background and the philosophy of science finds its echo to-day in the movement to develop the study of these subjects in universities and schools, here and abroad.

This insistence was handed on by Ferguson to Thomas Stewart Patterson, Professor of Organic Chemistry from 1919 to 1942, who, by his inclusion of the history and philosophy of chemistry in the course leading to the Honours Degree in Chemistry during this century, gave other universities a lead for the future. Ferguson has often been criticised on the grounds of his inactivity on the experimental side of his profession, but perhaps a little unfairly. It is the duty of a professor to advance his subject by teaching and research, and to serve his University faithfully. Ferguson served the University faithfully for nearly half a century, and who can maintain that his historical research did not contribute to our store of knowledge as much as the experimental research of many another? He was, moreover, a good teacher, at any rate in his earlier years, and, what is important, if he did not himself do experimental work, he did encourage the development of the subject within his Department, so that all branches were represented in it by the opening years of the twentieth century.

Closely bound up with the University Department was the chemical section of Queen Margaret College, which was established to deal with women students and became an integral part of the University in 1893. It was here that Henderson was appointed to his first lectureship in 1889, and this separate lectureship continued for many years, its last occupant being H. W. Bolam (1909). Chemistry was also taught and developed in the Glasgow and West of Scotland Agricultural College (1899).

During the first twenty-five years of this century there were, I think, three major events in the development of chemistry within the University, and all occurred in 1919 immediately after the first World War. In that year the Gardiner chair of Organic Chemistry was founded, endowment being provided by Sir F. C. Gardiner and W. G. Gardiner, two Glasgow shipowners, who also at the same time endowed the Gardiner chair of Physiological Chemistry in association with the chair of Physiology, thus giving early recognition to a branch of chemistry which was soon to become of major importance. To these chairs were elected T. S. Patterson and E. P. Cathcart. The third event of that year was the election of George Gerald Henderson to the Regius chair in succession to John Ferguson. Henderson's name will always loom large in the history of chemistry in Glasgow, for until his retirement in 1937 he was undoubtedly its dominating figure.

o

Prior to 1919 he had occupied the chair at the Royal Technical College, and it is necessary at this point for us to devote some attention to developments there during his tenure of office.

At the opening of the century, schemes were afoot to rebuild the Glasgow and West of Scotland Technical College, then housed in very antiquated buildings. These schemes soon bore fruit and the first block of the present College was opened in 1905 although it was not finally completed until 1910. Upon entry into the new chemical laboratories in 1905 Henderson proceeded at once to build up a flourishing school in association with Thomas Gray, professor of Technical Chemistry. During his period there, in 1912, the name of the College was altered to the Royal Technical College and it was affiliated to the University—a happy union of the two great educational institutions of Glasgow. A consequence of this affiliation was the development of the Honours Degree in Applied Chemistry, which could be taken by study in both institutions and which has formed the initial training of many industrial chemists now occupying important positions at home and abroad. On Henderson's election to the University chair in 1919, the chair of Chemistry in the College was divided into a chair of Organic Chemistry and a chair of Inorganic Chemistry.

Henderson then, came to the University as a man of ripe experience and acknowledged leadership, and for the next eighteen years he and Patterson guided the destinies of the school of chemistry. Before his retirement he had taken part in the planning of a new Department of Chemistry worthy of Glasgow University, and the present magnificent laboratories opened shortly before the late war are a lasting monument to the labours of Henderson and Patterson. It was during this period that I received my own chemical training in the University, and I remain full of gratitude and respect towards my two old teachers, whose kindness and encouragement meant so much not only to me but to all their students. Sir Ian Heilbron in his recent Henderson Memorial Lecture to the Royal Institute of Chemistry has paid a tribute to Henderson which will be endorsed by all Glasgow chemists of to-day. This is hardly the place to recount his personal charm and his mannerisms, but I would stress the great influence which he exerted, not only in Glasgow but throughout the country, on the relationship between the universities and industry. Henderson worked incessantly for the establishment of a true co-operation between the two, recognising its necessity in the modern world, and the satisfactory development of this co-operation is due in no small measure to his efforts.

Upon Henderson's retirement in 1937 he was succeeded in the Regius chair by George Barger, until then professor of Chemistry in Relation to Medicine in the University of Edinburgh. Barger occupied a unique position in chemistry. Not only had he a long record of brilliant researches in the alkaloid field, but he enjoyed a very great international reputation. He was a magnet for young chemists from all over the world, and his laboratory in Edinburgh was always filled with foreign students. I myself have vivid recollections of my own period as one of his staff : we were at that time a cosmopolitan crew frequently using German as our only common language. Barger was a man of great personal charm, a great linguist and a wise and generous professor. Glasgow, however, was not to have the benefit of his counsel for long, for a year later he died with tragic suddenness while on a visit to Switzerland. Fortunately, the University was able to elect as his successor another brilliant chemist, the present Professor J. W. Cook. Under his guidance the new Department has come into being. Upon retirement of Professor Patterson in 1942 the Gardiner chair became a chair of Physical Chemistry with J. M. Robertson as its first occupant. With this development, proper recognition was given to an important branch of chemistry, and the rather anomalous relationship which had hitherto existed between the Regius and the Gardiner chairs was clarified.

Changes too have occurred since Henderson's day in the Royal Technical College. On Henderson's election to the Regius chair at the University, Thomas Gray, the Young professor of Technical Chemistry since 1903, became Director of the chemistry school at the Royal Technical College. At the same time Henderson's chair was divided, Ian Morris Heilbron becoming professor of Organic Chemistry and Forsyth James Wilson professor of Inorganic Chemistry. This state of affairs did not last long, for Heilbron occupied the chair for only one year, and when he left in 1920 Forsyth Wilson took over the Organic Chemistry chair and Robert Caven became professor of Inorganic Chemistry and held that position until his sudden death in 1934. After Caven's death there was a reversion to former practice the two chairs being again merged. Forsyth Wilson now became Freeland professor of

Chemistry, having as his colleague in the chair of Technical Chemistry, William Cumming, who had succeeded Gray in 1933. Wilson, like Caven, died in office in 1944 and after a brief inter-regnum due to war circumstances Frank Stuart Spring succeeded to the Freeland chair in 1946. Spring and Cumming, the present professors, then are the counterparts of Henderson and Gray earlier in the century, the apparent confusion in the history of chemistry at the College during this century having been due to the experimental trial of a system in which there were three professorial chairs.

These bald historical facts do not give a full picture. Two things, research and teaching must be considered in addition. It is difficult and perhaps invidious to single out individual pieces of research from the whole mass of work done during this century. It is only natural to find that with the steady increase in facilities and funds for research and the growth in numbers of the chemical staff that a considerable variety of subjects was studied. It is, however, true that up to the time of the first World War the out-standing figure in organic chemical research was T. S. Patterson and in physico-chemical research F. Soddy. Soddy, before coming to Glasgow in 1904, had been a student of Rutherford and Ramsay and had, while with the latter in London, collected the gases emanating from radium bromide and shown that helium was present in them. An allied problem, that of the relationship between uranium and radium, was one of Soddy's main interests in Glasgow. The idea of radioactive decay gradually evolved and Soddy's experimental skill rendered possible the clarification of the main features of the uranium and thorium decay series. In his last publication from Glasgow he determined the atomic weight of lead from the mineral thorite, and showed that it was nearly 208, an abnormally high value. It was in these investigations on radioactive decay that the existence of the same element in modi-fications with differing atomic weights first came to light and for such modifications Soddy proposed the name " isotopes ". Few discoveries resting on experimental work can have had a greater bearing on future developments than this—a fact more readily appreciated in these days when the study of atomic fission has become a matter of vital importance not only to the scientist but to the whole community. T. S. Patterson, who had learned his first chemistry at the Technical College, had studied later in

Heidelberg and had been on the staff of the Yorkshire College at Leeds, brought to Glasgow a deep interest in stereochemical problems. During the succeeding years a steady flow of work came from his laboratory, dealing mainly with the problems of optical activity in organic compounds, work which established him as one of the leading workers in this field.

The war naturally caused some restriction of activity, but organic research continued under Patterson, and on the physical side A. W. Stewart, Soddy's successor when the latter went to Aberdeen, carried out investigations on absorption spectroscopy in collaboration with R. Wright, then his assistant ; their work on the relation between unsaturation in organic compounds and their absorption spectra is pioneer work in a field of great importance to chemistry at the present time. From 1919 onwards both organic and physical research continued their forward march. On the organic side the stereochemical work of the Patterson school still dominated, but was reinforced by the terpene and rubber researches of Henderson. Henderson had developed these lines of work on substances of natural origin throughout his period at the Royal Technical College and, although it cannot fairly be claimed that they yielded spectacular results, their introduction to the University is a matter of considerable interest, since the natural product field was then entering upon a period of great development which has culminated in many of the most spectacular achievements of modern organic chemistry—the structural elucidation and synthesis of alkaloids, plant and animal pigments, vitamins, hormones and carbohydrates. Other types of organic work which developed after the first World War included the studies in heterocyclic and polycyclic chemistry of S. H. Tucker, the numerous studies on molecular rearrangements among nitrogen compounds by T. S. Stevens and among sulphur compounds by D. T. Gibson and J. D. Loudon, and, during a short period, work on the structure of the tannins by A. Russell. Barger's Glasgow period was too short for him to make any lasting mark on the school, but under its present head organic research has entered on a period of intensive development. With his interests and great achievements in natural products and in the chemistry of polycyclic compounds, particularly in relation to cancer and to other problems in medicine and biology, Professor Cook's school now stands in the forefront of progress. A similar expansion on the organic side is occurring in the Royal Technical College, where Professor F. S. Spring, who succeeded the late F. J. Wilson in 1946, has brought to the College an intense interest in the natural product side of chemistry.

On the physico-chemical side, since 1919 one remembers best perhaps the work of S. T. R. S. Mitchell on the effects of circularly polarised light on chemical reactions, and the recent brilliant applications of the method of X-ray analysis to structural chemistry by Professor Robertson. Mention too must be made of Professor Cumming's elegant investigations at the Royal Technical College on explosives and their relation to industrial hazards in which he has made extensive use of absorption spectroscopy in solving difficult problems of great interest chemically and biologically.

The undergraduate courses in chemistry during this century have, of course, undergone various modifications with the passing of time, but their framework owes much to G. G. Henderson who, because of his career, first in the University then in the Royal Technical College and again in the University, had a unique opportunity to plan them in detail and to effect a real co-ordination between the courses in pure and applied chemistry. Of his success in these matters there can be no doubt, for men from his schools are to be found occupying prominent positions everywhere. The list is too long to give in full, but among present holders of academic chairs of chemistry in this country, Sir Ian Heilbron (London), Alexander Robertson (Liverpool), J. M. Robertson (Glasgow) and myself (Cambridge) are all Glasgow men, and the same is true of Sir James Irvine, Principal of St. Andrew's University, and W. R. Boyd, lately Professor at Southampton. In industry, too, one thinks of A. Fleck, J. Rogers, J. Ferguson, W. W. Lumsden, all of I.C.I. Ltd., A. Davidson, P. W. Tainsch, B. G. McLellan, T. F. Macrae and many others occupying leading positions. On this score Glasgow has already a record in this century of which it can justly be proud. As one who learned his chemistry in this University during the nineteen-twenties, the features which stand out now in my memory as characteristic of Glasgow undergraduate courses are the insistence on thorough training in quantitative methods, the introduction to research methods in the final year of the B.Sc. course, and the compulsory course in the history and philosophy of chemistry so ably and wisely introduced by Professor Patterson. In these respects the Glasgow curriculum differed from those of many other universities ; other features were common to most courses of chemical study but they were, in the majority of cases, given by excellent teachers, of whom Glasgow has had many.

No picture of twentieth century chemistry would be complete which did not pay some attention to local industrial development, the more so as much of it has to be attributed to the work of men trained in the chemical schools of the University and the Royal Technical College. Earlier in this lecture I have discussed the state of chemical industry at the turn of the century, and in many respects the events of that period formed the pattern for what was to come. The heavy alkali industry has not returned, nor, indeed, is it likely to do so on economic grounds, but during the twentieth century acid production has continued and indeed expanded to meet the demands of Scottish industries of many types including, of course, the explosives industry, which is a large consumer. It is of interest to note that the first *Tentelew* contact plant for sulphuric acid to be used in Britain was erected at Ardeer in 1911 in connection with the Nobel Explosives Company, which has in more recent years been associated with the erection of plants for the production of synthetic ammonia and its oxidation to nitric acid. These landmarks in heavy acid manufacture are intimately bound up with the astonishing growth of the explosives industry in Scotland—particularly in Ayrshire—which now supplies practically all the industrial explosives used in Britain and has markets all over the world. The progress of the Nobel company, which since 1926 has been a component of I.C.I. Ltd., is a fascinating one, but I cannot deal with it in detail here. Many of the major advances in the development of high explosives of all types for blasting purposes, propellants, detonators, etc., have been made here in the West of Scotland, and the men produced by the Glasgow School of Chemistry have played a large part in them. During recent years important research developments have occurred at Ardeer which are bringing the same company into new fields of endeavour, amongst others the production of cellulose derivatives of new types, and an artificial protein fibre Ardil, akin to wool in its properties.

Another organic chemical industry which has developed in Scotland, and is thus related to the Glasgow school, is that dealing with synthetic dyestuffs and pharmaceuticals. This has been almost wholly in the hands of Scottish Dyes Ltd., now a constituent of I.C.I. Ltd. Scotland has good reason to be proud of the achievements of that company, notably in the field of vat dye-stuffs, for its products in that range were among the first effective challengers to the supremacy of the German dyes. It is of some interest to note that the synthetic dyestuffs industry really owes its origin in Scotland to the first World War, and there is also no doubt that the same war gave a great stimulus to explosives pro-duction in Ayrshire. To-day Glasgow and the West of Scotland can show in addition a wide range of chemical manufactures ; the remarkable variety of products already noted by G. G. Henderson when he surveyed the field at the opening of the century is still evident and shows no sign of disappearing. It is perhaps appropriate to mention here that a feature of the chemical scene in Scotland is the excellence of her chemical plant manufacture, an important factor in industrial development.

I have endeavoured so far to sketch an outline of recent chemical history in Glasgow, and I feel it would be well to take stock of the position now in relation to possible future develop-ments. The Glasgow School of Chemistry has, since the days of Cullen and Black, had the normal alternating periods of activity and repose which are a feature of all academic schools, but those comparatively quiet periods have never led to retrogression, so that it stands to-day on a solid footing as one of the largest schools in Britain with active and expanding research activity. This latter is the true sign of health in an academic school of chemistry—where it is absent the subject will languish to the detriment not only of the University but also of the community at large, for academic strength and industrial strength are indis-solubly linked. Chemical industry, too, has gone far since those early days in the eighteenth century which have been described elsewhere by Dr. Fleck, and it now stands equipped as never before to expand and develop still further. One must plead for a continuation and a strengthening of that co-operation and under-standing between academic and industrial chemistry, which was the aim of the early pioneers of the Glasgow school and of so many of its later members. There is in this both opportunity and national duty, for the progress and strength of Britain in future years will, to a large extent, be measured by her application of chemical discovery to the service of the community. That Glasgow can contribute much to this end, and so be worthy of her great heritage, I have no fear. Let the courage and vision of the pioneers who founded the Lectureship we now commemorate, serve as an inspiration as their successors build for a glorious future!

REFERENCES

H. H. Browning, *The Andersonian Professors of Chemistry*.

Glasgow University *Calendar*, 1900-1946.

G. G. Henderson, *Chemical Industries*, Glasgow, 1901. (Prepared for the British Association, Glasgow Meeting.)

A Brief Description of the Royal Technical College. (British Association Handbook, Glasgow, 1928.)

I. M., Heilbron, *The Life and Work of George Gerald Henderson*. (Royal Institute of Chemistry, London, 1947.)

Obituary Notices :

G. G. Henderson, *Obituary Notices of Fellows of the Royal Society* 1944, *4*, 491.

J. Ferguson, *J.C.S.*, 1917, *111*, 333.

NOTES ON CONTRIBUTORS

BROOM, ROBERT, B.Sc., M.B., C.M., M.D., D.Sc. (*Glas.*), F.R.S. Hon. D.Sc. (*South Africa, Cape Town, Witwatersrand, Columbia, Stellenbosch*), LL.D. (*Glas.*). Keeper of Vertebrate Palaeontology and Anthropology, The Transvaal Museum, Pretoria. Sometime temporary Assistant in Chemistry (*Glasgow*), Professor of Geology and Zoology (*Stellenbosch*). Author of numerous books and papers, chiefly on palaeontology and anthropology, with excursions into chemistry, medicine and philately.

BUTLER, J. A. V., D.Sc. Courtauld Research Fellow (*Courtauld Institute of Biochemistry*, London). Formerly Rockefeller Foundation Fellow (*Rockefeller Iustitute for Medical Research*, Princeton, N.J.). Author of various text-books and articles on physico-chemical themes.

CLOW, ARCHIBALD, M.A., Ph.D., D.Sc., (*Aberdeen*) Science Producer to the British Broadcasting Corporation. Formerly Carnegie Teaching Fellow (*Aberdeen*). Author of various memoirs on applied chemistry of the industrial revolution, and on magneto-chemistry.

CRANSTON, JOHN A., B.Sc., D.Sc. (*Glas.*). Senior Lecturer and Chief Assistant in Chemistry (*Royal Technical College*, Glasgow). Author of *A Rational Approach to Chemical Principles* and of other books and memoirs, chiefly on radio-activity and on physical chemistry.

FLECK, ALEXANDER, B.Sc., D.Sc. (*Glas.*), F.R.I.C. A Director of Imperial Chemical Industries, Ltd.; Chairman of Scottish Agricultural Industries, Ltd. Sometime Assistant in Physical Chemistry (*Glasgow*) and physical chemist to the Glasgow and West of Scotland Radium Committee.

GREGORY, JOSHUA C., B.Sc., F.R.I.C. Hon. Lecturer in History of Science (*Leeds*). Formerly Lecturer in Chemistry (*Leeds*). Author of *A Short History of Atomism from Democritus to Böhr, Combustion from Heracleitos to Lavoisier*, and other memoirs on the history of science.

GUTHRIE, DOUGLAS, M.A., F.R.C.S. (*Edin.*). Lecturer in History of Medicine (*Edinburgh*). Formerly Aural Surgeon, Edinburgh Royal Hospital for Sick Children. Author of *A History of Medicine*, and of other papers on the history of medicine and on oto-laryngology.

HOWIE, ROBERT C., B.Sc., A.H.-W.C., F.R.I.C. Lecturer in Metallurgy and in History of Chemistry (*Heriot-Watt College*, Edinburgh). Formerly Lecturer in Metallurgy (*University College*, Cardiff).

KENDALL, JAMES, M.A., D.Sc. (*Edin.*), F.R.S. Professor of Chemistry (*Edinburgh*). Formerly Professor of Chemistry at Columbia University and, later, at Washington Square College (*New York*). Author of *At Home among the Atoms*, *Young Chemists and Great Discoveries*, and of other books and papers on chemical subjects.

KENT, ANDREW, M.A., B.Sc., Ph.D. (*Glas.*). Lecturer in Chemistry and in History of Chemistry (*Glasgow*). Author of various papers on organic and historical topics.

MACKIE, J. D., C.B.E., M.C., M.A. (*Oxon.*). Professor of Scottish History and Literature (*Glasgow*). Previously Lecturer in Modern History (*St. Andrews*), and Professor of Modern History (*London*). Essayist, reviewer and broadcaster on many historical themes.

PARTINGTON, J. R., M.B.E., D.Sc. Professor of Chemistry (*London*). Formerly, Lecturer and Demonstrator in Chemistry (*Manchester*). Author of *The Origin and Development of Applied Chemistry*, *A Short History of Chemistry*, and of other text-books and memoirs on inorganic chemistry, and on the history of chemistry.

PATTERSON, T. S., (*vide* p. xv.).

READ, JOHN, M.A., Sc.D. (*Cantab.*), B.Sc., (*London*), Ph.D. (*Zürich*), F.R.S. Professor of Chemistry, United College (*St. Andrews*). Formerly Lecturer and Demonstrator in Chemistry (*Cambridge*), and Professor of Organic Chemistry, Pure and Applied (*Sydney*). Author of *Prelude to Chemistry*, *Humour and Humanism in Chemistry*, and of numerous text-books and papers on organic and historical chemistry.

THOMSON, GEORGE, B.Sc., Ph.D., (*Glas.*) Lecturer in chemistry (*Glasgow*). Author of " James Watt and the Monkland Canal " and other antiquarian studies, and of memoirs on physical chemistry.

TODD, A. R., D.Sc. (*Glas.*), Dr. phil. nat. (*Frankfurt*), D.Phil. (*Oxon.*). M.A. (*Cantab.*), Fellow of Christ's College, Cambridge, F.R.S. Professor of Organic Chemistry (*Cambridge*). Formerly member of staff, *Lister Institute of Preventive Medicine*, Reader in Biochemistry (*London*), Sir Samuel Hall Professor of Chemistry (*Manchester*). Author of numerous scientific papers.

WHITTAKER, SIR EDMUND TAYLOR, Kt., F.R.S., Hon., LL.D. (*St. Andrews* and *California*), Sc.D. (*Dublin*), D.Sc. (*Manchester*,

National University of Ireland). Formerly Fellow of Trinity College, Cambridge, Royal Astronomer of Ireland, President of the Royal Society of Edinburgh, and until 1946, Professor of Mathematics (*Edinburgh*). Author of *The Beginning and End of the World*, *Space and Spirit*, and of other books and memoirs.

APPOINTMENTS SINCE 1747 TO THE STAFF OF THE CHEMISTRY DEPARTMENT, GLASGOW UNIVERSITY

Degrees are as at times of appointment, and of Glasgow University unless otherwise stated : the University is then indicated for only the last-mentioned in a group of degrees of common origin.

*Member of the Chemistry class at Glasgow.

Thomas Anderson (1)	M.D. (Edin.)	1852
*William Carrick Anderson (10)	M.A., B.Sc.	1894
*Mary M. Andross (18)	B.Sc.	1922
*John G. Auld (16)	B.Sc., Ph.D.	1937
Geoffrey M. Badger (21)	M.Sc. (Melbourne), Ph.D. (London)	1946
George Barger (1)	M.A., D.Sc. (Cantab.), F.R.S.	1937
*James Bell (14)	B.Sc.	1929
Joseph Black (3)	M.D. (Edin.)	1756
*Robert D. Blair (14)	B.Sc.	1929
Herbert W. Bolam (4)	B.Sc. (Edin.), Ph.D. (Leipzig)	1903
John C. D. Brand (9)	M.Sc., Ph.D. (London)	1947
*Robert Broom (19)		1883
*Charles Buchanan (11)	B.Sc.	1922
Joshua Buchanan (19)		(?) 1884
John Carrick (10)		1747
*Donald Chisholm (14)	B.Sc.	1924
Erich Clar (21)	Dr. Ing. (Dresden)	1946
Robert Cleghorn (3)	M.D. (Edin.)	1791
*Eva S. E. Coleman (11)	B.Sc.	1920
James Wilfred Cook (1)	Ph.D., D.Sc. (London), F.R.S.	1939
William Cullen (3)	M.D.	1747
J. G. Dalzell (10)		1873
*Catherine F. Davidson (12)	B.Sc.	1918
Cecil H. Desch (6)	Ph.D. (Würzburg), D.Sc. (London)	1908
James Johnston Dobbie (10)	M.A. (Glas.), D.Sc. (Edin.)	1880
*Edith F. M. Dunn (11)	B.Sc.	1922
Charles Edward Fawsitt (6)	Ph.D. (Leipzig), D.Sc. (Edin.)	1905
*John Ferguson (10)	B.A., M.A.	1868
*Alexander Fleck (13)	B.Sc.	1912

*James D. Fulton (11)	M.A., B.Sc.	1924
David T. Gibson (14)	M.Sc.(Belfast), Ph.D.(London)	1924
Thomas H. Goodwin (9)	B.Sc., Ph.D. (Birmingham)	1944
*Samuel H. Graham (10)	B.Sc.	1947
Thomas Gray (4)	B.Sc. (London)	1893
William C. Gray (6)		1919
Frank D. Gunstone (9)	B.Sc., Ph.D. (Liverpool)	1946
Frank Hargreaves (12)		1914
Margaret B. Haugh (15)		1918
*Robert Hay (6)	B.Sc.	1921
*Andrew Henderson (10)	M.A., B.Sc.	1908
*George Gerald Henderson (10)	M.A., B.Sc.	1885
*John B. Hutchison (10)		1874
William Irvine (3)	.M.D.	1769
John C. James (9)	B.Sc., Ph.D. (London)	1948
*Elizabeth G. Kennedy (12)	B.Sc.	1917
*Andrew Kent (17)		1923
Joseph Knox (7)	D.Sc. (Aberdeen)	1919
*William R. Lang (10)	B.Sc.	1892
*George Lean (10)	B.Sc.	1896
*Christina T. Lewin (18)	B.Sc.	1922
*James D. Loudon (14)	B.Sc.	1931
*Irene M. McAlpine (17)	B.Sc., Ph.D.	1929
Robert McCourtney (10)		1914
John McCrae (4)	Ph.D. (Heidelberg)	1903
*Walter P. McCulloch (14)	B.Sc.	1922
*Elizabeth MacDougall (13)	B.Sc.	1918
Norah A. McGinnis (10)	A. M. (Queen's, Kingston), D.Phil. (Oxon.)	1943
*Thomas McGregor (13)	B.Sc.	1928
*John P. McHutchison	M.A., B.Sc.	1919
*Isabella McLaren (18)	B.Sc.	1922
*Andrew McMillan (11)	M.A., D.Sc.	1911
*John A. Mair (13)	B.Sc., Ph.D.	1927
*Peter Maitland (17)	B.Sc.	1925
*Stanley F. Marrian (10)	B.Sc	1941
*John M. Martin (13)		1909
Edmund James Mills (10)		1862
*Stotherd T. R. S. Mitchell (13)	B.Sc.	1924
*James D. Morrison (10)	B.Sc.	1946
*Jane Morrison (15)	M.A.	1919
*James Stanley Muir (10)	B.Sc.	1890
*Matthew A. Parker (5)	B.Sc.	1902
*Agnes M. Patterson (18)	B.Sc.	1922

Thomas Stewart Patterson (5)	B.Sc. (London),	
	Ph.D. (Heidelberg)	1904
E. F. Pollock (11)	Ph.D. (?)	1913
J. Holms Pollok (19)		1884
William Ramsay (10)	Ph.D. (Tübingen)	1874
Rowland I. Reed (9)	B.Sc., Ph.D. (London)	1946
*Alec. C. Ritchie (10)	B.Sc.	1947
*James Roberts (10)		1898
*John Robertson (17)	B.Sc.	1924
*John McGregor Robertson (14)	B.Sc.	1923
*John Monteath Robertson (2)	M.A., Ph.D., D.Sc.	1942
John Robison (3)	M.A.	1766
Alfred Russell (20)	D.Sc. (Belfast)	1931
*Annie R. Russell (15)	B.Sc.	1915
Felix Schwarz (10)	B.Sc. Tech. (Manchester)	1946
*Robert Scott (10)	M.A.	1908
*Jean M. Semple (11)	B.Sc.	1920
*Robert Christie Smith (13)	M.A., B.Sc.	1921
Frederick Soddy (8)	M.A. (Oxon.), F.R.S.	1904
*Andrew R. Somerville (10)	B.Sc.	1946
*Robert Somerville (11)	M.A., B.Sc.	1924
James C. Speakman (9)	M.Sc., Ph.D. (Sheffield)	1946
*Thomas S. Stevens (11)	B.Sc.	1922
*Alfred W. Stewart (8)	D.Sc.	1914
*Elizabeth C. Stewart (15)	M.A., B.Sc.	1924
Walter Stewart (10)	—	(?) 1866
*Frederick R. Storrie (11)	B.Sc.	1926
*James Sword (14)	M.A., B.Sc.	1922
*David Thomson (11)	M.A., B.Sc., Ph.D.	1910
*George Thomson (17)	B.Sc.	1927
*John Millar Thomson (19)		1869
*Robert Dundas Thomson (19)	M.D.	1841
Thomas Thomson (3)	M.D. (Edin.)	1817
*John Todd (14)	B.Sc., Ph.D.	1934
S. Horwood Tucker (5)	B.A. (Oxon.), M.Sc. (London)	1921
*Alexander Walker (17)	B.Sc.	1924
*Mona M. Walker (5)	B.Sc.	1922
Ernest Warhurst (9)	M.Sc., Ph.D. (Manchester)	1944
*James S. Watson (10)	B.Sc.	1947
William Marshall Watts (10)	D.Sc. (?)	(?) 1866
*John L. T. Waugh (10)	B.Sc.	1947
*J. G. White (10)	B.Sc.	1946
Samuel Whyte (12)		1913
Robert Wright (13)	M.A., B.E., D.Sc. (Belfast)	1915

AUTHOR-INDEX

SUBJECT-INDEX

PRINTED IN GREAT BRITAIN BY ROBERT MACLEHOSE AND CO. LTD.
THE UNIVERSITY PRESS, GLASGOW, FOR JACKSON, SON AND CO.
(BOOKSELLERS), LTD., PUBLISHERS TO THE UNIVERSITY, GLASGOW